3-52-172-14dt

Twenty-Five Years of Chemical Engineering Progress

TWENTY-FIVE YEARS OF CHEMICAL ENGINEERING PROGRESS

Silver Anniversary Volume

AMERICAN INSTITUTE OF CHEMICAL ENGINEERS

Edited by

SIDNEY D. KIRKPATRICK

Editor of *Chemical & Metallurgical Engineering*

CONTRIBUTORS

W. L. BADGER
LAWRENCE W. BASS
CHARLES OWEN BROWN
HAL B. COATS
JOHN V. N. DORR
FRANCIS C. FRARY
EDWARD C. HOLTON
JOHN C. HOSTETTER
HENRY HOWARD
MARTIN H. ITTNER
W. S. LANDIS
E. H. LESLIE
ARTHUR D. LITTLE
ALBERT E. MARSHALL
GEORGE P. MEADE

A. V. H. MORY
WILLIAM D. MOUNT
GEORGE OENSLAGER
HORACE C. PORTER
S. T. POWELL
MARK E. PUTNAM
GEORGE RICHTER
RALPH W. SHAFOR
HOWARD W. SHELDON
W. B. VANARSDEL
EDWARD R. WEIDLEIN
ARCHIE J. WEITH
DAVID WESSON
ROBERT SPURR WESTON
ALFRED H. WHITE

FRED C. ZEISBERG

Essay Index Reprint Series

ORIGINALLY PUBLISHED BY THE INSTITUTE

BOOKS FOR LIBRARIES PRESS

FREEPORT, NEW YORK

First Published 1933
Reprinted 1968

LIBRARY OF CONGRESS CATALOG CARD NUMBER:

68-55837

MANUFACTURED
BY
HALLMARK LITHOGRAPHERS, INC.
IN THE U.S.A.

CONTENTS

FOREWORD

TWENTY-FIVE YEARS is a brief interval in the history of engineering, yet it encompasses practically the whole of the development of chemical engineering as a profession in the United States. At the time the American Institute of Chemical Engineers was founded in Philadelphia on June 22, 1908, chemical engineering was generally regarded as a hybrid of chemistry and some form of engineering—civil, mechanical, electrical or a mixture of all three. It was not until the years immediately following the outbreak of the World War that the chemical engineer came to be recognized in his own right. In the feverish excitement of supplying munitions—first for our Allies and later for ourselves—he received his real baptism of fire, to emerge with almost universal recognition of what is perhaps his most important function, namely, to translate the reactions of the laboratory into the large-scale, successful operations of industry. This in a sense involved a trinity of functions—design, construction and operation—in all of which the chemical engineer has shown marked proficiency. Likewise, it was demonstrated that he also had a most important part in research and development work.

With the return of peace came the gradual realization that the training and experience of the chemical engineer fitted him for broader duties than those of the specialist in the production processes of chemical industry. A grounding in economics, ability in handling men and a faculty of getting at the fundamentals of any problem led many chemical engineers into executive positions, not only in production, but in research, sales and general administration. At the same time the field of chemical engineering was rapidly expanding as it became apparent that the unit operations of the purely chemical processes underlay the technology of a broad range of industries.

As chemical engineering greatly widened its sphere of usefulness, the Institute grew in numbers and influence until today it is accepted as a branch of engineering, younger and smaller but as important in its field as are the four older and so-called Founder Societies of mechanical, civil, electrical and mining engineers.

When the Institute met in Washington, D. C., in December, 1932, for its twenty-fifth annual meeting, more than a thousand engineers had met its qualifications for active membership. Through the work of its important committees it had formulated and held high the standards of those who practice the profession of chemical engineering. It early interested itself and later helped to guide the work of schools and colleges in improving the training of those who answer this specialized calling. It had built an impressive literature of chemical engineering in its own *Transactions* and in the textbooks and periodicals stimulated by its example. Lastly, through unselfish contributions to the nation in times of war and peace, it had risen to a position of eminence in the public esteem.

All these phases of the progress of the profession—as well as the extremely interesting history of the organization itself—are duly recorded in "The Silver Anniversary of Chemical Engineering in America" which was issued as a souvenir pamphlet at the time of the Washington meeting. It is the purpose of the present volume to reflect in somewhat greater detail the record of the remarkable rôle played by chemical engineering in the development of American industries since 1908. It is altogether fitting that this volume should be issued in June, 1933, almost exactly twenty-five years after the founding of the Institute. It is a pleasant coincidence that this anniversary should come at a time when the engineering profession, as well as the nation as a whole and, in fact, much of the world, have centered interest and attention in the Century of Progress Exposition in Chicago. Chemical engineering has been pleased to have been able to contribute its share in this whole remarkable record of progress.

A further word about the plan and purpose of this volume is perhaps in order. In some measure it attempts to reflect the trend of chemical engineering development in the principal industries served by that technology. Certain of the more important unit operations are likewise reviewed. Logically, it would seem, the volume begins with the contributions of research and ends with a forward-looking chapter on chemical engineering education—our means of building for the future of the profession.

The men who have contributed these discussions are recognized as leading authorities in the fields they represent. Some have reflected largely their personal reminiscences and observations of the past quarter of a century. Others have given us more exhaustive and scientific reviews. It is hoped, therefore, that the reader will accept this volume, not as a carefully balanced and coordinated textbook, but rather as an authoritative array of essays—each interesting in itself and contributing something to the extremely broad picture of the whole development of chemical engineering in American industry.

Although prepared primarily for the membership of the Institute, it is hoped that this volume may serve a useful purpose in our schools and libraries where a record of chemical engineering advances may stimulate further study and progress. Chemical engineering has been aptly called the engineering of the future. If this volume, with its records of the past, is able to contribute some measure of inspiration for the important work of the future, its editor and contributors will feel amply rewarded for the effort invested here on behalf of the profession.

SIDNEY D. KIRKPATRICK

New York, N. Y.
June, 1933

CHAPTER I

CHEMICAL ENGINEERING RESEARCH

Lifeblood of American Industry

By Arthur D. Little

President, Arthur D. Little, Inc., Cambridge, Mass.

R ESEARCH has one characteristic in common with lightning—
one never knows where it may strike. Chemical engineers saw
no necessity of putting up protective rods when Ramsay began an
investigation of the abnormalities in the specific gravity of nitrogen,
or when Dewar undertook the liquefaction of air. There seemed
little probability that chemical engineering would be struck in either
case. Nevertheless, chemical engineers ultimately found themselves
engaged in the development of high-pressure processes for the recovery, from natural gas, of helium, which inaugurated a new epoch in
aerial navigation. They were equally busied with the large-scale
production and fractionation of liquid air as the source of oxygen,
and of nitrogen for ammonia syntheses and cyanamid; of argon for
filling incandescent lamps of a new order of efficiency; and of neon
which flames in red in countless advertising signs. Incidentally, every
picnic basket now carries a thermos bottle, the lineal descendant of
the Dewar flask.

Research, whether fundamental or applied, is the lifeblood of
chemical engineering. It provides the new facts, new materials, new
processes, and new methods of control upon which the progress of
chemical engineering depends, and it inspires the theories which give
better understanding and thereby suggest new lines for the attack of
problems. Research, moreover, reacts upon itself to constantly accelerate its own momentum by the development and application of
new research tools. It provides new mathematical concepts and
methods as signally exemplified in those derived from the phase rule
of Willard Gibbs; it enriches the equipment of the laboratory by the
spectroscope, the ultramicroscope, the interferometer, pH indicator,
Pyrex glass and the photo-electric cell. It projects our vision into
the interior of matter by the X-ray.

For many decades research in the United States was a precarious

1

and stunted growth upon a rocky soil. Today its creative power is so generally appreciated that great foundations are available for its support; universities, corporations and private agencies vie with one another in the equipment and maintenance of imposing laboratories, and the current triumphs of research are blazoned in the press, not always accurately, as front-page news.

Many individuals, events and agencies have contributed to bring about this recent and remarkable assimilation of the research idea. Chemistry, which owed so much to Richard Boyle, Cavendish, Priestley and Dalton in England, soon crossed the Channel and received such further development at the hands of Lavoisier, Berthollet, Gay-Lussac and Wurtz that it was claimed with some justification to have become a French science. Later its allegiance seemed to have been transferred to Germany. Research found there an atmosphere so hospitable and stimulating and was so liberally supported by government and industry that in the later decades of the nineteenth century "Made in Germany" became the hallmark of chemical science. Chemical thought was dominated by the theories of Ostwald, Fischer, Meyer, Wöhler, Kekule and Liebig. Chemical literature was, for a time, little more than an anthology of contributions from German laboratories, while the world noted with appreciation, tinged with envy and some solicitude, the many and often amazing conquests of German chemical industry.

The comparatively limited opportunities at home for instruction in the higher branches of chemistry and the prestige of great names in Germany naturally led the more serious students of the science to turn to the German universities for the completion of their training. The Ph.D. there obtained soon became the almost indispensable requisite for professorial advancement in the universities of America.

The research idea thus acquired in the laboratories of Germany was presently domiciled here by a long line of young, brilliant and enthusiastic exponents, conspicuous among whom were Remsen, Crafts, Chandler, Silliman and, later, A. A. Noyes' and G. N. Lewis. The inspiration which they brought naturally resulted in a marked improvement in standards of instruction and gradually developed a more general interest in chemistry itself. Many factors and a far greater number of men are, of course, responsible for this growth of interest in chemistry and for the broader recognition of the relation of science in general to progress and to human welfare.

The impact upon the public mind of a succession of great inventions based on science—the telephone, the phonograph, moving pictures, liquid air, the radio, the incandescent lamp and the multitudinous applications of electricity, together with such epochal discoveries as the X-rays and radium—created an esteem for science not only in its popular aspect as the master magician from whom any marvel was to be expected but also as the provider of foundations for great and profitable industries. Electrical toys and Chemkraft sets stimulated juvenile interest. Boys were busied building radio cabinets, and Willie, making mud pies in the back yard, was called into the house to show father how to get KDKA.

For many years the Gospel of Research was preached to congregations of skeptical manufacturers, who, in slowly increasing numbers, moved, hesitantly, forward to the anxious seat. One of the most notable and persuasive of the exponents of industrial research was Robert Kennedy Duncan. His books, "The Chemistry of Commerce" and "The New Knowledge," attained wide and effective circulation by the clarity of his presentation and the skill with which argument was buttressed by convincing facts. Edwin E. Slosson, the author of "Creative Chemistry" and for years editor of *Science Service*, founded by E. W. Scripps, possessed to a remarkable degree the rare faculty of popularizing science without distorting the outlines of its findings. As writer and lecturer he reached large audiences and lifted them to a plane of understanding and appreciation of their debt to science.

In a democracy the support of research depends very definitely upon popular appreciation of its aims, methods and achievements. It is, therefore, highly important that these be placed before the public in understandable, interesting and accurate form. Since the most direct method of reaching the public is through the press, it is gratifying to note the radical and significant change which recent years have brought in the editorial attitude toward scientific news.

Not only is the amount of space given to scientific news and subjects patently much greater than was the case twenty-five years ago, but both the quality of the material itself and the manner of its presentation are of a distinctly higher order. The absent-minded professor, the long-haired inventor, the Altoona cobbler with a formula for burning ashes, Garabed, Jernegan and the sea serpent have given place to serious reports of scientific meetings and to special articles by recognized authorities. Science is now news where once it was a joke. You can perhaps remember the famous Moon Hoax.

Meanwhile, the creative power of research was being strikingly exemplified in the remarkable growth of certain great corporations whose activities were based on science. Among the scientists whose work was, in large part, responsible for this growth were Whitney, Steinmetz, Coolidge and Langmuir of the General Electric Company's laboratory; Willson, Becket, Chaney and Curme of the Union Carbide & Carbon Corporation; Herbert H. Dow of the Dow Chemical Co.; Baekeland and Redman of the Bakelite Corporation; Reese, Comey, Irenée du Pont and Stine of the du Pont Company, and J. J. Carty and F. B. Jewett, directing the amazingly extensive research program of the American Telephone & Telegraph Company.

Stimulated by these examples of profitable research and menaced by the flood of new processes and products from other laboratories, manufacturers more generally sought to insure their dividends through the aid of science.

The Eighth International Congress of Applied Chemistry brought together in 1912, at Washington and New York, several thousand industrial chemists from all over the world. The impression derived from its proceedings as published in twenty-four volumes is that of an airplane survey of the status of applied chemistry throughout the world. The mass effect of its papers and demonstrations upon our own industrialists was in a sense not unlike that of the Centennial on the thought of American manufacturers. The notable success of the Congress upon both its scientific and social sides was conspicuously due to the personality of its president, Dr. William H. Nichols, and to the remarkable organizing and executive ability of its secretary, Dr. B. C. Hesse.

The most influential factor among those responsible for the higher appreciation of chemistry by industrialists and the general public was, undoubtedly, the World War. It put upon us the sudden obligation of making for ourselves the thousands of chemical products for which we had formerly relied on Germany. Dyestuffs, potash, synthetic drugs, T.N.T. and poison gas became staple topics of conversation. Membership in the American Chemical Society increased from 7,417 in 1915 to 12,203 in 1918, or 64.5 per cent.

Conspicuous among the developments resulting from the war, and which made especially severe demands upon chemical engineers, was the work of the Chemical Warfare Service and its Research Division. The latter owes its inception to the late Dr. Van H. Manning, at that time director of the U. S. Bureau of Mines. The rapidity with which this research was organized and got under way in many laboratories and plants was largely due to the initiative of Bradley Dewey and Dr. W. K. Lewis. Dewey was later commissioned as Colonel in charge of gas-mask manufacture and conducted with remarkable efficiency the operations of several great plants in which some 15,000 workers were employed. In recognition of this accomplishment he was awarded the Distinguished Service Medal. The research organization of the Chemical Warfare Service developed into a staff of 1,900 people, of whom 1,200 were technical men.

Among the more notable lines of research conducted by the Division were investigations leading to the following: the development of highly activated charcoal, for which Dr. H. B. Lemon, Colonel F. M. Dorsey and Dr. N. K. Chaney were largely responsible; the production of a new type of soda lime under the direction of R. E. Wilson; gas-mask design and manufacture, with which Dewey, Lewis, Dr. Yandell Henderson and Professor W. E. Gibbs were prominently identified; research directed to offense, the direction of which was assigned to Dr. James F. Norris; and the defense research headed by Professor A. B. Lamb. Much valuable assistance in the conduct of both these lines of research was contributed by Dr. G. A. Hulett.

While it is impossible even to touch upon the many activities of the Research Division under the direction of its chief, Colonel George A. Burrell, or to refer to the many valuable contributions of the members of the staff, the reader is referred for further details to Colonel Burrell's comprehensive article in the issue for February, 1919, of the *Journal of Industrial and Engineering Chemistry*.

Charles H. Herty stated in 1921, "When the full history of this war is written, I think one of the outstanding chapters is going to concern the remarkable results obtained in research at American University Experiment Station, and at Edgewood Arsenal in the building of that wonderful plant."

The construction of the Edgewood Arsenal plant, to which Dr. Herty refers, went forward rapidly during the hard winter of 1917-18 under the direction of Lieutenant-Colonel Ragsdale and Lieutenant-Colonel Chance. Colonel William H. Walker of the Chemical Warfare Service was presently placed in charge of operations and expansion. His position, in view of the highly dangerous character of the work and the necessity of developing new methods and equipment to operate under extremely hazardous conditions, was one of heavy responsibility, and his remarkable record of production was recognized by the award of the Distinguished Service Medal. Among other products there was produced at Edgewood more than 5½ million pounds of chlorpicrin, 3¼ million pounds of phosgene and nearly 1½ million pounds of mustard gas, and the estimated capacity at Edgewood and its allied plants on January 1, 1919, was 8 million pounds per month of mustard gas alone.

Precisely as the Civil War led to the chartering of the National Academy of Sciences in 1864, so the World War brought into being, virtually at the request of the President of the United States, the National Research Council in September, 1916. The Council rapidly developed into a powerful and far-reaching agency for the promotion and coordination of research in the several sciences and became notably effective as regards chemistry through its Division of Chemistry and Chemical Technology and the activities of Maurice Holland, Director of the Division of Engineering and Industrial Research.

Although industrial chemistry in its modern sense may be said to have begun as long ago as the French Revolution with the invention by Le Blanc of the soda process, it was nearly one hundred years thereafter before chemical engineering began to be dimly recognized as a distinct profession. In November, 1887, the faculty of Massachusetts Institute of Technology appointed a committee "to consider instruction in engineering as relating especially to applied chemistry," and in the faculty meeting of December of that year it was voted to establish a course in chemical engineering. The course schedule was adopted in February, 1888, and went into effect the following autumn, the first class in chemical engineering ever graduated receiving its diplomas from the Institute in 1891. In the Institute catalog for 1888-89 the new course was designated as "Course X—Chemical Engineering," followed by the statement, "This course is arranged to meet the needs of students who desire a general training in mechanical engineering, and at the same time to devote a portion of their time to the study of the applications of chemistry to the arts, especially to those engineering problems which relate to the use and manufacture of chemical products."

Even at that time and for many years afterward there was little distinction between industrial chemistry and chemical engineering. The "chemical engineer" was still a mechanical engineer who had acquired some knowledge of chemistry. As C. M. A. Stine said in 1928: "The chemical engineer is a comparatively recent product of our industrial development; a couple of decades ago we find but little mention of him. When the American Institute of Chemical Engineers was organized the conception of chemical engineering was rather hazy. What was actually realized was the fact that those engaged in industrial operations needed to supplement the results of the purely chemical research worker in order to adapt these results to use by the manufacturer. . . . The acceptance and adoption of chemical engineering in the family of applied science has been perhaps the most important factor in expediting the application of scientific development to the improvement of living conditions."

A new conception of chemical engineering was presented in a report which the writer of this chapter had the honor of submitting to the Corporation of the Massachusetts Institute of Technology in December, 1915, and which led to the foundation of the School of Chemical Engineering Practice at that institution. After referring to the extraordinarily varied and severe demands upon the members of this comparatively new profession and the many problems involved in the training of those who were to practice it, the report proceeded to define as follows the field of chemical engineering:

"Any chemical process, on whatever scale conducted, may be resolved into a coordinated series of what may be termed 'unit actions,' as pulverizing, mixing, heating, roasting, absorbing, condensing, lixiviating, precipitating, crystallizing, filtering, dissolving, electrolyzing and so on. The number of these basic unit operations is not very large and relatively few of them are involved in any particular process. The complexity of chemical engineering results from the variety of conditions as to temperature, pressure, etc., under which the unit actions must be carried out in different processes and from the limitations as to materials of construction and design of apparatus imposed by the physical and chemical character of the reacting substances. . . . An ability to cope broadly and adequately with the demands of his profession can only be attained through the analysis of processes into the unit actions of which they are composed and the close study of these basic unit actions as they are carried out on the commercial scale under the conditions imposed by practice."

This conception of chemical engineering is now generally accepted, and as pointed out by Stine in the paper first referred to, "Perhaps the characteristic which most differentiates the chemical engineering of today from the earlier activities of those interested in this field is the quantitative treatment of these various unit operations, and it is this exact and quantitative treatment of these operations which constitutes the province of modern chemical engineering."

Chemical engineering research, as distinguished from purely chemical research, is, therefore, directed toward the improvement, control and better coordination of these unit operations and the selection or development of the equipment in which they are carried out. It is obviously concerned with the testing and provision of materials of construction which shall function safely, resist corrosion and withstand the indicated conditions of temperature and pressure.   Its ultimate objective is so to provide and organize the means for conducting a chemical process that the process shall operate safely, efficiently and profitably.   "Twenty years ago," to quote Stine again, "the results of laboratory research were submitted to the politely tolerant and somewhat disdainful consideration of the design engineer and were considered by a group of men who had not yet learned mutual respect and appreciation, through experience, of the tremendous value of a type of cooperation which, to my mind, represents the very keystone of the modern industrial arch of chemical manufacturing."[1]

Today the chemical engineer is the recognized connecting link between the laboratory and the plant, and one of his most important functions is that of converting laboratory findings into terms of plant operation on the commercial scale.   Chemical engineering research thus begins in the laboratory and proceeds by steps from laboratory apparatus through to pilot plant and finally to the design or selection of equipment for the full-scale operation of the developed process.

The professional status of the chemical engineer was definitely established by the organization, June 22, 1908, of the American Institute of Chemical Engineers and the promulgation of its rigid requirements for admission.   Sixty chemical engineers paid dues that year as members.   The number had increased to 101 in June, 1909, while on December 31, 1931, the Institute had grown to include 832 active members and 182 associates.   Through its meetings, publications, committees and student chapters the Institute has powerfully stimulated chemical engineering research and has exerted a beneficially persuasive pressure which has resulted in raising the standards of chemical engineering education.

The foundation in 1907 of the Perkin Medal, which has been called the Badge of Knighthood in American Chemistry, was almost contemporaneous with the organization of the American Institute of Chemical Engineers.   The medal is awarded annually by a committee representing five national chemical societies "for the most valuable work in applied chemistry."   The roster of its recipients now carries twenty-six names, and the record of their performance constitutes an epic of chemical engineering achievement.   There is a striking testimonial to the high quality of American chemical engineering research and practice in the fact that at least fifteen of the

---

[1] "Chemical Engineering in Modern Industry," by Charles M. A. Stine. *Transactions*, A. I. Ch. E., Vol. 21, 1928.

twenty-six awards of the medal to date have been made to members of the American Institute of Chemical Engineers. To appreciate the significance of these awards within the Institute and the momentous bearing upon industry of the work of their recipients one has only to recall that J. B. F. Herreshoff received the medal for his contributions to metallurgy and the contact process for sulphuric acid; E. G. Acheson for carborundum and artificial graphite; Charles M. Hall for the aluminum process; Herman Frasch for desulphurizing petroleum and for subterranean sulphur mining; L. H. Baekeland for Velox photoprint paper and Bakelite; Charles F. Chandler for noteworthy achievements "in almost every line of chemical engineering," while among the later recipients in the Institute whose work is known to all of us are such men as Willis R. Whitney, M. C. Whitaker, Hugh K. Moore, Richard B. Moore, John E. Teeple, Eugene C. Sullivan and Herbert H. Dow.[2]

Nowhere has chemical engineering research found greater scope or encountered more difficult problems than in the rapidly expanding field of high-pressure and high-temperature work. Temperature and pressure, either alone or in association with catalysts, are the most effective agencies for accelerating chemical reactions, but it is only within comparatively recent times that their higher ranges have been generally available. That they are so today is a notable triumph to chemical engineering research and practice, which has provided materials of construction, designed safe and efficient equipment and provided methods of control—all by means so radically novel as to constitute together a new technology. In this country the pioneer in this research was the U. S. Fixed Nitrogen Research Laboratory, which Dr. A. B. Lamb organized in 1919 and which was brilliantly seconded by the Pittsburgh laboratory of the U. S. Bureau of Mines. Other notable contributors were the Research Laboratory of Applied Chemistry, the Massachusetts Institute of Technology, which began its high-pressure work in 1925 and which was almost immediately followed by the installation of high-pressure laboratories at Yale, University of Illinois and University of Wisconsin. Due credit should also be given to the steel companies and equipment manufacturers who fabricated parts to meet the rigid specifications imposed by the extraordinarily severe conditions under which plants were to operate.

It became necessary to develop special steels and alloys; to forge

---

[2] Editor's Note: Dr. Little himself was the Perkin medalist for 1931 and Mr. George Oenslager, also a member of the A. I. Ch. E., received the 1933 award.

thick-walled vessels to withstand pressures up to 15,000 pounds; to develop new types of compressors and new piping, valves and fittings. The known behavior of thin-walled vessels at high temperatures proved an unreliable guide to that of vessels with walls several inches thick, and the deterioration of strength with time of service at high pressures required careful study. The new technology demanded super-refractories, which were developed only by much research, and the selection of effective catalysts required even more intensive study.

The new technology is strikingly exemplified in the United States plant for the separation of helium from natural gas at Amarillo, Texas. The plant operation is there controlled by thermocouples for temperature readings, orifice meters for measuring gas flows, differential meters to indicate height of liquid in different parts of the unit, pressure gauges, and, most essential, automatic helium recorders which give the purity of the helium produced throughout the whole 24-hour period and which depend for their operation upon thermal capacity. Any given foot of gas is brought from room temperature to 300 deg. below zero and back to room temperature in less than a minute total elapsed time. The helium is shipped in cars carrying heavy-walled, seamless steel tanks holding 200,000 cu. ft. of free gas at a tank pressure of 2,000 lbs. to the square inch.

Another of the earlier and still one of the largest high-pressure plants in the United States is that of Commercial Solvents Corporation for the production of methanol from the fermenter gases, the composition of which by volume is about 40 per cent hydrogen and 60 per cent carbon dioxide. The latter is separated and converted to dry ice.

The operations of few industries have been more radically transformed by chemical engineering than those of petroleum refining. Here the petroleum technologist is of necessity a chemical engineer. The high pressures and temperatures and the dangers of corrosion, fire and explosion inherent in the materials and process all call for the highest expression of the skill of the chemical engineer, and its application has within recent years radically transformed refinery methods and equipment. For every chemical engineer employed in the industry twenty-five years ago there are today at least fifty so employed, and they are far better trained. The older equipment has been largely replaced by units of new design with far greater throughput capacity. Pipe stills have replaced batch stills. Lubricants are improved by high-vacuum distillation. Highly efficient bubble towers have been substituted for old-fashioned fractionating columns.

Elaborate provision has been made for effective heat transfer and heat exchange. Pressures and temperatures and the size of equipment have steadily gone up. The first pressure still was built for the Burton process. Its cylindrical shell was built of ½-in. mild steel and was 8 ft. in diameter and 20 ft. long. It held 6,000 gallons. The working pressure was 100 lbs. with a factor of safety of 5, and the operating temperature was around 700 deg. F. Today pressures in cracking processes commonly range from 400 to 700 lbs. at the tube still outlet, and working temperatures from 700 to 900 deg. F. The tendency is toward still higher pressures and temperatures: 1,000 deg. F. and 1,000 lbs. are not uncommon, and these figures are being further raised in some new plants.

Where once the "wild" fractions of casinghead gasoline were lost by wasteful "weathering," high-pressure rectification now stabilizes the product and recovers the propane and butane, widely distributed and utilized as a new type of gaseous fuel. The evaporation of gasoline during storage is minimized in tanks provided with floating roofs or breathing bags and protected against undue absorption of solar heat by white or aluminum paints.

Hydrogenation, based on the fundamental work of Sabatier and Senderens, led ultimately to the remarkable work of Bergius for the production of oil through the hydrogenation of coal at high temperature and pressure. Although the synthetic production of mineral oils can hardly be of more than academic interest in this country for many years, the possibility of the application of the general Bergius procedure to the amelioration of heavy oils and still bottoms was quickly recognized here. In 1927 the Standard Oil Company of New Jersey began research on a great scale at Baton Rouge, Louisiana, and a few years later a hydrogenation plant with a daily capacity of 5,000 barrels was started at Bayway, N. J., and the first unit was brought into operation in August, 1930. Thus applied, hydrogenation permits of the production at will of a wide variety of gasolines, other light hydrocarbons, and oils, and by the variation of carefully controlled conditions the products may be either of paraffinic or aromatic types. As an incidental advantage the sulphur present in the raw material is evolved and separated as H_2S.

The new technology has opened up a new and important field for the gas industry, since it has demonstrated the possibility of making a wide range of products from water gas. Methanol, of course, and some isopropyl and higher alcohols are now made from carbon monoxide and hydrogen by pressure catalytic processes, and it is even possible to produce the whole range of paraffins from methane to wax from these two gases. Ammonia and carbon dioxide are caused to react at 1,500 lbs. pressure and 150 deg. C. to produce urea available as a concentrated fertilizer and as a base for synthetic resins. We now produce synthetically methanol at the rate of millions of gallons a year. The price has been cut in half to the great advantage of the plastics industry, which consequently has available cheaper formaldehyde as a raw material for synthetic resins.

While it is one thing to develop methods and equipment for the production of compressed or liquefied gases and highly corrosive compounds, it is still another matter to develop equipment for their safe and economical transportation. So successfully, however, have the chemical engineers cooperated with the equipment makers that anhydrous ammonia is shipped in tank cars carrying 50,000 lbs., chlorine in cars of 30,000- and 60,000-lbs. capacity, while liquid carbon dioxide, sulphurous acid, propane and butane are transported as freely as fuel oil.

The most spectacular, however, of all high-pressure developments is, of course, that concerned with the production of synthetic ammonia, which has proceeded in this country along lines involving modification of the original method of Haber. Pressures in the various plants range from 3,000 to 4,000 lbs. as a minimum to 10,000 to 15,000 lbs. as a maximum. Through the operation of these processes the price of anhydrous ammonia has within a few years' time been reduced from 30 cents to as little as 5 cents a pound, with the result that ammonia is now one of the cheapest alkalies, and is available as a raw material for many uses from which it was previously precluded by its cost. The present daily capacity of more than 1,000 tons of the synthetic ammonia plants in the United States alone represents an advance which, in 1903, when the Atmospheric Products Company, at Niagara Falls, was operating the Bradley and Lovejoy process would have been regarded as bordering on the miraculous.

The quality of American chemical engineering and that of the research behind it is evidenced by the development of so many industries and the rise of so many corporations of imposing magnitude that it is impossible to make more than casual reference to a few illustrative examples here. Any adequate survey of the creative influence of chemical engineering upon American industry would expand this chapter to the proportions of an encyclopedia.

There are now more than two thousand makers of chemical engineering equipment and supplies in the United States. Many of them maintain extensive laboratories with semi-works or full-scale equipment for demonstration purposes and for the development or testing of new processes. To them we are indebted for many widely used appliances such as the Bethlehem pulverizer, the Oliver filter, the Dorr thickener and classifier, the Sharples supercentrifuge and many precision instruments for record and control. They have made Pyrex glass available in laboratory apparatus and in such things as bubble towers of commercial size. Other contributions range from rubber-lined tanks and corrosion-proof alloys to intricate ceramic structures.

The resourcefulness of the American chemical engineer was many times strikingly exhibited during the war, as, for instance, when the du Pont Company increased its annual capacity for military powder from 8,400,000 lbs. in 1914 to 440,000,000 lbs. It was shown again by John E. Teeple, to name one among many, by his development of the potash industry based on the complex brines of Searles Lake.

In 1893 the Willson process for calcium carbide provided a foundation upon which has been reared the great structure of Union Carbide & Carbon Corporation with thirty or more subsidiaries making a wide range of electric-furnace products and synthetic organic chemicals, liquid air, metals, alloys, batteries, and carbons for arc terminals, brushes and electrodes.

The Willson process branched and rooted like the banyan tree, and in 1907 the American Cyanamid Company was incorporated as another of its vigorous trunks. Cyanamid was first made commercially in Europe in 1905. Its manufacture was begun at Niagara Falls, Canada, in 1909, where the American methods, for which W. S. Landis was largely responsible, have reduced the consumption of raw materials by 20 per cent, although Canadian cyanamid carries 20 per cent more nitrogen than that made in Europe. Still more significant is the fact that the labor employed in Europe per unit of production is three times that required in the Canadian plant, where hand labor does not touch the product until it reaches the crude cyanamid stage.

In striking contrast to the attitude of labor in some other countries, and particularly in England, the American Federation of Labor, in 1919, published its conviction that "the increased production of industry resulting from scientific research is a most potent factor in the ever-increasing struggle of the workers to raise their standard of living."

In reviewing the remarkable development of chemical industry in America since 1907 the American Institute of Chemical Engineers can say, "All of this I saw and much of this I was." Membership in the profession has kept pace with this development. In 1910 there were only 869 chemical engineering students out of a total enrollment of 23,241 in our engineering schools, whereas Dr. John C. Olsen, for many years Secretary of the American Institute of Chemical Engineers and more recently its President, reported in 1931 that the engineering schools and universities having specialized chemical engineering courses had a total enrollment of 5,000 chemical engineering students and were annually graduating not far from 1,000 as chemical engineers.

Meanwhile, business has learned that research pays dividends. In 1907 the average executive could find time to steal away to an occasional ball game, but he could rarely be induced to waste an afternoon in visiting a research laboratory. That his attitude today is a radically different one is demonstrated by the success of the tours to industrial research laboratories organized and conducted under the auspices of the Division of Engineering and Industrial Research of the National Research Council. Eighteen laboratories in all were visited on the two tours, and the total of the two groups of bankers, general managers and other executives who participated was 138. The reaction of all of them was enthusiastic and sincere and may perhaps be summarized by the statement of a banker, who said, "It was one of the most instructive and inspiring experiences of my business life."

The laboratory has gained recognition as the nursery of industry, and M. C. Whitaker, in the paper which followed his reception of the Perkin Medal, said, "We believe that the place to start and finish a real chemical engineering problem is in the research laboratory." It is to the laboratory that we must look for those advances in fundamental science which provide new opportunities for the chemical engineer.

CHAPTER II

ACIDS AND HEAVY CHEMICALS IN RETROSPECT

By Henry Howard

Consulting Engineer, Newport, R. I.

IN WHAT FOLLOWS I shall attempt to set down the high-lights of heavy chemical development as I have observed them during the last 25 years (1908 to 1932 inclusive). As I have had personal contact with a good many of these, I must beg indulgence if I couch much of this history in the form of reminiscence of a fairly personal tone.

Sulphuric Acid

During the period covered by this report there were no such fundamental changes in the manufacture of sulphuric acid as characterized the preceding 25 years. The contact process had already received its initial development and a number of far-reaching improvements had also been accomplished in the older chamber plants.

In 1908 the Badische Anilin u. Soda Fabrik and the Bayer Co. at Leverkusen, were both producing huge quantities of strong sulphuric acid, and large quantities of oleum, using the Badische contact process. Meister, Lucius & Bruning, at Hoechst, were operating a process of their own development which was not as good as the Badische, but at the same time was giving them all the strong acid and oleum they needed for their very large works.

The Mannheim process, using iron oxide, was even at that time considered obsolete, although quite a large tonnage was being produced by its use in England, France, Germany and the United States. In Russia the field was held by the contact process of the Tentelevski Chemical Works. This process, in Europe, was probably second in its perfection of development to the Badische and in some respects was possibly superior. Its patents did not infringe Badische's and it is an interesting commentary on the honesty and unbiased character of the German courts that, as the result of a long suit instituted by Badische to prevent Tentelevski from licensing plants in Germany, the German court decided in Tentelevski's favor against Badische; by 1908 several plants of Tentelevski design were already operating in Germany, Holland, England and one in the United States.

15

In the United States in 1908, the General Chemical Co. was producing practically all of its concentrated acid by the Herreshoff contact process. The Merrimac Chemical Co., at Boston, had a very successful installation of the Tentelevski process. The New Jersey Zinc Co. and Harrison Bros., of Philadelphia, were using the Grillo-Schroeder process and in addition there were quite a number of small installations of the relatively inefficient Mannheim iron-oxide process.

At this period it was much more difficult to design and operate a contact sulphuric plant than is the case today, for the reason that the price of pure sulphur was so much higher than the price of sulphur in the form of pyrites, that nearly all the production of commercial sulphuric acid was made from the burning of pyrites. This necessitated a very careful purification of the gases to remove all traces of dust and particularly of arsenic which most of the pyrites contained in substantial quantity.

The period of 1908 to 1914 witnessed the greatest development of mechanical furnaces for burning fine pyrites. This improvement was forced by the huge quantities of pyrites fines which were available at very low prices and, up to that time, could only be burned in old-fashioned shelf burners which required much hand labor. McDougal's mechanical furnace, described by Lunge years before, had made little if any progress in the sulphuric-acid field in the United States. The small-capacity Herreshoff mechanical furnaces had, however, been making substantial gains for a number of years, and this was followed by the Wedge furnace in much larger sizes and shortly afterwards by large Herreshoff furnaces.

Such enormous increase in the use of mechanical fines furnaces created a new problem—dust. The first solution to this problem was given by the Howard dust chamber which I had designed to enable us to burn "washed spanish fines." At the time I started on the problem, this was a waste and unsalable product in Spain and could be bought very cheaply. In fact, a Spanish mine made us a present of 500 tons for experimental purposes. The design of this dust chamber was radically different from any in use up to that time and was, I believe, the first one designed on really scientific principles. It was described by Lunge in his 1913 edition of "Sulphuric Acid." By the outbreak of the war, this dust chamber was in use in nearly all the principal acid works in the United States and Europe. Shortly after the War, Dr. Carl Duisberg, chairman of the I. G. Farben Industrie, told me they had used it in Germany in the war plants for the production of sulphuric acid from gypsum, with portland cement as a byproduct.

This chamber was highly efficient and could have been made more so if the increased cost of the installation had warranted it. Its basic principles were exactly opposite to those generally used before. Whereas existing chambers used baffle plates or other means of changing and interfering with the flow of the gas, in the Howard dust chamber every precaution is taken to prevent stirring up the particles. Many plates were introduced parallel to the flow of the gas so as to reduce the distance through which the dust had to fall before coming to rest. Material can be settled out in this chamber which passes through the ordinary cyclone separator like smoke.

The Howard dust chamber has been largely superseded by the Cottrell precipitator which has the advantage of working continuously without periodic cleaning. The greatest credit is due the Research Corp. and the Western Precipitation Co. for the magnificent way in which they overcame the many difficult problems encountered in perfecting this radically new method of dust removal. The whole question, however, resolves itself into one of capital investment and I think it probable that there are still numerous problems that might be handled more economically by a modified Howard dust chamber design.

Up to the outbreak of the War, there was a very limited demand in the United States for any sulphuric acid stronger than 97 per cent H_2SO_4. The great bulk of concentrated sulphuric acid, prior to that time, was sold as oil of vitriol (66 deg. Bé.). During the war, however, the enormous demand for high explosives, and later on the development of the dye industry in the United States, created an ever-increasing need for oleum which was generally sold with 20 per cent free SO_3, although increasing tonnages of oleum containing 60 per cent free SO_3 are being sold today.

One of the most remarkable and radical designs for the contact process was developed by E. I. du Pont de Nemours & Co. during the War. Up to that time and, in fact, even at present there was and still is a very large quantity of lead required in most of the contact-process plants for the purification and cooling system. This was almost entirely done away with and iron and steel substituted in the du Pont process. This was made possible first by the fact that only sulphur was burned, eliminating all serious dust problems; and second by the clever design of the plant which provided either that only strong sulphuric acid should come in contact with the iron or steel apparatus, or that the temperature should be kept high enough to prevent all condensation of sulphuric acid and its accompanying corrosion of the iron.

Before 1913 it was possible to keep pretty well posted on all the developments of the sulphuric acid and alkali industry by reading the latest editions of Lunge's unequaled books on the subject. It seems to me out of place, therefore, to repeat the relatively complete descriptions given in his 1913 edition. It is a pity that no one with practical experience has stepped in to fill his place. To cover the progress from 1913 to the present time as completely and efficiently as this work used to be done by Lunge, would require at least five or six hundred pages and innumerable drawings and illustrations. It is a work that ought to be started by a young man of practical experience such as Lunge possessed, for he could follow it along for years to come, getting out a new edition every five or six years.

Vanadium Catalysts

Prior to 1924 or 1925, nearly all of the contact sulphuric acid made in the United States depended upon platinum as the catalyst. Even the old Mannheim iron oxide process was no exception, for it could not have been operated without the platinum catalysts at the end. About this time the vanadium catalysts began to make very substantial progress and this, combined with the fact that a considerable percentage of sulphuric acid in the United States was made from pure sulphur, has permitted a great simplification in the whole plant with corresponding reduction in its cost.

Platinum, as ordinarily used in platinized asbestos, is easily poisoned, especially by arsenic, while the vanadium catalyst is said to be immune. With Texas sulphur as the source of SO_2, practically all purification can be eliminated and a very cheap and efficient plant is thus made possible. In any plant where purification is necessary, as when sulphur is obtained from metallurgical sources, the cost of purifying the gas for a platinum mass may not be so much greater than the cost of purifying for vanadium. With properly purified gases, platinized asbestos will have a life of many years.

I was informed a few months ago that the converter for one of the plants which I had designed for the Grasselli Chemical Co., and which was started in 1922, had its first contact-mass renewal in the spring of 1932. During the whole of this period it was operated at an average of 50 per cent over its designed capacity. When you consider that, as an outside figure, the platinum in the contact mass does not exceed 5 to 10 per cent of the cost of a complete contact plant and that the cost of the vanadium catalyst is also a material amount, it will be seen that it takes only a very slight advantage in yield on the side of platinum to make its use more economical. Therefore, the best argument for the use of vanadium is in its immunity to poisoning and not in its lower first cost. In fact, I was informed recently by the Silica Gel Corp. that when silica gel is the supporting medium for platinum the mass becomes immune to the same poisons to which vanadium is immune. The explanation advanced is that the pores in the silica gel are too small to allow the poisons, which are in the nature of fumes and not true gases, to enter and establish contact with the platinum. I am unable to say how far this statement has been borne out by actual experience.

Tests do indicate, however, two advantages which a platinum mass has over a vanadium mass. First, there is a wider range of temperature over which the platinum mass will give a good conversion. The vanadium is stated to be more delicate and require closer regulation of temperature to get maximum conversion of 97 to 98 per cent. This is probably not a serious handicap where you have a perfectly uniform supply of SO_2 as in a plant producing acid from sulphur or pyrites; but in handling waste gases from smelter operations, where variations in composition are continually occurring, the ability of the platinum to give higher yield over a greater range of temperature has a very real value, especially where government regulations are stringent as to the amount of SO_2 discharged into the air.

Secondly, the platinum catalyst does not need so large an excess of oxygen as the vanadium catalyst. Unless this can be overcome, it is a serious and far-reaching objection to the use of vanadium. For instance, with platinum as a catalyst, when burning sulphur, excellent conversion can be obtained with up to 10-per cent SO_2 and fairly satisfactory conversion at concentrations even above this point. I am informed that in order to get equally good results with the vanadium catalyst the concentration of the SO_2 should not be over 8 per cent. If this is true it means, for instance, that if you have a plant with a maximum capacity of 100,000 lb. of sulphuric acid per day from sulphur, based on using a 10-per cent SO_2 gas and with a platinum catalyst, and you then change over to a vanadium catalyst, the capacity of your entire plant will be reduced to 80,000 lb. per day. In order to get the same capacity you not only have to use larger blowers but also more power in moving the larger quantity of gas required per unit of acid made. To what extent these disadvantages are offset by the simplification in the purification apparatus, I am unable to say.

From an engineering standpoint, some of the most interesting developments during the past ten years have been in the stainless steels and the special alloys which have been introduced, notably by Krupp in Germany and also in this country.   These corrosion-resisting alloys of high tensile strength and great durability open up an entirely new technique in the construction of chemical apparatus, particularly in that of dealing with heavy acids, especially phosphoric and nitric.   These alloys are used in many cases to replace lead or earthenware, giving a great increase in the life of apparatus and a decrease in the cost of repairs and renewals.   In the old days, when dealing with much of our chemical apparatus, we felt that it was wise to set aside a large reserve for obsolescence, but only a comparatively small allowance for depreciation.   This was because the current wear and tear was so terrific that the plant was being continually rebuilt and renewed as an operating expense, so that it was always in about the same condition of partial decay.

One of the most interesting examples of a modern contact plant that I have seen is that of the Merrimac Chemical Co. at Everett, Mass.   The plant was described in detail by Daniel S. Dinsmore in a paper read before the Institute of Chemical Engineers on June 10-12, 1931.   In this plant the air is first dried and then pumped into a burner which is under pressure and is fed with molten sulphur. From the burner, after slight cooling, the SO_2 goes at a temperature of about 300 deg. C. directly into the converter, containing a Monsanto vanadium mass.   All purification is eliminated except for the drying of the air in a sulphuric acid tower before it reaches the Roots blower and sulphur burner.   The plant burns 50,000 lb. of sulphur per day and is handled by one man on a shift with the addition of one mechanic during the day shift.   Sulphur is delivered in a special car which holds enough for one day's run.   Its contents feeds into a tank where the sulphur is melted by steam coils.   From here it is pumped directly to the sulphur burner.

The converter is said to give 97 to 98 per cent conversion of SO_2 to SO_3.   An interesting and notable feature about this plant is that the floor space for the complete installation is only about 112 sq. ft. per ton of sulphur per day while the adjoining old plant for the Herreshoff process, including pyrites burner rooms and purification system, requires over 1,000 sq. ft. per ton of sulphur per day.   It should be remembered, however, that this great saving is primarily due to the use of pure sulphur instead of pyrites.   Furthermore, if silica gel is as satisfactory a carrier as represented, an equally good and perhaps even better installation might be made with platinum as a catalyst.

Chamber Process

The chamber process for the manufacture of sulphuric acid is still a very important element in production, especially in the fertilizer field where weak acid only is required. One of the notable improvements in the chamber operation during the last ten years has been the introduction of nitrous gases made by the oxidation of ammonia. Except in cases where there is a good market for the sodium bisulphate which was a byproduct in the old method of potting nitre, the ammonia oxidation process shows substantial savings. It also has the advantage of being very easy to control and regulate. The raw material is generally "B" grade ammonia liquor shipped from the byproduct coke ovens in tank cars. The feed of nitre to the chamber process is then regulated by the feed of the ammonia liquor to the stripping column where the ammonia is flashed off in a steady stream and led mixed with air and with some preheating to the platinum gauze where it burns to the lower oxides of nitrogen.

This reminds me of the changes that have taken place in methods of supplying nitre to the chamber process within my recollection. My father, A. P. Howard, was vice president and superintendent of the Merrimac Chemical Co., beginning about 1872. I can remember, at the age of ten years, in 1878, visiting the works where there were several small sets of acid chambers. Brimstone imported from Sicily was the source of sulphur and was burned in large brick burners on iron pans which formed the bottom of the burners. The burner tops were also covered with cast-iron plates, and on these plates there were lead pans for concentrating chamber acid to 58 to 60 deg. Bé., utilizing the waste heat of the burning sulphur. This acid was in turn fed to a Gay Lussac tower. The acid leaving the bottom of the tower, and containing the recovered nitrous gases, was then quite completely denitrated in a small, quartz-packed steam column about 2 ft. in diameter and 6 ft. high. Nitrous gases coming from the top of the column, mixed with steam, were carried by means of an earthenware pipe into the first chamber and the acid running from the bottom of the column was also allowed to run into the first chamber by gravity. Acid for feeding the pans on top of the burners was also taken from the first chamber.

As a matter of fact, only a few years before my first visit, the chambers were run without even the Gay Lussac tower, all the nitrous fumes being allowed to escape. Nitric acid was introduced into the system by "potting" Chile nitrate of soda, which was charged in small rectangular cast iron pots about $10 \times 12 \times 8$ in. deep with four legs about 3 in. long cast on the bottom. These were introduced directly into the burner where the sulphur was burning. Sufficient 60 deg. Bé. sulphuric acid was added to the nitrate of soda to drive off the nitric acid and leave a strongly acid bisulphate of soda in the pot. The pots were, of course, charged at regular intervals and removed with a special fork of wrought iron. They were slightly flaring, so that when the nitre cake had cooled and solidified it would fall out when the pot was turned up-side-down.

Operating in this way, without a Gay Lussac tower, the nitrate of soda required was about 11 per cent of the weight of sulphur charged in the burner. My father managed to get hold of a book on sulphuric acid and with the aid of that constructed the first Gay Lussac tower which resulted in cutting the nitre consumption down to about 5 per cent or even slightly less. It was just about this time (1878) that a lead burner named Bowman came over from England and applied for work. He had been employed by Mr. Glover in the acid works where the Glover tower was developed and he persuaded my father to allow him to build a similar tower for one of our chamber sets at Woburn. This was, so far as I know, one of the earliest Glover towers built in the United States. It worked pretty well and was used for a number of years.

Ten years later I entered these works as chemist and one of my first problems was to provide a better connection between the burners and the Glover tower. This presented an interesting little problem in chemical engineering, although there was no profession called by that name at that period. The connection then in use consisted of a cast-iron pipe lined with tile set in fireclay cement. Under these conditions the iron pipe corroded rapidly and the sulphate of iron so formed would force the lining away from the shell, allowing more and more acid to condense on the pipe so that, in a comparatively short time, it was eaten through. Acid dripped on the floor, soaking into the foundations under the burners and under the tower where it combined with the lime in the mortar, forming bulky sulphate of calcium and resulted in heaving both the burners and the tower foundation out of line. An analysis of this situation convinced me that the covering should have been on the outside instead of on the inside of the cast-iron pipe, thereby keeping it so hot that no acid could condense. The connection made in this manner was, of course, a complete solution to the difficulty and illustrates the innumerable problems of similar nature which were arising and being overcome almost daily in the acid industry at that period.

To return again to the question of nitre supply to the chambers, in 1908 the supply in the United States was generally furnished by comparatively large nitre pots set in brick work and heated by the heat from burner gases. In fact, the pots were generally set directly in the gas stream. At that time in Europe, the general custom was to use weak nitric acid from the nitric acid plant, and to introduce this at the top of the Glover tower. By using this weak acid it greatly simplified the operation of nitric acid plants where the object was usually to produce as much strong acid as possible. I introduced this practice at the Merrimac Chemical Co.'s works in 1905 upon my return from Europe and it was also adopted in many other works in the United States. It is not, of course, applicable to fertilizer plants which do not produce nitric acid. Even at present it is economically possible in works where nitric acid is still being made from nitrate of soda and sulphuric acid. Because of the high price obtained for the byproduct, sodium bisulphate, I am informed that in one case, at least, synthetic nitrate of soda, i.e., nitrate of soda made from the neutralization of nitric acid (obtained in its turn from the oxidation of synthetic ammonia) is actually being used for the manufacture of nitric acid according to the old process.

Another method which was economical and satisfactory consisted of introducing the nitrate of soda in solution either as a spray into the first chamber or, as I believe was first used by the Virginia-Carolina Chemical Co., in an intermediate tower located between the Glover and the first chamber where the temperature was claimed to be sufficiently high to obtain perfect denitration. The solution of nitrate of soda was run over this tower in a continuous stream. The tower itself was said to be an excellent sulphuric acid maker. The acid running out at the bottom was kept separate and retained for use where the sodium sulphate would not be objectionable as, for instance, in the manufacture of superphosphate.

In 1890 it was considered good practice in the chamber process to burn 1 lb. of sulphur for 20 cu. ft. of chamber space. By 1908 this had changed to 1 lb. to 9 or 10 cu. ft., which meant that so far as the chambers themselves were concerned, the production had been a little more than doubled. However, this was not all clear gain. What had made the speeding up of the reaction possible was the operation of the chambers with a much greater percentage of lower oxides of nitrogen in circulation, and in order to avoid losing these, it was necessary to have a much larger Gay Lussac tower for the recovery of these nitrogen compounds than would have been necessary at the lower rate of operation. This in turn meant that a much larger Glover tower was necessary to take care of the larger quantity of hot gases coming from the burner and to give the larger quantity of strong acid which would be required for feeding the larger Gay Lussac towers.

Another change which resulted in increased capacity was the substitution of water sprays in place of steam for supplying the water necessary for the chamber process. This, of course, avoided introducing the latent heat of the steam as well as its sensible heat.

I personally introduced water sprays in the chambers at Merrimac as early as 1903 but used them only in the first and second chambers. On my European visit in 1905 I was interested to find that sprays were being used extensively and that steam had been entirely displaced in most of the up-to-date plants. This practice was put into effect at our works immediately upon my return. As an example of the extreme slowness with which ideas of this sort make progress in the United States, I know of several very large chamber sets which were still using steam as late as 1920 in spite of what would seem to be the obvious advantages of water sprays.

Still another change which was introduced about this period was the much more efficient air cooling of the lead walls of the chambers. In order to accomplish this, the horizontal members of the frame which formerly had been used to support the lead, were done away with, open-work floors between chambers were provided for the admission of cooling air and very large ventilating stacks on the top of the building supplied the draft for drawing the air up between the chambers. In spite of all these methods it was customary to run the chambers at a considerably higher temperature than had formerly been the case, and this in turn made it necessary to construct the chambers of heavier lead. The result of all this evolution was that large towers with more liberal pumping arrangements and lead fans for more draft represented a larger and larger percentage of the cost of the plant, so it was not a very long step to abandon the chambers and work the process entirely with towers and this was actually done in a number of installations. A notable design of this type is that of Larison at Anaconda which has worked well and produced large tonnages of sulphuric acid.

The Opl tower system was developed in Austria over 20 years ago but has not so far as I know made any progress in this country. The Schmiedel box is another development which received quite a little publicity four or five years ago but apparently made no progress in the United States.

The Gaillard spray tower chamber is well spoken of but I do not know of any installations in this country. Gaillard was a pioneer in the development of spray towers. His sulphuric acid concentrating tower was extensively used in Europe as early as 1914. His residence and his own works were located at Barcelona, Spain.

In the development of intensively worked chambers, the Mills-Packard system is perhaps the most interesting and radical departure that we have had in sulphuric-acid design. It consists of water-cooled chambers built in the shape of truncated cones. The Armour Fertilizer Co. have two Mills-Packard chamber sets, one located at Jacksonville, Florida, and the other at Wilmington, North Carolina. These sets have been operating for a number of years and are stated to have proved quite satisfactory. Some changes were made in the method of construction when they put them up. The cost of manufacture has not been out of line and there has been no trouble from leakage of water into the chambers. They are fireproof and will stand high wind and are stated to be best suited for southern conditions where it is hot so much of the year. Production keeps up during summer, nitre consumption is normal, i.e., about the same as with the old-fashioned sets. The investment cost is low per unit of capacity. Good operation has been obtained at a capacity of $2\frac{1}{2}$ cu. ft. per lb. of sulphur burned, and this same company has worked in their old-style chambers to a capacity of 5 to $5\frac{1}{2}$ cu. ft. per lb. of sulphur burned.

In spite of all these developments it is undoubtedly true that by far the largest tonnage of chamber-acid production is still in lead chambers. The explanation of the persistence in the use of chambers lies in their simplicity and relative cheapness of construction. This is especially true today owing to the low cost of lead.

On the other hand, however, rapid progress has been made with contact process. The size of units has been increased continuously and the cost of plant per ton of capacity steadily reduced. Moreover, the wear and tear on a well-built, well-designed contact plant was found to be very much less than on a chamber plant, so that today I doubt whether anyone who has had equal experience in building and operating both types of plant would consider the construction of a chamber plant, even for weak acid.

One very interesting and possibly far-reaching development of recent years is the flash-burning of finely pulverized, sulphur-bearing ore. This method would appear to be particularly applicable in the metallurgical field where huge quantities of sulphur-bearing ore have been finely pulverized to permit concentration by the flotation process. Such ores are difficult to burn in the old-fashioned mechanical pyrites furnaces which, moreover, require a very large plant investment. Flash-burning of pyrites was described in a paper by Freeman, read before the summer meeting of the American Institute of Chemical Engineers in June, 1931.

A similar principle has been perfected by the Consolidated Mining & Smelting Co., of Canada, Ltd., at Trail, B.C. Here the installation for flash-burning is applied to zinc blend and the roasting is carried on more efficiently than before and entirely without the use of any auxiliary fuel such as has been necessary for the dead-roasting of this material in the furnaces formerly used. Moreover, the capacity of these flash-roasting furnaces is enormous and the capital investment a fraction of the cost of the old mechanical furnaces. This field should be a very fertile one for designers and inventors at the present moment, and although many difficulties may be encountered, I feel confident of the ultimate success of this method.

NITRIC ACID

Two revolutions in the manufacture of nitric acid have taken place since 1908. At that time practically all the acid produced in this country was condensed in earthenware or glass apparatus. High-silicon iron had been used for the concentration of sulphuric acid in Europe as early as 1905 by Bencker & Co. as a substitute for porcelain or glass dishes in the old cascade system for the concentration of sulphuric acid. My recollection is that Bencker told me the castings contained about 15 per cent silicon. A few years later high-silicon iron, under the name of Duriron, was beginning to be used for the entire construction of a nitric acid plant. This got away from the continual breakages and leaks which were so hard to overcome when using earthenware apparatus and also made possible the construction of larger units than had previously been the practice. A much greater efficiency of the whole plant was also obtained by the addition of liberal absorption towers, taking the exhausts from all the earthenware or Duriron condensation units, thus saving all the lower oxides which came off. These towers were, of course, packed with coke or acid-resisting material, water being recirculated over the back tower and then working gradually forward, countercurrent to the gas. Three to six towers in series were used, giving nitric acid of 36 to 40 deg. Bé. I saw these towers in use in nitric acid works in Germany in 1905 and introduced them at the nitric plant of the Merrimac

Chemical Co. immediately on my return. Dr. Charles L. Reese carried out a similar program on a much larger scale at about the same time, or possibly earlier, at the duPont works. This resulted in increasing the yield in both his works and ours from around 92 per cent of the theoretical up to 97 per cent or 98 per cent and yet, strange as it may seem, one of the largest works in this country continued operating without this system as late as 1920.

The second revolution in nitric-acid production was much more significant than the one just described and involved its manufacture by the oxidation of atmospheric nitrogen, either directly or indirectly. The direct method was never used on any very large scale in the United States but was carried out extensively in Norway with the exceedingly cheap water power there available. However, with the development of the Haber process for the production of ammonia from atmospheric nitrogen, it was found to be exceedingly simple to convert this ammonia into lower oxides of nitrogen simply by burning it in air in the presence of a catalyst. For this catalyst platinum gauze has been almost universally used. There are two general methods of carrying this out, one at atmospheric pressure and the other at a considerably higher pressure. The latter process has been developed and patented by the duPont Co. and is used in their own works as well as by a number of licensees. Probably the ·greatest tonnage of nitric acid is, however, produced by the other process at atmospheric pressure. It is said to give somewhat higher yields than the duPont process but with a considerably more expensive absorption plant, because, under pressure, the absorption goes much more quickly and the absorbing apparatus is less costly. The old method of making HNO_3 from nitrate of soda, however, is by no means done away with. With so many plants making the acid from ammonia, byproduct sodium bisulphate, which used to be a waste product very difficult to sell in the large quantities in which it was produced, has now become relatively scarce. At any rate, it is no longer a waste product. The price has gone up to such an extent that it looks as if there would always be a certain number of plants where it would be found profitable to continue the manufacture from nitrate of soda, simply for the sake of the byproduct, sodium bisulphate.

MURIATIC ACID AND SALT CAKE

This whole problem has been so completely changed around by new conditions, that old manufacturers, brought up in the LeBlanc soda process, would be dazed at the present situation. Soda ash and caustic soda are no longer produced from decomposition of common salt by sulphuric acid, which involved the production of immense quantities of muriatic acid and, in turn, of chlorine and bleaching powder. The process is now frequently reversed and electrolytic chlorine is combined directly with hydrogen to form synthetic hydrochloric acid of great purity and high concentration. Sulphate of soda, however, is still needed for various purposes such as the manufacture of glass, the sulphate process for kraft paper and the manufacture of glaubers salt, used extensively in dyeing. There is hardly any other chemical whose price has fluctuated more than sulphate of soda. Sometimes it is sold at a considerably higher price than its equivalent in soda ash and at other times as low as $3 a ton. Large quantities are produced as a byproduct from other processes. Since byproducts are inevitable and the material must be sold or thrown away, the price may go way down. On the other hand, conditions may change so that the amount of byproduct sulphate produced is less than the amount consumed and the price again goes way up. Then you have to jump in at once to its manufacture from common salt and sulphuric acid. This demonstrates the fact that it is always difficult to have to deal with a process which produces two products in a definite proportion, each of which must be marketed. You nearly always find that there is a feast with one and a famine with the other and that they are practically never on a balance. When at the Merrimac Chemical Co., I have seen stocks of muriatic acid stored all over the yard in quantities of 20,- or 30,000 carboys. Then, perhaps, two years later a shortage of muriatic acid would develop and huge stock piles of sulphate of soda would appear, only to be stored out-of-doors, exposed to the rain, because their value was so low you could not afford to build a building to keep the weather off. Hand salt-cake furnaces were generally used in this country up to the beginning of the present century, but by 1908 the Mannheim mechanical furnace was being extensively employed, although at that time its application was almost entirely limited to the decomposition of salt with sodium bisulphate.

About 1908 improvements were made in the furnace which allowed sulphuric acid to be directly combined with salt in the furnace and this, with slight modifications, is the apparatus used today in making sulphate of soda and muriatic acid from common salt.

In the condensation of muriatic acid, much progress has been made. In 1908 absorption towers of sandstone, packed with coke, were still extensively used. No artificial cooling was provided for the acid with the result that very large towers were required for a small amount of gas and the yields were none too good. In Germany, however, as early as 1905 I saw small earthenware towers in use with acid recirculating over them and the heat removed by cooling coils, or their equivalent, introduced into the acid circulation system of each tower. This resulted in an enormous increase in efficiency and made it easy to produce stronger acid. At that time there used to be two qualities of muriatic acid produced, one called "pot acid," the other "furnace acid." The pot acid was relatively pure and nearly free from sulphuric acid, while the furnace acid always contained a considerable percentage of free H_2SO_4 which had been driven off by the high temperature of the furnace. An elaborate process perfected by the Verein Chemiker Fabriken was supposed to overcome this impurity and consisted in passing the gas through scrubbing towers, fed with oil, which was supposed to have a selective absorption capacity for sulphuric acid, while allowing the muriatic acid gas to pass through. The Bayer Leverkusen works brought about purification by means of an absorption tower in front of the regular tower, over which impure muriatic acid was recirculated. Later on it developed that all that was necessary to remove the sulphuric acid was first to cool the gas thoroughly and then to filter it through a bed of carefully sized coke, through 10 and on 20 mesh. By this simple method all the acid can now be turned out of quality which is even better than the acid formerly called "pot acid."

It is a hard question to predict the future of manufacture of sulphate of soda and muriatic acid from common salt and sulphuric acid. It is another case of one product depending upon the demand or sale of another and no one can foretell what the years will bring forth.

Glaubers Salt

Radical changes have been made in the method of producing this product by the adoption of continuous crystallizers, notably the Swenson-Walker crystallizer, which consists of a stationary, water-cooled, U-shaped trough of considerable length, generally placed in banks of two or three. These troughs are provided with stirrers or scrapers and have given very satisfactory results in many fields. The Zahn rotating-drum crystallizer is also used for a considerable production of glaubers salt and is also said to give excellent results.

Continuous centrifugals have made a good deal of progress during the period under discussion, but the most recent progress has been rather disappointing, which I feel certain is due to faults in the respective designs and that continuous centrifugals will sooner or later completely displace the batch variety.

ALUMINA AND SALTS OF ALUMINUM

There has been very little change in the manufacture of alumina or hydrate of alumina from bauxite since 1908 except as regards the scale of operation. The Bayer process still holds undisputed control of the field in the United States. This process is well suited to the treatment of bauxite reasonably low in silica and as long as such ores are available in such large quantities as at present, the outlook for the development of the many processes which have been proposed for treatment of clay and other ores is decidedly poor.

About 1911 a great deal was expected of the Serpek process. At that time a fairly good-sized semicommercial plant had been successfully operated by the Aluminium Francaise, at St. Jean de Maurienne, Savoy, France. The results with this semicommercial plant had been so encouraging that a large full-sized plant was in course of construction, costing three or four hundred thousand dollars. I knew Serpek quite well. He was a very brilliant fellow, and his calculation had all been checked and rechecked by the French engineers. Everyone was full of enthusiasm. Old Daniel Guggenheim was a relative of one of the officials in the French company. They were so sure of the success of the plant that they advised him immediately to start construction of a similar unit in this country. He asked me to come in and advise him. I strongly advised against building until the large-scale plant in France had been tried and found successful, my reason being that there are so many things which make a difference between a small-scale and a large-scale operation. He probably saved at least half a million dollars by following my advice, because the French plant was an absolute failure. The Aluminum Co. of America, a little later, also carried out large-scale experiments in this country which were unsuccessful.

The Serpek process consisted in passing atmospheric nitrogen over bauxite heated to about 1,600 deg. C. The nitrogen had to be free from oxygen and the oxygen in the air was converted into carbon monoxide which was inert in the reaction. The result was the formation of aluminum nitride which, on treatment with caustic-soda solution, formed sodium aluminate and ammonia gas. This reaction in the French plant was carried out in a cement-kiln type of apparatus about 250 ft. long and 8 or 10 ft. in diameter. The hottest zone of this kiln was heated electrically. The whole process failed because of the difficulty of bringing a large enough quantity of hot nitrogen in close contact with alumina heated to the right point. The white-hot bauxite, lying in the bottom of the kiln, exposed only a comparatively small surface in proportion to its weight. One group after another seemed to think they could solve the difficulty, but so far as I know, there is no commercial plant using this process today.

The old Bayer process was originally invented by Dr. J. K. Bayer, an Austrian chemist who did all his development work in Russia. The first plant was in the works of P. K. Oushkoff in his plant at Elabouga on the Kama River, not far from the Ural Mountains. I went out there in 1893 and spent ten days in the plant and was so favorably impressed with the process that I bought the American patent for the Merrimac Chemical Co. The contract provided that Bayer should design the plant and come to the United States to supervise its erection and put it in operation. This he did, but the plant was considerably larger than that which he had in operation in Russia and caused many new problems to be encountered. Before we had this plant in operation, Paul Heroult, the inventor of aluminum in France, had obtained rights for France for this process and came over to study the plant we were erecting. This was the beginning of a long friendship with Heroult which lasted until his death in 1914. Since 1908 there has been no fundamental change in the carrying out of the Bayer process except that a much larger apparatus is used and Dorr thickener equipment has been applied in separating the fine from the coarser hydrate of alumina. Hand filter presses have been abandoned to make room for the modern type of filters, with a great saving in labor.

ALUM AND SULPHATE OF ALUMINA

When I first went into business we were just in the transition period from potash and ammonia alum to sulphate of alumina. No such radical change has, of course, taken place since 1908. The iron-free alum is practically all made by dissolving hydrate of alumina in pure sulphuric acid, the hydrate of alumina generally being obtained from the Bayer process. Nearly all of the ordinary commercial sulphate of alumina is made by dissolving bauxite in sulphuric acid, settling the solution, concentrating it until it solidifies to the proper strength on cooling, then grinding and shipping. The only notable modification in this process is the introduction of continuous operation instead of batch operation, continuous operation having been developed with the aid of Dorr equipment. This method has been by no means universally adopted, however, as many manufacturers still believe that a properly designed plant built for batch operation is preferable. I have not had any personal experience with a continuously operated plant, but judging from the description by G. E.

Walker, which was published in *Chem. & Met.*, Nov. 17, 1924, considerably more evaporation was required than is necessary in at least some of the batch-operated plants with which I am familiar. I believe, however, it might be possible to overcome this objection.

Attempts to substitute clay for bauxite as a raw material are continually being made, but I understand that by far the largest quantity of aluminum salts is still produced from bauxite. The impression which seems to have been prevalent in the United States for the past 30 years that there is a shortage of bauxite is far from true and never has been true during that period.

CHAPTER III

ORGANIC CHEMICAL INDUSTRIES OF THE UNITED STATES HAVE MADE MOST PROGRESS SINCE 1908

By M. E. Putnam
Production Manager, Dow Chemical Company, Midland, Mich.

I N THIS CHAPTER an attempt will be made to outline the status of the organic chemical industry, to explain its unique position in America at the beginning of the period under consideration, to discuss in some detail a few of the more interesting developments, and to summarize briefly the progress made. The past 25 years unquestionably cover the period of the most rapid and important development which the industry has ever had in this or any other country. We have grown from a nation largely dependent upon foreign countries to one that supplies all of the major pharmaceutical, textile and industrial needs for 120,000,000 people, and in addition does considerable exporting.

Epoch-making developments always have basic underlying causes. In examining the setting which made this organic chemical development possible, we must look for things peculiar to this country, otherwise the advance would have been made concurrently in other countries. Probably the two most important factors were the well developed sources of raw materials, and an enormous domestic market. We had the further advantage of equipment manufacturers who could meet any reasonable demand. Even with these advantages we would have been handicapped except for a large number of men with sound chemical and scientific training who could, and did, cooperate with men experienced in heavy chemical production and other types of manufacturing. With the stage all set and significant progress beginning to be made, the advent of the World War shut off the main source of supply of organic chemicals, not only from this country but from the entire civilized world outside of Germany. Thus it will be seen that we had the most favorable set-up imaginable for rapid development of the organic chemical industry. The only element lacking was experience.

Situation in 1908. Properly to understand the progress made, it is necessary to consider the situation at the beginning of this period.

33

In 1908 we had well developed coke ovens which were great potential sources of benzol and toluol. Naphthalene, phenols and cresols were produced by the Barrett Co. directly from coal tar. Schoellkopf, Hartford and Hanna manufactured a limited line of dyestuffs, Heller and Merz made dyes of the eosin type, and some other manufacturers assembled colors for printing inks and paints. The wood distillation industry was in a relatively strong position. The country was well supplied with acetic acid, methyl alcohol, and acetone. Ethyl alcohol was also available in quantity. Synthetic aliphatic compounds were just struggling into existence. Chloroform was made by the action of bleaching powder on acetone.

In the early part of the period under discussion, the Dow Chemical Co., which had already achieved success in the manufacture of chlorine and bromine, turned attention to the organic field as an outlet for its products. The first attempt resulted in the manufacture of chloroform by a purely synthetic process, the raw materials being carbon in the form of charcoal, hydrogen from iron and water, and chlorine. On the face of things, an attempt to manufacture chloroform by this scheme showed evidence of remarkable faith in the theories of organic chemistry. However, as actually carried out, the process was not quite such a strain on one's chemical credulity.

Commercial Synthesis of Chloroform. Charcoal and sulphur were heated together to produce carbon bisulphide. Sulphur and chlorine were allowed to react, with the formation of sulphur chloride. Then the carbon bisulphide was treated with the sulphur chloride, and carbon tetrachloride formed. The carbon tetrachloride was reduced with fine iron and water under carefully controlled conditions, and chloroform resulted. At first the carbon bisulphide was purchased from the Taylor Process Co., but as soon as the chloroform business was definitely established a plant was built for its production.

This process involved several interesting chemical engineering problems. All of its reactions required careful heat control. All were corrosive; some were violent. New types of apparatus had to be evolved. To the best of my knowledge, the large rotating tumbler with accurate heat control was first used in this plant for organic reactions on a large scale. At the cost of much work and at least one explosion, relatively safe ways of reacting carbon bisulphide and sulphur chloride were found. New columns were developed for accurately fractionating chloroform and carbon tetrachloride, both of which were too corrosive for the ordinary columns then in use. Later, carbon tetrachloride proved of much greater importance than the chloroform for which the process was originally designed. With the further progress of chemical engineering in solvent recovery in the dry cleaning field, this material will continue to increase in importance.

Hydrocarbon Derivatives. More recent developments in the aliphatic field, by the Carbide and Carbon Chemicals Corporation, have started with hydrocarbons as a raw material. Among the more important products are ethylene chloride, propylene chloride and chlorohydrin. In the case of these compounds the problem was two-fold; first, the manufacturer had to overcome the scientific and engineering difficulties inherent in pioneer enterprises, and second, it was necessary to find a suitable market or practical use for the product. In this case the first two compounds found a use in the field of special solvents. Chlorohydrin, in addition to becoming the starting point for a whole series of solvents, was also used to produce glycol which has found a wide use in automobile radiators to prevent freezing, and in the manufacture of explosives. Chlorohydrin is also a starting point for various organic syntheses.

Acetic Anhydride. At the beginning of the period under consideration, acetic acid was well known in industry as an organic acid and in the form of calcium acetate was used as a raw material for acetone but it found little application in the synthetic field except for the production of esters. War developments brought about a demand for acetic anhydride. This was used in quantity for the production of cellulose acetate coatings for combat airplanes, as well as for aspirin manufacture. The manufacture of acetic anhydride involved numerous technical difficulties, which were solved promptly. Acetic anhydride assumed increasing importance with the development of acetate silk, and today ranks among the more important synthetic chemicals.

Acetic Acid. Monochloroacetic acid production grew along with the production of synthetic indigo. Its use, however, was not confined to indigo but extended to the production of pharmaceuticals and lachrymatory material (chloroacetophenone) for filling shells.

These new uses, together with increases in the old, led to the search for a source of glacial acetic acid independent of the wood distillation industry. This was found in acetylene, Two processes are in use; in the older, by means of a catalyst, acetylene is combined with water to form acetaldehyde which in turn is oxidized to acetic acid. In the newer process, sodium acetate is produced directly by the action of caustic soda upon acetylene, with the evolution of hydrogen. The production of acetic acid and its derivatives can now, if necessity should arise, become entirely independent of the wood distillation or fermentation industries.

Aniline Processes. Turning to the field of aromatic compounds, an outstanding development in the industry was the manufacture of aniline, one of the most important chemicals used in dye and rubber manufacture. At the beginning of the period under discussion this country was entirely dependent upon foreign sources of supply. After several abortive attempts by other concerns, the Benzol Products Co., organized in 1912 by The Barrett Co., General Chemical Co. and Solvay Sales Corp., successfully undertook the manufacture of aniline. This was a very timely key development, in that this organization was just nicely under way in the manufacture of aniline and other basic intermediates at the time the World War broke out. The organizers of the Benzol Products Co. are to be especially commended for building up their business in the face of bitter and unscrupulous foreign competition at a time when the tariff and the public did not give them the backing to which they were entitled.

As a result of the world shortage of aniline caused by the War, numerous plants sprang up in various parts of the country. Most of these used modifications of the older Perkins process, although at least two processes, one dispensing with the use of nitric acid by substituting sodium nitrate and another using sodium sulphide and obtaining hypo as a byproduct, were in operation. After the confusion and excitement of the War had died away, three main producers were left using the Perkins process which had been greatly improved by changes in size and design of apparatus and by the application of sound chemical engineering to each step of the process. These improvements, together with a better knowledge of acid recovery and low-cost nitric acid from synthetic ammonia, brought production costs down to a point heretofore not even hoped for, especially during the hectic days of the War.

Since 1918 an aniline process has been developed using chlorobenzol and ammonia. It involves the use of relatively high pressures, a catalyst, and especially designed equipment. With cheap chlorobenzol and ammonia this process has made very rapid progress, and notwithstanding its recent development accounts for a relatively large percentage of the aniline used in the country at the present time.

Synthetic Phenol. One of the first major organic chemical industries to develop as a direct result of the World War was the manufacture of synthetic phenol. At first, the problem was to get phenol quickly at any price. Plants were hastily thrown together; as many as 15 were in operation at one time. However, as it became evident that the War was to have considerable duration, plants were rebuilt with greater efficiency and with more regard for chemical engineering principles. Among the organizations which entered this field was that of Thomas A. Edison which succeeded in manufacturing some product, and in getting a glowing write-up of its achievement in the *American Magazine.* However, the game was too stiff, and regardless of the unlimited demand for phenol at tremendous prices this plant was unable to continue.

As the War progressed and the prices more nearly approached reason, the weaker and less experienced firms dropped out. The total production at one time exceeded 320,000 lb. per day, which was a tremendous quantity of a difficult synthetic material to be produced by an industry less than three years of age. These plants were fairly well designed and operated with a reasonable degree of efficiency. This development made possible the manufacture on a very large scale of picric acid which was one of the most important high explosives used by the allies and was an important factor in winning the War. After the Armistice, these plants stopped production, leaving the country with such an enormous stock of phenol that everyone lost interest in its further production.

Even at the close of the World War, however, the problem of manufacturing really cheap phenol had not been solved. Generally the problems of mass production and low costs are solved simultaneously. In this case, however, due to war conditions, low costs followed to some extent but did not keep pace with increased production.

For some years after the War, the country obtained its phenol from excess war stocks. As these approached exhaustion, phenol manufacture was undertaken by four companies, namely, the Bakelite Corp., Monsanto Chemical Works, the Southern Dyestuffs Co., and the Dow Chemical Co. The first three of these used modifications of the sulphonic acid process. The rapid development of the plastic industry furnished a large market. The experience of these companies has been a battle against cost. The Bakelite Corp. dropped out. The Rubber Service Laboratories took over the Southern Dyestuffs Co. and were themselves absorbed later by the Monsanto Chemical Works. Developments in the sulphonic acid process have been such that it is only possible for a manufacturer of sulphuric acid and caustic soda to operate under present price conditions.

The Dow Chemical Co. developed the chlorobenzol process which operates under high pressure and makes possible the production of very cheap phenol, provided that cheap chlorine and caustic soda are available. It is possible to operate the process so that diphenyl oxide will be produced. This material is a valuable liquid for high temperature heat transfer work and is used to some extent in the perfume industry. Other byproducts of this process are paraphenylphenol (a raw material for synthetic varnish resin) and orthophenylphenol which by itself, or in the form of derivatives, possesses unique and important germicidal and fungicidal properties. Because this process readily lends itself to production methods and low labor costs, and because of the importance of its byproducts, it occupies a leading position in the production of synthetic phenol. It would have been virtually impossible to have carried out this process without the improvements in welding and high-pressure technology which have been developed largely since the War.

As though, seemingly, the development of two independent processes were not sufficient for a basic material like phenol, physical chemistry and chemical engineering applied to coke-oven byproducts have furnished a very large supply of low-cost phenol for the plastic industries and potentially made available a much larger supply.[1]

The fundamental scientific facts relating to the three processes listed above, with the exception of part of the chlorobenzol process, were known before or during the War. However, the application of science and sound chemical engineering and manufacturing principles has since brought down the cost of production to a fraction of the previous figure.

Diphenyl. An entirely new material to be produced commercially during the last few years is diphenyl. This was first produced by the Federal Phosphorus Co. of Anniston, Ala., for heat transfer purposes, for which it is admirably adapted, in this respect closely resembling diphenyl oxide, which has been mentioned in connection with the phenol synthesis. The resemblance between diphenyl and diphenyl oxide goes further, in that, when chlorinated, both give commercially valuable products especially for dielectric purposes. Diphenyl also serves as a starting point for the synthesis of para-hydroxydiphenyl which is used in self-drying varnish resins.

---

[1] See McCloskey, G. E., "Coal-Tar Distillation by Hot Gas at Coke-Oven Plants," *Chem. & Met. Eng.*, Vol. 39, p. 333-5 (1932).

Monochlorobenzol. Another starting point for important products not manufactured in this country at the beginning of the period under consideration is monochlorobenzol. The production of this material was not begun until after the World War started. The demand for military purposes (for the manufacture of dinitrophenol) and for dye manufacture caused American chemical manufacturers to take an early interest. The first plants were crude affairs, giving very poor yields of a rather inferior product due to improperly designed equipment and a lack of fundamental knowledge of most of the factors involved. Corrosion was an extremely troublesome problem. The byproducts were large in quantity, and practically worthless. Today the manufacturing difficulties have been very largely overcome. The byproducts have all found a use either in their own right or as derivatives, and as far as tonnage is concerned chlorobenzol ranks among the largest synthetic organic products.

Phthalic Acid. The commercial adaptation of the Gibbs process for the direct oxidation of naphthalene to phthalic acid by the Monsanto and Selden companies is a development of outstanding importance to the American chemical industry. Its benefits are distributed among the manufacturers of pharmaceuticals, perfumes, synthetic resins and dyes. The dye manufacturers probably profit most, as phthalic anhydride is the starting point for a large number of vat dyes of the anthraquinone and indanthrene types. Its manufacture is a fine example of chemical engineering ability applied to a very difficultly controlled reaction.

Dyestuffs. During the past 25 years the organic chemical development which has most attracted and interested the general public has been that of the dye industry. At the beginning of this period the industry had a small but sound development in the Schoellkopf plant at Buffalo. Its position was greatly strengthened by the development of sources of raw materials and intermediates before the War. Accordingly, when European supplies were shut off this organization was in a position to expand at a tremendous rate. Naturally, under the circumstances, the early expansion was along the lines most easily developed. It so happened that the dyes thus produced were unsuited to many uses to which they were put, and American dyes temporarily received a bad reputation, when in reality the manufacturers should have received considerable credit for meeting the situation as well as they did.

The dye which always has been, and still is, used in by far the largest quantities is indigo, which on account of its romantic history and production possibilities has long interested both the chemist and manufacturer. The large and expensive plant required, together with involved process and uncertainty regarding the length of the War, caused manufacturers to hesitate at first. However, in the summer of 1916, this problem was attacked by the Dow Chemical Co., and very early in 1917 synthetic indigo was being produced in Midland. E. I. du Pont de Nemours & Co. and the National Aniline and Chemical Co. came into the field later, and the three plants now not only supply American needs but export large quantities. This accomplishment, while important from an economic standpoint, was even more important from a moral standpoint because it tended to remove the heretofore strong doubts as to whether America could produce a self-contained and vigorous dye and organic chemical industry. Later, developments have been confined principally to vat dyes and direct colors of the naphthol A. S. type. The American dye industry is now one of the most complete and important in the world.

Pharmaceuticals. In the synthetic pharmaceutical field some progress had been made before the period under consideration, particularly by the Heyden Chemical Co. who were manufacturing salicylic acid and salicylates prior to 1908. During and since the War, remarkable progress has been made in synthetic medicinals. Salicylates, especially aspirin, are the most important from a tonnage as well as value standpoint. Acetphenetidine, antipyrene, barbital and its derivatives, and synthetic germicides are now made in quantities sufficient to meet this country's needs and of a better quality than previously known.

The foregoing account of the development of the organic chemical industry during the past 25 years is necessarily very incomplete. Further, the emphasis is based on personal interest and knowledge rather than on any attempt to treat the various developments in exact accordance with their relative importance. However, it is hoped that it will contribute in some measure to the purpose for which this book has been planned, namely, to recall the remarkable progress of chemical engineering in all of our various industries.

CHAPTER IV

SOLVENTS SHOW STRIKING ADVANCES SINCE 1908

By Fred C. Zeisberg

Technical Investigator, Development Department,
E. I. du Pont de Nemours & Co., Wilmington, Del.

WHEN the American Institute of Chemical Engineers was founded in 1908, lacquer solvents, and the solvents closely related to them, were manufactured exclusively from agricultural products. Acetone and acetic acid, the latter used to esterify alcohols to produce a line of indispensable acetates, were derived from wood distillation, as was methanol. Ethyl alcohol and fusel oil resulted from the fermentation of grain (starch) or molasses. Butyl alcohol was a laboratory curiosity and none of the commercial solvents was being produced synthetically.

In the 25 years which have elapsed since then a marked change has come over the picture. Agricultural products as raw materials for solvent manufacture, while still important, have had to yield place to petroleum and coal. Today acetone, for example, while still made from an agricultural product, corn, is no longer a primary product from this raw material, and must share the market with synthetic acetone made from petroleum hydrocarbons. At least as much acetic acid is made from calcium carbide as from wood distillation. Ethyl alcohol is still made largely by the fermentation of molasses, but a not inconsiderable amount is made from ethylene recovered from byproduct gases evolved in the cracking of petroleum. More methanol is produced synthetically from water gas than by wood distillation. Fusel oil has a host of competitors: Pentasol, synthetic amyl alcohol made from petroleum; secondary amyl and butyl alcohols made from olefines recovered from oil cracking gases; isobutyl alcohol and amyl alcohols made by a synthetic process from water.gas simultaneously with synthetic methanol; and butanol made from ethylene from oil cracking gases. Cellosolves, trade name for a series of chemical compounds unheard of 25 years ago, have appeared, as has Petrohol (synthetic isopropyl alcohol). These latter are derived from by-products of the petroleum industry.

41

An attempt will be made to trace the development of these solvents in the United States, and to indicate what part chemical engineering has played in this development.

Acetic Acid. Acetic acid is not in itself a solvent, but the acetates are extremely important, so that a word or two about developments in acetic acid manufacture over the past 25 years is not amiss.

In 1908 acetic acid was one of the important products of the wood distillation industry, appearing on the market as calcium acetate. Except for a little made by fermentation, wood distillation was the only source of acetic acid. During the World War a synthetic process was developed by Shawinigan Chemicals, Inc., of Canada, in which acetic acid was made from calcium carbide, through acetylene and acetaldehyde. This same process was first installed in the United States in 1928 at Niagara Falls by Niacet Chemicals Corp.

The appearance of synthetic acetic acid seemed to sound the death-knell of calcium acetate from wood distillation: that the wood distillation industry has survived is a tribute to the chemical engineer. First fermentation acetone, then synthetic acetic acid and finally synthetic methanol encroached on wood distillation markets. Better chemical engineering, involving, along with minor improvements, rapid kiln drying of wood to supplant yard drying of a year or more, rotation charging of retorts to effect fuel economy and permit continuous extraction of the gases and distillation of the liquors, and finally the development of direct extraction processes for acetic acid, thus avoiding the use of lime and sulphuric acid to obtain the acetic acid, have permitted the wood distillation industry to survive.

The first of the direct acetic acid processes was the Brewster process, utilizing ethyl ether for the cold extraction of the acid liquor. The Suida process, using wood oils for hot vapor extraction, has had considerable development. More recently ethyl acetate has been used for cold liquor extraction, and still more recently E. B. Badger & Sons Co. have developed a process using combined solvents, with isopropyl ether, a chemical commercially available only within the past few years, to produce glacial acetic acid direct by extraction of the liquor in the cold. Another process of recent development, the so-called Othmer process, uses normal propyl acetate for cold extraction of liquors.

The acetic acid of pyroligneous liquors from wood distillation has also been converted into sodium acetate, now required for acetic anhydride used in cellulose acetate manufacture, which has involved the application of chemical engineering to the wood distillation industry at still another point.

A rough measure of the replacement of wood distillation acetic acid by synthetic acetic acid is given in Table I.

Table I. Acetic Acid Consumption in the United States

[Data in 1000 lbs. 100 per cent. acetic acid]

Year	Wood·Distillation	Synthetic	Total	Synthetic Per cent.
1923	40,160	688	40,848	1.7
1925	42,715	2,295	45,010	4.9
1927	62,285	8,183	70,468	11.6
1928	55,925	17,885	73,810	24.2
1929	57,268	37,332	94,600	39.5
1930	51,750*	36,250	88,000*	41.2
1931	42,799	35,081	77,880	45.0

*Estimated.

Acetone. In 1908 acetone was not of great importance commercially. It was recovered as part of the "wood alcohol" from the pyroligneous liquors condensed when wood was destructively distillated for charcoal production. Later, methods were devised for separating it from the wood alcohol, and in so far as this supply was insufficient, it was supplemented by acetone made by destructively distilling calcium acetate, itself a product of wood distillation. The enormous requirements of acetone for cordite manufacture in Great Britain, as a consequence of the World War, could not be met from this source. This led the British government to take up a process of fermenting corn with a particular organism, now called *Clostridium acetobutylicum,* which had been isolated by Weizmann. After many difficulties the process was worked out on a commercial scale, and operated at first in England, but, realizing that the operation could most economically be carried out near the source of the raw material, two distilleries in Canada and later, through the Allied War Board, two distilleries at Terre Haute, Ind., were equipped to carry out the process. These plants were operated solely for acetone production: the larger simultaneous production of butyl alcohol had no complete immediate commercial use and was simply stored.

At the conclusion of the War one of the plants at Terre Haute was purchased by the Commercial Solvents Corp., with the intention of operating it for the simultaneous production of acetone and butyl alcohol, for by this time butyl alcohol and its derivatives had demonstrated their substitutability for fusel oil as nitrocellulose lacquer ingredients, and nitrocellulose lacquers of the Duco type were being used in enormously increasing quantities by the rapidly growing automobile industry. Later, a second and much larger plant was built at Peoria, Ill.

Acetone produced from the destructive distillation of calcium acetate could no longer compete with what might be regarded as byproduct acetone from butyl alcohol manufacture and gradually passed from the picture. About 1928 acetone from a new source was placed on the market by the Carbide and Carbon Chemicals Corp. This acetone was made by the dehydrogenation or controlled oxidation in the vapor phase of isopropyl alcohol, in turn made by absorbing propylene from oil cracking gases in sulphuric acid and hydrolyzing the resulting isopropyl sulphate. This latter process involves more complicated chemical engineering than fermentation acetone, but despite this has been able to compete in the face of a continued downward trend in acetone prices.

Acetone, *per se,* although important in photographic film manufacture, is not one of the major solvents, but the growing importance, in the past few years of the cellulose acetate industry, which requires acetone as an essential process ingredient, assures a continued consumption of this chemical. Moreover, a continuation of the downward trend in acetone prices will have a tendency to bring about its utilization as a raw material for further organic syntheses in which chemical engineering will play an important part.

Table II.   Acetone in the United States
[Data in 1000 lb.]

Year	Production	Imports	Exports	Apparent Consumption
1925 13,300		400	?	13,700
1926 21,500		300	?	21,800
1927 25,500		200	?	25,700
1928 25,100		50	5,000	20,150
1929 .... 35,300*		40	8,000	.....
1930 .... 20,100*			3,600	.....
1931 26,056		0	3,900	22,156

*Commercial solvents only.

Methanol. In 1908 wood distillation was the only source of methyl alcohol, or methanol, as it is now called, and remained so until 1927, when the du Pont company began producing methanol as a byproduct of its synthetic ammonia manufacture. In the gas stream going to the catalyst chambers of the synthetic ammonia plant was a small amount of carbon monoxide which was removed by converting it catalytically to methane which was innocuous as opposed to the catalytically poisonous carbon monoxide. It was found that the substitution of a methanol catalyst for the methanation catalyst was just as effective in removing the carbon monoxide, consumed less hydrogen, and in addition permitted the recovery of this carbon monoxide as marketable methanol instead of practically worthless methane.

Later, demands for methanol exceeded the amount recoverable as a byproduct, and a separate plant in which either methanol or a combination of methanol and higher alcohols could be produced, was erected, and began production in 1929.

Commercial Solvents Corp. also installed a synthetic methanol plant in 1929, to utilize waste hydrogen and carbon dioxide from the fermenters. This development is interesting in that it utilizes carbon dioxide instead of the carbon monoxide generally used in this process. Carbide & Carbon Chemicals Corp. began the production of synthetic methanol in 1929, and Roessler & Hasslacher Chemical Corp. in 1930.

The processes employed in all of these plants consist in passing a mixture of hydrogen and an oxide of carbon compressed to several hundred atmospheres, over a catalyst maintained at a temperature of 300 deg. C. and upward. Chemical engineering of a very specialized nature is necessary for a proper selection of materials of construction and in the design of equipment which will maintain the necessary high temperature without overheating from the exothermic synthesis processes, and which will keep the reacting gases properly confined.

The amount of penetration of synthetic methanol into the market formerly enjoyed exclusively by the wood distillation product is shown by Table III:

Table III. Production of Methanol in the United States

[Data in 1000 gals. 100 per cent methanol]

Year	Wood Distillation	Synthetic	Total	Per cent. Synthetic
1924	5,500	0	5,500	0
1925	5,800	0	5,800	0
1926	6,400	0	6,400	0
1927	5,700	500	6,200	8.0
1928	6,500	2,100	8,600	24.5
1929	5,900	4,100	10,000	41.0
1930	5,000	7,500	12,500	60.0
1931	1,700	7,700	9,400	81.9

The increase in production of total methanol shown here is more rapid than the general increase in industry in the United States. This is the result of a continued drop in the price of methanol, permitting its utilization for new purposes such as for anti-freeze in automobile radiators. At a sufficiently low price it might also be used as a motor-fuel, in admixture with certain types of petroleum distillates.

Ethyl Alcohol. Ethyl alcohol is the oldest known organic solvent, but until almost the time of the formation of the American Institute of Chemical Engineers it was used in the United States largely for beverage, and to a very small extent for medicinal purposes. The high tax made it too expensive for industry in general. On Jan. 1, 1907, however, denatured alcohol, tax-free, was made legal. This resulted in an enormous development of industrial alcohol, as may be seen from Table IV:

Table IV. Production of Denatured Alcohol in the United States

[Data in 1000 gal. denatured alcohol]

Year*	Production	Year*	Production
1907	1,780	1920	28,836
1908	3,321	1921	22,389
1909	4,556	1922	33,346
1910	6,079	1923	57,565
1911	6,881	1924	67,687
1912	8,095	1925	81,808
1913	9,832	1926	105,376
1914	10,405	1927	95,449
1915	13,986	1928	92,418
1916	46,679	1929	106,960
1917	55,680	1930	105,788
1918	50,163	1931	86,309
1919	38,271	1932	78,330

*Fiscal year ending June 30.

About 40 per cent of the denatured alcohol used in the United States goes into a non-solvent use, namely, is employed for automobile radiator anti-freeze.

In 1908 cereals were virtually the only source of raw material for ethyl alcohol manufacture, and fermentation was the only process. In the 25 years which have elapsed, while the process has remained unchanged, cereals have been largely replaced by molasses, and since this is mostly imported the alcohol industry has tended to migrate from the corn belt to the sea coast. Around 1911 the du Pont company operated a small alcohol plant in Georgetown, S. C., which used sawdust as a raw material. This was hydrolyzed with acid, after which the process was identical with that still used in fermentation alcohol manufacture. Cellulose, however, is either too costly to collect or more valuable for other purposes, and consequently this operation proved uneconomical.

Since the process has remained virtually unchanged, it is apparent that improvements have taken the form of better chemical engineering. Materials of construction have improved. Wood, formerly used for the construction of both beer stills and fermenters, has been replaced by copper for distillation equipment, and copper-bearing steel for fermenters. With steel, it is easy to construct closed fermenters, permitting the recovery of carbon dioxide evolved during fermentation, either as liquid or solid, which has led to the utilization of this byproduct.

In distillation, the application of the principle of azeotropic mixtures has been developed for the production of absolute alcohol at only a slightly increased cost over the usual 95 per cent, by volume, alcohol of commerce. Priority in this commercial development belongs to American chemists and chemical engineers. Absolute alcohol can be blended in any proportion with many petroleum distillates for motor fuel but this use, owing to the low cost of petroleum products in the United States, and to the practical difficulty that absorption of moisture causes a separation of the alcohol, has had a much more limited development than in other countries.

In 1929 Carbide & Carbon Chemicals Corp. put on the market synthetic ethyl alcohol made from ethylene from oil refinery gases. The ethylene is absorbed in strong sulphuric acid to produce monoethyl sulphate; and this is hydrolyzed to alcohol and weak sulphuric acid, which is concentrated for reuse. Potentially, alcohol from ethylene has possibilities of an extended development wherever the oil-cracking industry is carried out. Its economic development, however, depends on molasses costs, which at present are low owing to an overproduction of sugar.

In the fiscal year ending June 30, 1932, synthetic ethyl alcohol production was 7,500,000 gal. of 95 per cent alcohol, by volume, out of a total production, for the United States and Porto Rico, of 77,300,000 gal. of industrial alcohol, or 9.7 per cent.

Butyl Alcohol. As previously stated, butanol, as butyl alcohol is now called by Commercial Solvents Corp., did not have any large commercial importance until after the war. Then its availability in large amounts, and its lower cost as compared with fusel oil, for nitrocellulose lacquer manufacture, and the economy of using these quick-drying lacquers instead of the older slow-drying coach varnishes in the automobile industry, brought about a phenomenal increase in its consumption. Commercial Solvents Corp., until a few years ago, had a virtual monopoly on this commodity, so that a tabulation of the production of this company, as reported by them, gives a picture of the rapidity of this development.

Table V.   Production of Butanol by Commercial Solvents Corp.
[Data in 1000 lb.]

Year	Production	Year	Production
1920	2,600	1926	41,500
1921	3,500	1927	49,000
1922	6,900	1928	50,000
1923	5,800	1929	67,500
1924	13,600	1930	38,500
1925	26,500		

This process entails the fermentation of cornstarch. The corn is ground, the hulls and the germ are separated, the remaining starchy material is cooked, and the sterile mash is inoculated with a carefully prepared pure strain of the butylic organism. During the fermentation carbon dioxide and hydrogen are evolved and butyl alcohol, acetone and ethyl alcohol are formed in the solution. At the conclusion of the fermentation the dilute beer is distilled to yield the pure solvents. A bushel of corn produces approximately 8.4 lb. butanol, 4.35 lb. acetone, 1.75 lb. ethyl alcohol, 0.7 lb. hydrogen and 23.2 lb. carbon dioxide.

Since the mash is an ideal medium for the growth of many organisms present in the air, in the water supply, on the corn itself and on any dirt which might get into the process, and whose growth is inimical to the growth of the butylic organism, the difficulty of carrying on this fermentation on the commercial scale under the necessary sterile conditions can well be imagined. That it has been successfully done is a tribute to chemical engineering of the highest order.

Chemical engineering also had a large part, incidental to the main problem of maintaining sterile conditions, in the handling and processing of the corn and the handling and distillation of the large volumes of dilute solutions, and in the utilization of byproducts. Corn oil and corn germ meal were made almost from the beginning. Synthetic methanol, made from the waste carbon dioxide and hydrogen, appeared on the market in 1929. Within the past few years solid carbon dioxide, "dry ice," has been recovered from the carbon dioxide not required for methanol manufacture.

In 1931 butyl alcohol made from the fermentation of black-strap molasses by Publicker Commercial Alcohol Co. began to appear on the market. The technique of the process is much the same as that of Commercial Solvents Corp.: material handling is somewhat simpler, but the maintenance of sterile conditions is much more difficult.

In 1932 synthetic butyl alcohol manufactured by Carbide and Carbon Chemicals Corp. appeared on the market. Exact details of the process are not known, but the steps are probably ethylene, ethyl sulphuric acid, ethyl alcohol, acetaldehyde, aldol, crotonaldehyde, butyl alcohol. It is obvious that chemical engineering of the highest order is necessary in order to obtain a reasonable yield, even if all of the steps indicated are not carried out.

Secondary, Tertiary and Iso Higher Alcohols. The early history of the manufacture of this line of products, based on mineral rather than agricultural raw materials, harks back to the time of the foundation of the Institute. From 1900 to 1907 ether was manufactured at Richmond, Va., at the rate of about 1000 lb. per day, by treating ethylene from oil gas with sulphuric acid, but this proved unprofitable after the advent of tax-free industrial alcohol.

The first successful commercial attempt to make higher alcohols from olefines was in 1917, when the Melco Chemical Corp. made isopropyl alcohol from propylene, to be converted into acetone for the U. S. Aircraft Production Bureau. The armistice removed the need for acetone; work was continued, however, resulting in the offering of large quantities of isopropyl alcohol in 1921. This was followed by secondary butyl and amyl alcohols, tertiary butyl and amyl alcohols, and secondary hexyl alcohols, all now available in commercial quantities from several manufacturers.

The companies taking part in this development were the Standard Oil Co., Bayway, N. J., the Petroleum Chemical Corp. at Tiverton, R. I., whose plant was torn down but later rebuilt at Okmulgee, Okla., by the Doherty Research Co., a subsidiary of Cities Service Corp., and the Shell Union Oil Co. at Martinez, California. The main process is the same: an olefine derived from oil-cracking operations is absorbed in sulphuric acid to produce an alkyl sulphate, which is then hydrolyzed to yield the alcohol. An immense amount of chemical and chemical engineering research was necessary to work out methods of separating the olefine in sufficiently pure form, in establishing temperature and concentration conditions to effect selective absorption of the desired olefine, and in working out methods of fractionating the resulting alcohols and removing from them, or the raw materials used, such impurities as sulphur. These problems have been successfully solved and increasing amounts of these higher alcohols are being produced. The major part of their cost lies in the operations carried out and in fixed charges on the equipment: raw material is an insignificant portion of the total cost. Further improvements in chemical engineering, therefore, should make possible still further reductions in cost.

Another development based on mineral raw materials is the manufacture of a series of higher alcohols, of which isobutyl alcohol is the principal one, and normal propyl and secondary and isoamyl alcohols second in importance, which was begun by the duPont company at Belle, W. Va., about 1928. At first it was carried out as an adjunct to the methanol manufactured as a byproduct of gas purification for ammonia synthesis (see section on methanol), but was later taken up as a separate manufacture when the new methanol plant was built in 1929. This plant utilizes water gas made from coke; by the choice of a suitable catalyst, operating temperatures, and in some cases gas composition, the same plant can turn out at will either pure methanol, or a mixture of methanol and higher alcohols in various proportions. Among these higher alcohols there have been positively identified normal propanol; isobutanol; 2-methyl pentanol-1; 2, 4-dimethyl pentanol-1; as well as a number of still higher alcohols unnecessary to mention. A mixture of these alcohols, boiling within a specified range, has recently been adopted as a denaturing agent for industrial alcohol.

The higher alcohols made from olefines, as well as those synthesized from water gas, can be used as such and as their acetates, in the formulation of lacquers, in which use they are tending to displace normal butanol and its esters. They can also be converted by oxidation or dehydrogenation to ketones, and recent work along these lines indicates that a growing use for these alcohols will be as a raw material for the manufacture of ketones and other organic compounds. To a lesser extent these higher alcohols are finding use in flotation reagents, anti-foaming reagents in the beet-sugar and paper industries, hydraulic fluids, detergents and paint removers.

The lower-boiling higher alcohols such as normal and isopropyl alcohol are being put to uses in which, in general, they replace ethyl alcohol.

No production statistics are as yet available on this comparatively new industry, but the production of these higher alcohols, even in these depressed times, is well over 4,000,000 gal. per annum.

Synthetic Amyl Alcohol. About 1926 the Sharples Solvents Corp. at Belle, W. Va., began the production of synthetic amyl alcohol, made by chlorinating pentane to the monochloride, and then hydrolyzing with caustic soda to produce the alcohol. Thus a mineral raw product again came into competition with an agricultural one, and chemical engineering made it possible.

This operation has not been of large magnitude, in comparison with the total production of higher alcohols. From 1927, when the production was about 1,800,000 lb., the output increased gradually to around 5,000,000 lb. in 1931. Perhaps one of the most interesting outgrowths of this operation is the manufacture of a line of derivatives of Pentasol, such as amines and mercaptans. Late in 1932 the removal of the plant from Belle to Wyandotte, Mich., was announced.

Miscellaneous Solvents. There are a number of additional solvents whose more detailed treatment cannot be undertaken because of lack of space. Among them should be mentioned the glycols and the alkyl ethers of glycols marketed under the name of Cellosolve, whose manufacture was begun by Carbide & Carbon Chemicals Corp. in 1924. These are synthetic products based on ethylene from petroleum, and that they are available at all is due entirely to the research, ingenuity and perseverance of American chemists and chemical engineers.

Ethers, also, should be mentioned. Ethyl ether is produced by Carbide & Carbon Chemicals Corp. in conjunction with the production of synthetic ethyl alcohol from ethylene. This same company also produces iso-propyl ether, mentioned in the section on acetic acid. Dimethyl ether, produced from synthetic methanol, was placed on the market in 1932 by the duPont company.

There should also be mentioned the solvent naphthas of the petroleum industry, whose production is probably as great as that of all the other solvents combined, and which can now be produced to very exact specifications by a combination of stock selection, stock treatment (such as pyrolysis or hydrogenation) and careful fractionation. Indeed, no review of chemical engineering in the United States would be complete without mention of the application of fractional distillation to the petroleum industry.* This application has been very extensive over the past ten years and in addition to direct improvements in distilling technique has indirectly been responsible for bringing chemical engineers in contact with many other refinery problems of a chemical engineering nature.

Acknowledgment. It is a pleasure to acknowledge the assistance of a number of chemical engineers in the preparation of this chapter. Particularly, Arthur A. Backus, of the U. S. Industrial Alcohol Co., on industrial alcohol, M. B. Hopkins, of the Standard Alcohol Co., on solvent naphthas and synthetic alcohols, and Harry C. Merriam of E. B. Badger & Sons Co., on the wood distillation industry, were most helpful.

---

* Editor's Note.—See subsequent chapters on petroleum refining and fractional distillation.

CHAPTER V

TWENTY-FIVE YEARS OF PROGRESS IN PETROLEUM REFINING

By Howard W. Sheldon

Chief Chemical Engineer, Research and Development Laboratories, Socony-Vacuum Corporation, Paulsboro, N. J.

IN 1908 THE PETROLEUM REFINING INDUSTRY was one of considerable magnitude, employing approximately 15,000 men and producing products valued at more than $200,000,000. Today the industry has risen to fifth place in the value of manufactures, employing nearly 80,000 wage earners, and producing products valued at ten times as much as were those of 25 years ago.

Production of crude oil in 1908 was 178,527,000 bbl. valued at $129,000,000. Production increased rapidly until in 1929 it was over 1,000,000,000 bbl. valued at over $1,250,000,000. The present rate is in excess of 800,000,000 bbl., which is approximately equal to refinery consumption. There were approximately 100 refineries in operation in 1908, which number has increased to over 400 with a potential daily refining capacity of 3,856,300 bbl.

The first oil was produced from a well 69½ feet deep. The driller kept drilling deeper and deeper in his search for oil. In 1908 wells of 2,000 feet depth were not uncommon. Today there are several that are producing oil from depths of approximately two miles.

It has been estimated that only from one-fourth to one-sixth of the oil present in any one pool can be recovered by natural flow and pumping. Recent work on improved methods of recovery, such as flooding with water or chemicals, repressuring with air or with the natural gas that is produced along with the oil, have resulted in additional recoveries equal to or greater than those obtained by previous methods. These methods will become very important when the large pools of oil have exhausted their flush production.

Crude oil and its refined products are transported from one place to another by almost every means imaginable. The pipe line has grown from a 1½-in. pipe about 4 miles long to a system that rivals the railroad with its maze of main arteries and feeders. Natural gas produced in Texas and Oklahoma is distributed in Denver and Chicago, for industrial and household use. Crude oil from the same field is refined at St. Louis, Chicago, Detroit, Buffalo, and along the Atlantic seaboard. It is of interest to add that some of these pipe lines that were used to move crude to the Atlantic coast are now used to move finished products, such as gasoline and fuel oil, inland.

Prior to 1908 the distillation of petroleum was performed in batch stills of the cheese box and shell types. Very little progress had been made, other than increasing the size of the shell still from a few hundred gallons to about 1,000 bbl., and the use of vacuum and steam to obtain larger yields of distillate without cracking. Some attempts had been made at fractionation, but the old-time refiner was very reluctant to accept any new methods.

From the early days of the industry the products were finished by treating with sulphuric acid followed by neutralization with an alkali, and usually subjected to a final bleaching by sunlight. In some instances the lubricating oils were filtered through bone black in order to improve color.

One outstanding development prior to 1908 was the Frasch process for treating the high sulphur oils that were being produced at Lima, Ohio. This process consisted of distilling the "burning oils" from a still in which finely divided copper oxide was kept in suspension by agitation. The copper sulphide was converted again to the oxide by roasting, then ground and returned to the process in the next batch. The kerosene produced was of excellent quality. This process represented one of the first applications of technical methods to refining.

If one were to walk into a refinery early in the twentieth century, one would see a battery of stills of the cheese-box type and another of plain cylindrical design, the former set in one group and the latter set side by side in a bench. These stills were equipped with parallel tube type condensers, the condensate running to a "tail house" where the stream was diverted to any one of a series of tanks according to its gravity. In some of these refineries only naphtha, burning oil (kerosene) and residuum were made, while in others the residuum was distilled for the production of lubricating oils, paraffin, wax, coke, etc. The kerosene was refined by treatment with sulphuric acid and caustic soda. It was finished by bleaching with air in direct sunlight. The lubricating oil was redistilled and the wax removed either by cold settling or cold filtering. This oil was finished by filtering through bone black and finally bleached in open shallow pans.

Since 1908 radical changes have taken place in refinery operations. The most important of these changes will be discussed under the following headings: (1) cracking, (2) distillation, (3) refining, (4) dewaxing, (5) hydrogenation, (6) special products, (7) utilization of byproducts and (8) research.

PROGRESS IN CRACKING

The expansion of the automotive industry furnished the impetus for developing cracking processes so as to produce more gasoline from a barrel of crude petroleum. The first intensive study of this problem was begun in 1908 or 1909 by the Standard Oil Co. of Indiana, when, after an outlay of over $1,000,000, they put into successful operation the first commercial Burton still in 1912. These stills were simply cylindrical shells set horizontally over the firebox, and batch operated at about 95 pounds pressure. The coke formed in the cracking reaction settled to the bottom of the still, forming an insulating layer which necessitated heavy firing in order to get sufficient heat into the oil. This service was so severe that the still bottoms needed frequent renewal. Having this large volume of oil directly over the fire-box was extremely hazardous and resulted in several disastrous fires. In order to minimize this hazard, the Humphreys false bottom was installed inside the shell to collect the major portion of the coke.

The first important departure from the shell still was to follow boiler practice and suspend a bank of tubes in the combustion chamber below the shell. Here the heat was absorbed by the tubes instead of the shell and the oil circulated by heat convection through a drop leg, through the tubes, and up another leg into the shell. This was followed by the addition of a bubble cap tower in place of an aerial condenser for partial dephlegmation of the vapors leaving the shell. In 1920 more than 15,600,000 bbl. of gasoline were produced by this process.

In 1920 the second commercial cracking process, the Holmes-Manley, was put into operation by the Texas Co., and there are many of these units in operation today. In this process the oil is heated to cracking temperature in a pipe heater and then passed to a series of four vertical shells where the cracking reaction proceeds. No heat is applied to the bottom of these stills, a small amount being applied to the sides in order to maintain the temperature. A mechanical scraping device is installed to keep the sides of the still coke-free, the coke removed settling to the bottom of the still. In this process a further step forward was made, in that the tube bank is separated from the shell and the shell or cracking chamber is kept out of the fire zone or only fired sufficiently to supply the heat of reaction and that lost due to radiation. The thermo-syphon effect does not furnish a sufficiently rapid flow to prevent the tubes from becoming coked nor does it provide satisfactory rates of heat transfer, so positive displacement pumps are installed to insure rapid circulation. It was observed that with the higher rates of heat transfer thus obtained, it was possible to produce the desired cracking in a shorter time without over-cracking.

Since the cracking reaction is a function of both time and temperature, it soon became apparent that the desired result could be obtained in a variety of ways. Once-through processes, recycling operations, the use of reaction chambers where the oil could be held at cracking temperature for varying periods of time, formed the basis of a large number of processes, many of which have been very successful. The Cross and Tube-and-Tank processes made their appearance in 1921. These were followed by many others, such as the Dubbs, Jenkins, Fleming and Isom. These processes produce a large part of the world's gasoline requirements.

Prior to about 1926 the cracking processes were very inefficient thermally. In order to increase the heat recovery the hot oil type of unit was developed. In this unit the hot recycle stock, which is separated from the gasoline distillate in the dephlegmator, is mixed with preheated fresh feed and charged either directly or through vapor heat exchangers to the tube heaters. This change has materially increased the capacity of the units and economy of operation.

Further developments have been to increase the size of the units, and to use higher operating pressures. Operating pressures have been gradually increased from 95 lb. in the first Burton stills to 250, to 350, to 700 and finally to 1,000 lb. and over. During the past year the largest commercial unit as yet to be built was put into operation. This unit processes 19,000 bbl. of charging stock per day, which is a long step from that first Burton still in 1912 which charged a batch of 196 bbl. of gas oil.

Vapor-Phase Cracking. In the processes just mentioned, pressure was used in order to keep the products in the liquid phase as much as possible during the treatment. There was another type of cracking process, namely, vapor phase, developed during the same

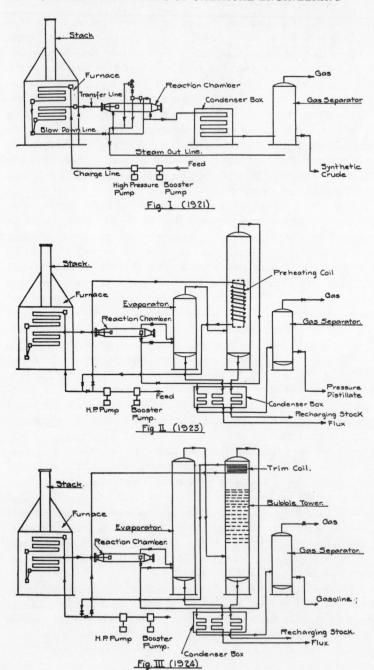

Fig. I (1921)

Fig. II (1923)

Fig. III (1924)

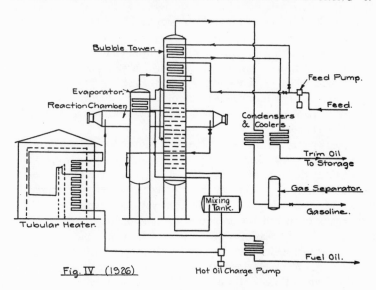

Fig. IV (1926)

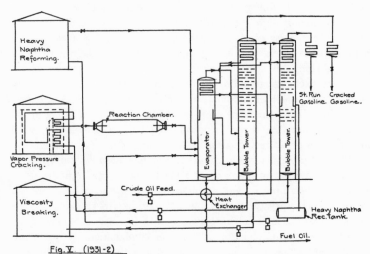

Fig. V (1931-2)

Figs. I.-V. Illustrate the Development of the Cross Cracking Process.

Fig. I. First unit built in 1921 producing synthetic crude.

Fig. II. First application of heat recovery with production of pressure distillate.

Fig. III. The addition in 1924 of the bubble tower for the production of end-point gasoline.

Fig. IV. Hot oil circulation utilized in 1926 for economy of heat.

Fig. V. Combination unit of 1931-2 in which such operations as liquid-phase and vapor-phase cracking, naphtha refining and viscosity breaking are accomplished.

period which became important later because of the demand for high anti-knock gasoline. It had been observed that by cracking at high temperatures and low pressures more unsaturated and aromatic compounds were formed, as well as a much larger quantity of fixed gases, than when cracking under liquid-phase conditions. It was also observed that the products produced were highly colored and difficult to treat so as to meet a satisfactory specification as to gum and color stability.

Greenstreet, Hall, Ramage, Rittman, Alexander and many others developed processes for vapor-phase cracking. There were many obstacles in the way of the commercial success of these processes, chiefly the lack of proper materials of construction and insufficient knowledge of the cracking reaction. It was the automotive industry that again furnished the incentive for an intensive study of this reaction. The increasing compression ratio in internal combustion engines created a demand for anti-knock properties in the gasoline that were not being obtained by the liquid-phase processes.

The Gyro (Pure Oil Co.), DeFlorez (Texas and Gulf) and Pratt (Lubrite Refining Corp.) vapor-phase processes were successful in producing high anti-knock gasoline in commercially practical units. The success of these units depends on having a clean stock to feed to the cracking tubes. Any tar present is deposited in the tubes and shuts down the plant in a very short time. Because of the poor heat exchange relationship between the metal tube and the oil vapor, either small tubes or larger tubes with solid cores are used to obtain a high turbulence. Many special alloys have been developed to meet the severe conditions of these processes, in which oil vapor temperatures of from 1,000 to 1,150 deg. F. are used.

The advance in cracking unit design has been so rapid in the last few years that in many cases a newly constructed unit would be obsolete by the time it was put into operation. The latest designs combine such operations as topping, liquid-phase cracking, vapor-phase cracking, naphtha reforming and viscosity breaking (mild cracking) to form a single unit. The combination of operations depends upon the stock to be processed and the quality of gasoline required. Some of these recent installations utilize a single furnace in which several separate heating coils are installed, each coil functioning independently of the others.

DISTILLATION OF PETROLEUM PRODUCTS

Since 1908 there have been many changes in equipment and methods used for the distillation of petroleum. The original shell still passed through a series of improvements. These changes were stimulated by the cost of fuel, which is the largest single item of operating cost in the refinery.

The first important change was from batch to continuous distillation. This was attained by arranging the shell stills in batteries of four to eight in such a manner that the oil could flow through them by gravity. A definite fraction of the crude was vaporized from each still by suitable adjustment of temperatures. Improvements were made in fire-box conditions, increasing the fuel economy and allowing higher rates of heat transfer through the shell. For example, carborundum muffles were installed in the fire-box under the shell. The fuel could be burned in this muffle with a minimum of excess air, the muffle radiating heat to the shell and the products of combustion going to the stack through a set of internal flues in the lower part of the shell. This was an application of the principle of the well known return tubular boiler, adding both capacity and efficiency to the shell still operation.

Various methods of recovering heat from the vapors leaving the still and the hot residuum have been developed. The first vapor heat exchanger or fore-warmer, as it was then called, consisted of a shell containing a worm to carry the vapor stream. This shell contained the next charge for the still which was preheated from 100 to 150 deg. F. This equipment was inefficient, cumbersome, and expensive. It is doubtful whether any of such installations were able to justify their cost. The first residuum exchangers were double pipe and found considerable use in the continuous battery for preheating the feed. The modern tubular exchanger was developed in the power plant. This type was adapted by C. H. Leach to refinery practice from which our present highly efficient vapor heat recovery systems have been developed.

About 1926 C. W. Stratford introduced a novel plan for obtaining high capacities from the shell still equipment at one of the large California refineries. A centrifugal pump was installed inside of the shell still, circulating the oil by jetting it against the heated sheet at a high velocity. This continuous sweep of oil over the sheet reduced the oil temperature of the film in contact with the metal and allowed much higher rates of heat transfer with less danger of overheating the oil. Rates as high as 40 to 50 per cent vaporization of 8,500 bbl. per day were obtained in a single 12 x 45 feet shell still.

In order to increase the fractionation between the cuts taken from each shell still, dephlegmating towers were installed. At first these were very crude, being vertical towers packed with flower pots, large boulders, scrap iron, etc. It was not long before the bubble-cap tower, which had been in use in the alcohol industry for some time, was utilized. This column has not changed greatly although there have been improvements in design to get better distribution of vapor and reflux, as well as to reduce the friction loss through the tower. This is especially beneficial in high vacuum towers to enable a more effective pressure at the point of vaporization. Appropriate fractions may be withdrawn from various decks in the column and at various stages additional reflux may be introduced. Stripping sections have also been provided. The whole column, in fact, replaces the separate devices which were used in a battery of shell stills, with the advantage that at every step there is accurate control of temperature and reflux.

Pipe Heaters. The pipe heater was developed in connection with cracking processes and came into general use about 1920. When its value as a means of safely and rapidly heating the oil had been proved, it was universally accepted for use with the fractionating column for the distillation of crude oil. The first pipe heaters were very crude, being made up of lengths of pipe either passing through or placed in the form of coils in a combustion chamber. These pipes became filled with coke in a very short time, as the result of excessive heating, probably caused by a combination of radiant and convection heat absorption and poor rates of fluid flow. Radiant heat was thought to be the cause, and furnaces were then designed in such a manner as to prevent, as far as possible, any radiation from the flame or furnace refractories reaching the tubes. Dutch ovens were added to the furnace, bridge walls were installed, and all the tubes placed behind them. This type of furnace was very inefficient as extremely high quantities of excess air had to be used to maintain reasonable furnace temperatures. The gases were then tempered by the use of flue gas recirculation which increased the unit capacity approximately 30 per cent because of the higher rates of heat transfer, and resulted in fuel efficiencies of 60 to 65 per cent. This change, however, required the installation of costly blowers and ducts, increasing the capital outlay and adding an operating expense for power and maintenance.

Furnace Design. As a better understanding of the relationships existing between fluid flow and heat transfer was attained, furnace design turned more and more from the convection type to that of radiant heat absorption. The Power Specialty Co. installed tubes in the roof of the combustion chamber, first covering them with refractory and then gradually removing sections of this material until the entire tube was exposed to the radiant heat. As soon as it was demonstrated that the amount of radiant heat absorption could be controlled, the developments were toward maximum heat pick-up in this section, amounting to as much as 85 per cent of the total heat input in the heater. Furnaces of this type are those of Foster-Wheeler with from two to four rows in the roof, M. W. Kellogg Co. with tubes on all four walls and the roof, DeFlorez with his cylindrical combustion chamber ·with vertical tubes around the circumference, and Alcorn with roof, wall and floor tubes. Heaters of this type are highly efficient, requiring only a slight excess of air over the theoretical required for the combustion of the fuel. Rates of heat transfer in the radiant sections of these heaters are in the order of 10,000 to 12,000 b. t. u. per sq. ft. per hr., as compared to 2,500 to 3,500 in the convection section. This results in lower furnace construction costs and a saving in pumping costs due to lower pressure drop through the tubing.

It is of interest to note that where the tubes exposed to radiant heat are placed in more than one row, the second row will absorb from 10 to 15 per cent as much heat as the first row, the third only 2 to 3 per cent as much as the first row, while the fourth absorbs almost no heat. These tubes, however, are of value for use as reaction tubes in certain types of cracking processes.

Vacuum Distillation. The use of vacuum for the recovery of higher yields of distillate oils is old, but the advantage of distilling lubricating oils at absolute pressures of 3 to 5 mm. Hg. as compared to 40 mm. was first recognized by Schulze and Steinschneider. The effect on the boiling point reduction with lowering of the absolute pressure is much more pronounced at these very low pressures than at a more moderate vacuum. Schulze designed a shell still with a large number of vapor outlets to prevent entrainment. These outlets were manifolded together so that no reflux could return to the hot oil in the still and be cracked. He provided the still with an aerial condenser and a separate condenser to which the vacuum pump was connected. By this means he was able to remove a small amount of a light odoriferous oil which otherwise must be removed by chemical treatment.

The first application of the pipe heater to vacuum distillation on a commercial scale was made at the Vacuum Oil Co. refinery at Paulsboro in 1927-1928. This was a two-stage atmospheric-vacuum unit having a daily capacity of 2,000 bbl. The design has proved very successful and today the majority of lubricating oil refineries have units of similar type, some of which process 14,000 bbl. of crude in 24 hr.

This type of operation is also used in rerunning treated pressure distillate from the cracking process. In order to get a color-stable gasoline, it is necessary to distill at temperatures sufficiently low to prevent decomposition of the acid esters that are present. In order to do this, the light end of the gasoline is distilled at atmospheric pressure and the balance at a pressure of 1 to 2 in. Hg. absolute.

Other means for supplying heat to the oil for distillation have been developed, the most noteworthy being the mercury vapor process of the Sun Oil Co. Mercury vapor has the property of not wetting the exchanger surface when condensing. With the elimination of this liquid film, very much higher rates of heat transfer are attained. In the distillation unit a series of towers is used with an evaporator at the base of each. With accurate temperature control, close-cut fractions are removed which it is claimed require little chemical treatment. These fractions can be used separately or blended as required to meet the desired specifications of the finished product.

The Govers process which was developed at the Indian Refining Co. at Lawrenceville, Ill., utilizes the vapors of diphenyl or diphenyl oxide as a heat carrier, the heat exchange taking place in a specially designed tubular exchanger, forced circulation of the oil being used to get high rates of heat absorption.

Treating and Refining Processes

The petroleum products that require treatment to meet the specifications demanded by market and service requirements may be divided into the following general classes: gasoline and naphtha, kerosene, insulating oils, lubricating oils, and wax. The treatment may consist of one or a combination of several distinct processes. These processes may be classified according to the materials used for treating, such as (1) sulphuric acid, (2) solvents, such as sulphur dioxide and nitrobenzene, and (3) chemical reagents, such as chlorine, hypochlorite, caustic soda, anhydrous aluminum chloride, and "doctor" solution. (Doctor solution consists of a solution of litharge in aqueous caustic soda.) In the refining process the treatment of petroleum fractions with solvents or chemical reagents is frequently followed by filtration. Various types of natural and activated clays have come into use, displacing the bone charcoal formerly extensively used for decolorizing the oil.

Sulphuric acid is today as it was in 1908, the principal reagent used for refining petroleum products. The ease of application and of sludge removal, as well as the low cost, has made it a successful competitor with all other processes. During the last 25 years the apparatus used for treating has undergone considerable change, especially that required for the treatment of light oils. The quantity and concentration of the sulphuric acid used depends upon the nature of the crude from which the stock was produced and upon the grade of finished oil required.

The procedure for treating lubricating oils, which remained almost unchanged from 1908 until relatively recently, is about as follows: The oil is charged into a cone-bottomed agitator having a capacity up to about 2,000 bbl. This agitator is equipped with air lines for mixing the batch and is lead-lined if 66 deg. Bé acid or weaker is used. After the acid has been pumped into the agitator and the mixture contacted sufficiently by blowing, the air is shut off to allow the sludge formed by the reaction to settle to the bottom of the agitator, from where it is immediately withdrawn. The oil is allowed to stand for several hours to allow a quantity of very finely divided sludge to settle. After this so-called pepper sludge has been withdrawn, the batch is transferred to another similar agitator where the acidity of the oil is neutralized with either caustic soda or soda ash. The soaps that are formed in this step are settled and withdrawn, after which the oil is washed with hot water, and finally blown bright (dry) with air. It may then be filtered through clay.

Continuous Treaters. Within the last year a continuous process for treating these oils has been put into operation at the refinery of the Vacuum Oil Co., Inc., at Paulsboro, N. J. This process was developed in cooperation with the engineers of the Sharples Specialty Co. In the process, the oil and acid are accurately measured to a mixing chamber, where the mixture is intimately contacted for sufficient time to complete the reaction. The mixture of acid-treated oil and sludge is then separated continuously in a centrifuge rotating at 15,000 r. p. m. The oil separated is finished in the same manner as the batch treated product. This process has the advantage of obtaining a much better separation of oil from the sludge with a corresponding increase in yield.

In the early days of oil refining, the light oils, such as gasoline and kerosene, were first treated in cone-bottomed agitators. Mixing was obtained by blowing with air or by drawing the mixture off the bottom of the agitator and spraying it in at the top. This method was very hazardous and all the agitators were equipped with explosion doors in the roof to minimize the danger in case of fire. The losses were high, as considerable quantities of the gasoline were carried off by the air used for agitation. In this process the acid treatment was followed by contacting with doctor solution. The oil was then neutralized, water-washed and either filtered through spent clay or redistilled with steam.

About 1915 the refiners adopted a system for the continuous application of acid, caustic, doctor solution, etc., to gasoline, which consisted of a series of connecting cylindrical vessels, each slightly inclined from the horizontal and provided with internal agitators. Each operation to be performed was done in one of these vessels, tanks being provided where the sludge or treating reagents could be settled before the oil passed to the next reaction vessel. The next development was the construction of a series of vertical towers, each provided with perforated plates to assure intimate mixing. Separate towers were provided for acid treating, washing, alkali and doctor treating as required by the particular stock being processed. This plant has been further modified by using orifice columns or Duriron nozzles to obtain sufficient mixing, these devices being placed in between the settling tanks from which the spent treating reagents are withdrawn. These plants have been made highly efficient. Being very flexible, they lend themselves to a wide variety of operation.

In the last few years the highly reactive gasoline produced by vapor-phase cracking required more accurate control of temperature, time and degree of mixing, than was obtained by the methods previously outlined. A continuous process is now in operation at several refineries in which the gasoline is mixed with the required amount of acid in a centrifugal pump, the mixture circulated through a reaction tank under controlled conditions of time and temperature, and the sludge separated from the gasoline by means of a DeLaval centrifuge. The gasoline is then neutralized with caustic and distilled with steam or under vacuum. Sufficiently low temperatures are maintained in this rerun operation to prevent the decomposition of the esters and polymerized products formed in treating, as otherwise the benefits of the treating operation would be destroyed.

Other Processes. The Edeleanu process for treating oils with liquid sulphur dioxide was developed about 1909 in Europe. It was not placed in commercial operation in this country until some time after 1918. The sulphur dioxide is a solvent for the unsaturated and aromatic hydrocarbons as well as some of the sulphur compounds. The naphthenes and paraffin hydrocarbons are only slightly soluble. The sulphur dioxide is soluble to a certain degree in petroleum and petroleum distillates. Sufficient liquid sulphur dioxide is used to form two layers, the lower one containing the aromatic and unsaturated hydrocarbons in solution, the upper layer being a solution of sulphur dioxide in the naphthenes and paraffins. These two layers are separated and the sulphur dioxide recovered for re-use by distillation. The degree of separation depends on the relative amount of sulphur dioxide used, the temperature, and the number of extractions performed. More recently a mixture of sulphur dioxide and benzene has been used in the Edeleanu process.

There are several large Edeleanu plants in successful operation. In California the process is being used for the production of transformer oils, lubricating oils, and an excellent quality of burning oil from high sulphur aromatic base crude oils.

Chemical reagents have been applied almost entirely to the treatment of gasoline and kerosene. Sodium hypochlorite has been used as a treating reagent for the conversion of certain organic sulphur compounds to less objectionable derivatives. It does not react with thiophene and free sulphur. Care must be used to prevent the formation of substituted chlorine compounds as well as the oxidation of other substances to form undesirable colored compounds. It has been the general practice to filter oils treated in this manner through bauxite. In addition, gasolines so treated require redistillation.

One of the most recent developments is the Lachmann process in which a zinc chloride solution of 70 to 85 per cent concentration is sprayed downward through a contacting chamber where it meets in counter-current the naphtha vapors being treated. Temperatures range from 265 to 410 deg. F. Concentration of zinc chloride must be maintained by careful control of operating conditions. It is claimed that gums and mercaptans are reduced to a minimum, and excellent color is obtained.

Other methods have been developed for treatment of gasoline in the vapor phase. The first one of commercial prominence was the Gray process in which the hot vapors were contracted with fullers earth. The fullers earth was heated by the hot vapors. The reaction is one of polymerization, to which the diolefins and other gum-forming constituents are susceptible. The utility of this process depends entirely on the nature of the distillate being treated. Many stocks do not respond to the process to a sufficient degree to give it an advantage over acid treating and rerunning.

Today's treating process for cracked gasolines must be one that will reduce sulphur, gum and color forming constituents sufficiently, without substantial reduction in anti-knock value.

Decolorizing Methods. Various types of filtering materials have been used for decolorizing oil. In 1908 bone black was used extensively. Today a few refiners still use this material for special products. Bone black has been supplanted by fullers earth, bauxite, silica gel, activated charcoals and acid-treated clays. Of these fullers earth and activated clays are in most general use. The method of filtration has varied from percolation, in which the oil passes through a bed of the absorbent, to the contact method, in which the oil and fine clay are intimately mixed and then separated by mechanical means.

In the percolation process, a 30-60 mesh clay is generally used as it permits a reasonable rate of flow of the oil and a sufficient decolorizing effect. A vertical tank is ordinarily used, approximately 10 x 30 ft. in size, equipped at the bottom with a perforated drainage plate covered with canvas to hold the clay. The oil is fed to the filter either by gravity or pressure. The latter is preferred in modern practice.

The usual custom is to allow the oil to soak in contact with the clay for 12 to 24 hrs. in order to guard against possible channeling in the filter. The first oil through the filter is decolorized to a greater degree than desired. As the process continues, the oil gradually becomes darker until the total blended filtrate has a color equal to that of the established standard. The filter is then allowed to drain, washed with naphtha to remove the oil, and steamed to remove the naphtha. The clay is then withdrawn and partially reactivated by burning.

Fresh clays are generally used for the lighter colored oils and the reactivated clays used for the darker oils being processed. Oils of high viscosity are sometimes filtered in solutions in naphtha. Better filter rates, and higher yields of oil per ton of clay are generally obtained. The temperature of filtration varies greatly; some oils must be handled hot, while others can be filtered cold. It is customary to install the filters in rooms where heating coils can be placed to prevent radiation losses from the filters.

Contact Filtration. In the contact filtration process, the acid treated fine clays are used either dry or in the form of a pulp. The amount of clay required varies widely, depending upon the effectiveness of the clay used, the nature of the oil being treated, the previous treatment the oil has received, and the amount of decolorization desired. In this process a predetermined quantity of clay is intimately mixed with the oil in a tank equipped with an agitator. The mixture is then pumped through a pipe heater where the temperature is raised to 350 to 650 deg. F., depending upon the particular stock being processed. The clay always contains considerable moisture which is flashed off in an evaporator. The mixture of clay and oil is then separated by filtration, using filters such as the Oliver, Sweetland, and Vallez. Heat exchangers are utilized in the plant for cooling the hot oil leaving the evaporator and preheating the mixture prior to its entrance into the heater.

There are several advantages in the contact filtration process, which may be summarized as follows: uniformity of product, ability to neutralize sour acid treated oils and thus eliminate neutralization troubles, lower cost of plant, and smaller quantities of oil in process at one time. The principal disadvantages of the process are the high cost of the clay and the difficulty in reactivating it for re-use.

Clay Regeneration. In regenerating coarse clays, it is necessary to remove the coloring material from the clay. It has been the practice to accomplish this by burning at temperatures low enough not to destroy the porosity of the clay. If temperatures above 1,050 to 1,110 deg. F. are used, the clay sinters and its decolorizing power is lost.

The first clay regenerating furnaces were of vertical gravity types, such as designed by Paris, Eby, Keubler, and others. The Bonnot rotary kiln was a decided step forward and consisted of a steel shell lined with refractory material, inclined slightly from the horizontal, and mounted on rollers so that it could be rotated about its central axis. The clay entered at the upper end and was discharged through the lower end. Fuel was burned at the lower end to heat the kiln and burn the carbonaceous material from the clay. The hot clay leaving the kiln was cooled in a second rotating drum in which the air used in the kiln was preheated.

The more recent improvements have been the use of Wedge and Nichols-Herreshoff multiple-hearth furnaces developed for ore roasting. In these furnaces, the clay is fed in at the top and is moved by sets of rabbles inward on one hearth and outward on the next as it passes through the furnace. These kilns are fired with oil or gas and the temperature of the various hearths can be controlled. The chief differences between these two furnaces are that the Wedge uses water for cooling the rabbles and the driving mechanism, and that the fuel is burned in a Dutch oven, whereas Nichols-Herreshoff uses air for cooling and burns the fuel directly on the hearth.

The same methods have also been tried for the reactivation of fine clays used in the contact process. The results have not been very encouraging; dust losses are extremely high and the efficiency of the reactivated product is rarely over 50 to 60 per cent of the original product.

DEWAXING LUBRICATING OILS

Nearly all petroleum oils contain paraffin wax; those of the asphaltic group have very little, while the semi-paraffinic and paraffinic groups often contain as much as 4.5 to 5 per cent. It has been the custom when distilling these wax-bearing crudes for the production of lubricating oils to separate two fractions. The lighter fraction (wax distillate) carries a large quantity of wax which separates in large crystals upon cooling. The heavier fraction, from which most of our viscous lubricating oils are produced, contains a wax which on cooling separates in crystals so small that the wax has been called amorphous. The smallness of the crystals in this latter case is probably due to the presence of colloidal inhibitors which retard crystal growth. The two lubricating oil fractions must be processed by entirely different methods in order to produce relatively wax-free oils.

Entrainment and lack of fractionating equipment in shell still operation allowed heavy viscous oils and crystallization inhibitors to be carried overhead into the wax distillate. This made it necessary to redistill the light oil fraction before the wax could be separated by chilling and pressing. This rerun operation has been eliminated by the use of the modern pipe heater and fractionating column. Increased yields of lubricating stocks have also been secured because of less decomposition and better fractionation. There has been little change during the past 25 years in the technique of wax removal from the wax distillate other than incorporating improvements in heat exchange and modern refrigeration.

Real progress has been made in handling the heavier oil fractions which contain the so-called amorphous wax. The fundamental basis of most methods of separating the petrolatum from the oil is the use of light solvents to create a relatively large difference in specific gravity between the solidified wax and the mixture of oil and solvent.

Cold Settling. In 1908 it was the practice to fill large storage tanks with the crude, or the topped crude cut back with naphtha, and depend on the gradual cooling during cold weather to effect a separation of the high-melting-point amorphous wax, by its gradual solidification and settling to the lower part of the tank. The clear upper portion of the oil was pumped off and distilled for the production of cylinder oil or "bright" stocks as they are called in the industry. A sudden period of warm weather would often set up sufficient convection currents in the tanks to destroy the effect of several months settling, or a period of extremely cold weather would congeal the entire mass and prevent settling.

These difficulties led to the development of the cold settling process in which artificial refrigeration was used. At first the solution of wax and oil was placed in rectangular tanks located in refrigerated rooms maintained at about 0 deg. F. With careful operation fairly satisfactory results were obtained; but the cost was high, due to expensive buildings, excessive refrigeration and very small capacity.

The next improvement was the tank type of cold settler. A standard vertical cylindrical tank was used, ranging in sizes up to 120,000 gal. capacity. Refrigerating coils were placed in horizontal layers at the top, so distributed that the heat could be extracted from the oil at a uniform rate over the entire surface, thus reducing the danger of setting up convection currents. Every precaution was taken to prevent agitating the contents of the tank. It was thoroughly insulated over its entire surface. The stock to be dewaxed was dissolved in naphtha in the proportion of 30 to 40 per cent stock and 60 to 70 per cent naphtha. This solution was cooled slowly at a uniform rate and when the temperature reached 8 to 10 deg. F., cooling was stopped and the mass allowed to settle for about 24 hr. The clear solution was then pumped off and the naphtha removed by steam distillation. The resulting bright stock had a pour point (A. S. T. M.) of about 35 deg. F., which was about the best that could be produced by the method. It required from 4 to 6 days for processing each batch through the equipment.

Centrifugal Dewaxing. In 1917 the Sharples Specialty Co. undertook the study of dewaxing various petroleum products, an investigation which resulted in the centrifuge process that is in universal use today for the separation of amorphous wax. In this process the solution of wax and naphtha is cooled at a carefully controlled rate with agitation to a temperature from 25 to 30 deg. F. below the pour point required in the finished product. The petrolatum which separates in the solution is removed by means of a high-speed centrifuge. These centrifuges revolve at 15,000 r. p. m. and multiply the effect of gravity several thousand times, thereby obtaining a rapid separation of the two products. The centrifuge process has resulted in large savings, because of the reduction of time, the elimination of the settling period, and the larger yield of lubricating oils which result because of more efficient separation of the petrolatum from the solution.

Another development of dewaxing is the Weir process, in which a filter aid is added to the chilled solution of the stock being treated. This mixture is then separated in a pressure filter. The bright stock solution is distilled with steam to remove the naphtha. The petrolatum is separated from the filter aid by heating and steaming. The hot filter aid is cooled by blowing with refrigerated gas, and is then returned to the process. The Weir process is under development at several refineries at the present time. The process has the inherent possibility of handling those stocks in which the waxes are too crystalline to centrifuge and not sufficiently crystalline to press.

Hydrogenation of Petroleum

The investigation of destructive hydrogenation of organic materials, such as brown coal, has been going on in Germany for a number of years. In 1927 the work of Bergius and the "I. G." had progressed to such an extent that the Standard Oil Co. of N. J. became interested in the possibilities of the process because of its basic relation to the general problem of crude oil conservation. An extensive laboratory program was carried out by subsidiaries of the Standard Oil Co. of N. J. with the conclusion that not only could liquid products be produced from coal but petroleum itself could be materially changed under controlled conditions of operation. It was found that such impurities in the crude as sulphur, nitrogen and oxygen could be almost completely removed as their gaseous hydrides, and the structure and size of the hydrocarbon molecules could be altered to that desired in the finished product. It was demonstrated that the following operations could be performed by destructive hydrogenation: low grade asphaltic crudes high in sulphur could be converted to gasoline and other distillates low in sulphur; low grade lubricating oils could be converted to a high grade product having a low temperature-viscosity coefficient and low Conradson carbon value; off-color kerosenes of poor burning qualities could be changed to high quality products; and gasolines having high sulphur content, poor color, and gum-forming constituents could be stabilized for color and gum, as well as desulphurized without material loss of anti-knock value.

Two 5,000-bbl. per day plants have been constructed, one in 1930 and the other in 1931. The results achieved in these plants have confirmed the findings of the experimental work. The hydrogen is compressed to approximately 3500 lb. pressure, mixed with the stock to be treated, and pumped through suitable heat exchangers and heaters into a reaction vessel containing a catalyst, where, at the desired temperature, the reaction is allowed to take place. From the reaction chamber the combined final products and gases pass through heat exchangers and coolers to a high-pressure separator where the liquid product is separated from the unused hydrogen and other gases. The liquid product then passes to a low-pressure separator, where a further separation of gas takes place, from which it goes to a distillation unit. The gases from the high-pressure separator are scrubbed with oil to remove hydrogen sulphide and returned to the system by means of a booster pump. Runs as long as eight months' duration have been made. Temperatures used in the process vary from 800 to 1025 deg. F. depending upon the type of reaction desired. It is of interest to add that the heat exchangers and reaction vessels are placed in huge reinforced concrete stalls. The process is costly, requiring expensive equipment; and because it operates at such high temperatures and pressures, maintenance charges are high. It is claimed that these disadvantages are more than offset by the large improvements in quality of products obtained.

Special Products

During the last ten years many special materials have been developed to impart specific qualities to certain petroleum products. The first important development was lead tetra ethyl. Thomas Midgley, Jr., of the General Motors Research Corporation, had found that lead tetra ethyl was efficient in raising the anti-knock properties of gasoline. The Standard Oil Development Co., in conjunction with the duPont company, developed a method for making this compound at a price sufficiently low to permit its commercial use.

Another product of importance from the laboratories of the Standard Oil Development Co. is "Paraflow," a viscous synthetic hydrocarbon material, which is a condensation product of chlorinated paraffin and naphthalene. This product has the property of reducing the pour point of wax-bearing oils with which it is blended. This enables the refiner to conserve a considerable quantity of the oil that would be removed with the wax if the lubricating oil were completely dewaxed for the production of very low pour point lubricants.

Sullivan and his co-workers have produced a synthetic lubricating oil at the laboratories of the Standard Oil Co. of Indiana. The process consists of polymerizing by means of aluminum chloride the unsaturated products obtained by cracking paraffin wax. The lubricating oil produced is highly resistant to oxidation and has a low temperature-viscosity coefficient.

UTILIZATION OF BYPRODUCTS

From the refining processes there is obtained a large number of byproducts, among which the most important are petroleum, coke, acid sludge, and gas.

Petroleum coke is produced chiefly in the cracking operation and is used for fuel. Its low ash content makes it a very desirable raw material for the manufacture of carbon electrodes and for those metallurgical processes which require an extremely high grade carbon. Many attempts have been made to briquette this coke for household use, but as yet none of these methods has achieved notable commercial success. Recently the Knowles process for coking topped crudes and the residuum from cracking plants has been installed at several of the larger refineries. The coke produced by this process is very dense, has a high fixed carbon content and resembles the metallurgical coke produced from coal. In this process the material to be coked is preheated in a pipe heater, from which it flows to one of a series of coking ovens. These ovens are 10 x 30 ft. and are floored with a special alumina-clay tile which serves as a hearth. The oven is fired by gas, which burns in a series of tunnels distributed underneath the hearth. At the beginning of the cycle, the hearth is heated to about 2300 deg. F. and cools to approximately 800 deg. F. when a 5- to 6-in. layer of coke has been deposited. The feed to the oven is then stopped but firing is continued until most of the volatile matter has been removed from the coke layer. The coke is pushed out of the oven with a ram, closely following the standard practice of the byproduct coke plant for the destructive distillation of coal. The overhead products during this operation are gas, gasoline and gas oil, sufficient gas being produced to fire the heater and ovens.

Acid Recovery. Large quantities of acid sludge are produced in the acid treatment of the various petroleum fractions. These sludges vary widely in character, depending on the nature of the oil being treated and the quantity of acid used. The sludges produced from light oils such as gasoline and kerosene are usually fluid, while those obtained from lubricating oils are extremely viscous. They oxidize and solidify rapidly and must be subjected to immediate treatment in order to recover their sulphuric acid content.

It has been the practice to transfer these sludges to a series of lead lined tanks having either cone or slanting bottoms and provided with open steam lines for agitation. The sludge is mixed with water or gas oil and water, and steamed for several hours. The free acid and the acid liberated by the hydrolysis of the acid esters in the sludge pass into the aqueous phase. This dilute acid, which is usually less than 25 deg. Bé is concentrated for re-use.

A pressure retorting method for processing sludges was developed at the Standard Oil Co. of California about 1925. This process is particularly successful for the sludges produced from light oils and distilled lubricating stocks. The conditions of operation depend upon the character of the sludge, the temperature usually being between 275 and 350 deg. F. and the pressure between 25 and 70 lb., with a heating time of one to two hours. The separated acid has a strength of 40 to 50 deg. Bé. The process is continuous. Larger yields of stronger acid are recovered, which result in a material saving in acid cost to the refinery. The residue from these operations is usually burned as fuel at the boiler house, stack temperatures being kept sufficiently high to prevent corrosion due to the acid nature of the products of combustion.

In 1908 and until 1920 the dilute separated acid was concentrated in pan-and-bench systems. The first stage was a series of lead pans and the second stage originally consisted of glass retorts or bottles, which were later replaced with cast iron stills set in the form of a cascade. This method of operation was extremely costly due to high maintenance charges, low fuel efficiency and a fume loss as high as 10 per cent. It was, without doubt, the most disagreeable part of the refinery yard for the workmen.

The Chemico process for acid concentration was put into operation in 1920 at Buffalo, N. Y., and since that time has been installed in a large number of refineries and chemical plants. It is a two-stage process based on the principle of passing a mixture of hot air and flue gases through the acid to be concentrated. Both stages are mechanically identical, the acid being concentrated to 57 to 60 deg. Bé in the first and further concentrated to 66 deg. Bé in the second. A quantity of tar separates after the first stage, which is removed before further concentration. The feed to each stage passes down a checker column where heat exchange is effected. The hot acid flows from this column into a bath where the hot gases from the furnace bubble through it. Cottrell precipitators are installed at the top of these columns to prevent the loss of SO_3. However, the SO_2 which is formed in the process escapes from the towers and is the source of a fume nuisance.

In 1921 Simonson-Mantius developed a vacuum process at the Vacuum Oil Co. refinery at Paulsboro, N. J. This process is operated in either single or double stages, depending upon the quality of finished acid required and the strength of the acid to be concentrated. Heat is applied in the first stage with steam, where the acid is concentrated to 55 to 60 deg. Bé. In the second stage, where higher temperatures are required, hot oil is circulated through a series of Duriron tubes. Any tarry material that separates after the first stage, is removed before charging to the second evaporator. Vacuum is produced by a specially designed antimony-lead barometric column. The lower temperatures and entirely closed system have the advantages of eliminating fumes and odor, decreasing fuel consumption and losses due to less decomposition of the acid.

The latest development for the recovery of acid sludge is the process of the Chemical Construction Co. installed at Petrolia, Pa. In this process the unseparated acid sludge is fed into a rotary kiln where it is heated to 400 deg. F. in the presence of a controlled quantity of air. The sulphuric acid content of the sludge is partly reduced to SO_2. The SO_2 gas is cooled and converted to SO_3 by oxidation with air in the presence of a vanadium catalyst. The SO_3 is absorbed in packed towers. A clean acid of any desired concentration can be produced. If the process is successful, it will make the refiner independent of the acid manufacturer, for sufficient sulphur can be converted to sulphuric acid in the plant to make up for the refinery losses.

The gas produced in the cracking process is the potential source of a large number of chemical products. Large amounts of unsaturated hydrocarbons, such as ethylene, propylene, and butylene, are present. Secondary propyl and butyl alcohols are being manufactured by first absorbing the hydrocarbon in sulphuric acid and then hydrolyzing the ester thus formed to the alcohol. Ethylene is being used for the manufacture of ethylene glycol, ethyl alcohol, and resins for use in the preparation of plastics and lacquers. The saturated gases have also been used for the preparation of solvents. In this process the hydrocarbon is first chlorinated and then esterified to form such compounds as butyl and amyl acetate.

RESEARCH AND DEVELOPMENT

The need of fundamental facts goes hand in hand with the development of an industry and this advance is accelerated as scientific principles are applied to the solution of its problems. There is no doubt that the progress of refining in America was retarded by the industry's belief that "common sense" and "prior practice" were sufficient for the design of new and larger refineries.

The advent of the cracking industry brought out the necessity of greater knowledge of the fundamental facts regarding petroleum. However, it was not until 1920 that any serious consideration was given to the problem, at which time several of the larger companies embarked upon definite research programs. The last 10 or 12 years have seen the beginning of a revolution in the industry. As one reviews the changes that have taken place even in the last 5 years, it is very difficult to picture the refinery of the future when, along with motor fuels and lubricants, there may be produced many synthetic chemical products.

In 1925 the American Petroleum Institute, through gifts amounting to $500,000 by John D. Rockefeller and by the Universal Oil Products Co., started a program of fundamental research in petroleum. A considerable volume of essential data and information has been obtained. The determination of specific and latent heats of petroleum fractions and compounds has given the industry fundamental data for the design of all types of heat exchange equipment.

One objectionable impurity in light petroleum products is sulphur, and it is found in varying quantities in all crudes. Sulphur compounds have caused the gasoline refiner a great deal of trouble due to the cost of treatment for their removal and their corrosive action on his equipment. A good start has been made in the A.P.I. program in the study of such sulphur compounds as the mercaptans, sulphides, disulphides and thiophenes.

Some work has been done on the isolation and identification of the constituents of crude petroleum and the determination of their physical properties. Of interest here is the A.P.I. program at the Bureau of Standards, and Edgar's work on hydrocarbons which resulted in the adoption of mixtures of iso-octane and heptane as a reference fuel for the evaluation of the anti-knock characteristics of motor fuels.

When there is considered the work of Midgley on lead tetra ethyl; of Bergius and others on the hydrogenation of coal and petroleum; of Edeleanu on the fractionation of petroleum with sulphur dioxide; of McAfee with anhydrous aluminum chloride; of Gray on the clay treatment of gasoline; of Sharples in the dewaxing of lubricating oils; of the Universal Oil Products Co. and most of the major oil refineries on cracking; of the development of the equipment to meet the demands of the modern refinery by such manufacturers as M. W. Kellogg Co., Foster-Wheeler, Badger, and many others, it is realized that the petroleum industry of today is very different from that of 1908.

Practically all of the major oil companies have recognized the importance of research and have established laboratories where a definite program can be carried to completion. In most of the laboratories a certain amount of work is being done on problems of more or less fundamental nature.

There are many important problems in every refinery that require careful investigation; questions involving cracking, distillation, treating with chemicals and solvents, the better utilization of byproducts and most important of all, the improvement of the quality of the products at lower costs of manufacture.

CHAPTER VI

CHEMICAL ENGINEERING CONTRIBUTIONS TO THE ELECTROCHEMICAL INDUSTRIES

By W. S. Landis

Vice-President, American Cyanamid Co., New York, N. Y.

MOST of the fundamental principles underlying the application of electric energy to chemical processes, either electrolytic or electrothermic, were discovered prior to the foundation of the American Institute of Chemical Engineers. Within the past quarter of a century the electrochemical industry has expanded enormously; this expansion, however, has included comparatively few new applications of the electric current to chemical processes outside the field of control apparatus. The chief development, therefore, is due almost entirely to the chemical engineer applying his knowledge of materials and engineering practice to the perfection of equipment, particularly by increasing the size and the life of units. His skill in manipulating the primary products of electrolytic cells and furnaces has greatly widened the use of the materials produced, to meet the constantly changing requirements of modern life.

In this field the chemical engineer is faced with a complex problem, the solution of which requires knowledge of the properties of a unique type of electric circuit, as well as an understanding of the complicated chemical reactions involved. In reviewing the progress made, the field has been divided into several more or less distinct groups, on account of the diversity of problems presented in each of the subdivisions.

Electroplating. The oldest of the commercial electrochemical processes, electroplating, dates back long before the founding of the Institute. Modern practice of the art, in the smaller establishments, differs very little from that of 50 years ago when plating was done in small baths with current supplied by batteries. Development of the dynamo replaced the inefficient primary cell by a mechanical source of power. With the widespread distribution of electric power the place of the small generating unit with its prime mover has been taken by the more economical motor-generator or converter set. The rectifier has not yet become a factor in plating, as it possesses certain inherent electrical characteristics that prevent the attainment of maximum economy in this service. These changes in the source of energy have enabled the plating unit to broaden its field greatly and to keep up with the greatly increased demand for ornamental and satisfactory mechanical objects.

Early plating practice was restricted to coatings of gold, silver, copper, and nickel, each object being individually cleaned, plated, and finished by hand. Today plating of brass, zinc, iron, cadmium and chromium has been added to the list with finishes not characteristic of any particular metal, and the plater is combining art with his technique. The advent of the automobile, the safety razor, the powder box, and the lipstick has caused a tremendous increase in the demand for cheap plated articles of the most varied kinds and sizes, and mechanical equipment has been forced on the industry, for cleaning, plating, and finishing operations. The chemical engineer was called upon to develop not only the required mechanical features, but also to insure proper electrical contacts in the bath, and to select materials of construction capable of resisting the corrosive action in the different steps of the process.

Electro-Refining and Extraction. Electrolytic refining of metals also antedates the founding of the Institute, although the art was previously devoted primarily to the refining of copper and the recovery of the noble metals. The fundamental principles developed in copper refining have later been applied to the treatment of other metals such as gold, silver, nickel, lead, and zinc; going beyond the simple refining operation they have become useful in the extraction of metals from ores. A purely chemical process is used to produce the solutions of the metals, and, following the principles developed in the refining of copper, the metal content of these solutions is recovered by a purely electrochemical process.

Two important factors in the refining of copper are the cost of power and the interest charges on the materials in process. The contributions by the power engineer have materially reduced the first item: contributions by the chemical engineer have been equally effective in reducing the latter. Development of larger cell units, of better circulation permitting increased current density, and particularly the maintenance of pure solutions by the development of purification equipment are all contributions of the chemical engineer. Purification of the solutions is an outstanding achievement in the refining industry; the solutions are extremely corrosive and require the development of highly efficient evaporators, pumps, and filters, not only to meet the specifications for purity but to withstand the intense corrosive action.

The copper refiner has not yet equipped himself, as have other industries, with the electric furnace for the melting of his finished products, but this development may come in the near future, being but an advance from the present restricted use in melting certain types of copper and copper alloys.

The chemical engineer has also contributed to the copper smelter in the development of higher grade refractories suitable for the non-ferrous industry. The Cottrell process is a standard tool in the non-ferrous industry.

Development of electrolytic recovery of the metals from their ores falls completely within the life-history of the Institute, and the chemical engineer has played a highly important part in these developments. Essentially they consist in a preliminary preparation of the ore, a leaching operation to remove inert gangue, purification of the resulting solution, rejecting interfering metals, and final electrolysis to recover the desired metal, with regeneration of the solute. Successful handling of enormous quantities of corrosive solutions, involving complicated filtration and purification methods, in competition with the older smelting processes, is a tribute to the skill of the chemical engineer. The scale upon which these complicated operations are carried out has necessitated a redesign of much of our chemical apparatus, to meet the exacting requirements of this new branch of metallurgy, in which the chemist has become as important an individual as the metallurgist. Copper and zinc have received most attention, but the methods are being extended to other metals.

The next step, which is yet in the stage of development, is the production of finished articles from such solutions, by modification of the electroplating process. Some progress has already been made, but much remains to be done before the process becomes universal for production of cylinders, tubes, and more complicated hollow-ware.

Alkali and Chlorine. Electrolysis of sodium chloride solutions for the production of caustic alkali and chlorine was an established industry in America prior to the foundation of the Institute having started about 1902 through the work of LeSueur and his associates. The procedure is based upon fundamental principles long established, but the development was delayed by lack of cheap electric power on a scale sufficiently large to make the electrochemical process feasible. Purely chemical processes for production of both caustic and chlorine had been in existence for a long time; the electrochemical process, therefore, had to face an already existing competitor. Through the ingenuity of the chemical engineer, in cooperation with the electrical engineer, machinery of large capacity for production of direct current was provided, permitting a correspondingly large cell unit. This effectively placed the electrochemical process in competition with the older methods.

The advances which have been made in the art during the last 25 years are mainly in the simplifying and improving of the cells used and in increasing the production. From 1883, the date of the first patent issued on electrolytic cells in the United States, up to 1907, 152 patents had been issued. Of these, only five have been in commercial use. During the last 25 years another 150 patents have been issued and the list of cells now in operation is not more than a dozen and in most of these many changes have been made from the original designs. Of the two distinct processes, the mercury and the diaphragm, the diaphragm has far exceeded the other in point of number and production. While the mercury process produces a purer caustic, the electrolytic is sufficiently pure for all purposes except the manufacture of rayon where soda ash caustic and that made by the mercury process have preference. As a result of this the diaphragm caustic producer has had to evolve a method of removing the salt. This is now accomplished and marks another improvement in the art.

In all the early cells of rectangular construction the anodes were made with joints within the cell and these joints were found to be a serious drawback and the development has been toward an anode without joints. Examples of this are seen in the K.M.L. cell of Allen and the Buck-McRae cell both of which are developments from the old Allen-Moore cell. The necessity of saving in cost at all points has resulted in the development of the circular type by Vorce which not only embodies an anode without joints, but also requires less floor space than any rectangular cell. In addition it is easier to repair and less expensive to build than any cell of equal capacity. Of all installations made during the last few years only two have been of rectangular construction while several thousand cylindrical cells have been installed. Notable in this respect is the replacement of the flat rectangular Billiter cell by the circular type.

The electrochemical process itself produced chlorine and a solution of caustic soda and sodium chloride; the chemical engineer thus was faced with the problem of separating the salts by evaporation and crystallization, and of reducing the gaseous chlorine to a transportable form. Through the development of satisfactory evaporating equipment for handling the peculiar corrosion problems presented by this solution and by the moist chlorine gas, this industry soon made great headway; today it ranks as one of our premier electrochemical industries. Continuous development of the cell has resulted in highly efficient, compact units with a long life. Diaphragms and electrodes have been much improved and adequate equipment for circulation of the solutions provided.

Drying, compression, and liquefaction of chlorine and development of suitable containers acceptable to the transportation systems, are wholly the work of the chemical engineer; most of the chlorine produced now finds its way into industry in the liquid form. Again the chemical engineer was forced to develop satisfactory equipment for the utilization of this chlorine in the complex bleaching and sterilization industries. His equipment for control of the feed is remarkable for its proportioning precision and long performance with minimum attention.

Production of chlorates is now entirely accomplished by electrochemical means. The original cells, small in capacity and equipped with costly platinum anodes, have in recent years been replaced; fused magnetite has been substituted for the platinum, and the size of the cells has been multiplied many times. Development of the magnetite electrode is an outstanding contribution of the chemical engineer, for service where insoluble anodes are required to resist oxidation.

Persalts and Peroxides. One of the recent electrochemical processes in this country is the production of the so-called persalts and peroxides, principally hydrogen peroxide of high strength. Formerly this product was made either from sodium peroxide, a secondary product of the electrochemical industry, or from barium peroxide, a purely chemical operation. Quite recently these older processes have been replaced by a new electrochemical process, involving oxidation on platinum anodes. In one modification, ammonium sulphate is oxidized to ammonium persulphate; and in another modification, sulphuric acid is oxidized to persulphuric acid. By chemical treatment these intermediate products are converted into hydrogen peroxide, which is recovered by distillation as a high strength solution.

The chemical engineer has been forced to redesign much equipment to eliminate all traces of decomposition catalysts, particularly iron and light metals, utilizing stoneware, glass, and aluminum alloys, protected by suitable non-metallic coatings.

Hydrogen and Oxygen. Electrolytic production of hydrogen and oxygen is one of the older electrochemical industries. As both products could be supplied by competitive chemical and physical processes, the electrolytic equipment was developed only in special cases and for small installations. Use of the electrolytic cell is essential in cases where specifications in regard to purity are extremely rigid. The comparatively low capital cost for a small electrolytic installation, compared with physical methods, such as production of oxygen by the liquefaction of air, advantageous only on a large scale, brought into existence many small electrolytic plants.

With the development of the synthetic ammonia processes demanding the local production of enormous quantities of very pure hydrogen, the chemical engineer undertook redesign of the early small cells; electrolytic equipment in sizes commensurate with the large volumes of hydrogen demanded by the synthetic unit is now available. These modern cells are of two types; the single cell with multiple electrodes and with capacities up to 18,000-20,000 amp.; and the compound cell, in which the units are arranged in series, like the plates and frames in a filter press. Both types are represented in some of the larger hydrogen plants. Construction of these large cells is a difficult problem. Proper distribution of current, prevention of interference by rising gas bubbles, diaphragms stable at the high operating temperatures, and even mechanical stress set up by the electrical characteristics of the unit all complicated the problem. Little relation in engineering features can be found between a 20,000-amp. cell of today and the 1,000-amp. cell used at the founding of the Institute.

Primary Cells and Storage Batteries. The primary cell as a source of direct current has almost disappeared from industry today, with exception of the dry cell for light service and the wet cell for signal service. Its place has been taken by the motor generator, the converter, the rectifier, or the storage battery. Even for call-bells or buzzer circuits the wet cell is rarely found, dry cells or small transformers being used for this service.

The dry cell has reached a very high state of development on account of its portability, convenience, and general reliability, but the chemical engineer has played a minor part in this progress. His contribution is mainly the production of chemicals of high purity and, to some extent, the automatic machinery used in producing the present cell.

The storage battery has replaced the older wet cell in many of its common applications, and has made a new field for itself in the automobile, portable or isolated lighting plants, and the radio. Two types are on the market, the lead cell and the Edison cell. The present lead cell is an achievement of the chemical engineer; the principle upon which it operates has been known for many years, but present-day service requires a radical departure from the original method of construction. In its development the outstanding feature of the past 25 years is the advent of the wood separator for insulating the plates of opposite polarity. An enormous amount of thought and inventive genius has been applied to this problem of inter-plate insulation, but a properly prepared flat sheet of wood has undoubtedly been the most satisfactory insulating material, judging by its widespread use.

The original battery plate, in which the active material was formed by the plate itself, has made way to the so-called pasted plate in which the active material is pressed or pasted into a suitable frame. These pasted plates possess much larger capacity per unit of weight than the old formed plates, but have less structural strength. The tubular type came into being just about the time when the Institute was founded. In this plate the active material is held in tubes of inert material, fastened together into a grid; nearly all the better types of batteries used for motive power are of this construction.

The advent of the self-starter in the automobile industry called for the most spectacular development of the storage battery. This service demands a special type of lightweight battery, made up of numerous thin plates and capable of a high power output over a very short period. This was an engineering problem pure and simple— the building of a structurally strong plate, as light as possible, and a container which now consists of a single piece of molded composition with three compartments, each constituting a single cell. These small, light batteries, weighing only 30-40 lb., will deliver as much as 1-2 hp. during the short cranking period of the automobile, a power output almost undreamed of 25 years ago from a unit of this size.

Airplanes are calling for still lighter batteries and new engineering principles are being utilized to develop a unit capable of performing the service required without too great a reduction in the life of the battery through saving of material.

Engineers have also played an important part in the development of the modern battery factory. The enormous demand placed on the industry by the automobile industry called for automatic machinery for casting the grids, automatic pasting machines to apply the proper amount of active material to the grids, and an almost automatic assembly line for welding and assembling the plates. He has also contributed to the improvement of the sanitary conditions in the battery plant, where the handling of lead products constitute a hazard.

For years engineers have been searching for substitutes for the lead battery, hoping to find a combination of greater chemical activity per unit of weight. At the present time only one substitute has obtained an important place in industry, the so-called alkaline or Edison cell. Certain limitations of the present alkaline battery restricts its use almost entirely to motive power applications. It is better adapted to discharge at a steady and comparatively low rate, and its high unit cost of construction precludes its use for automobile starting, where a heavy overload over a few seconds is desired.

The extremely complicated Edison battery is a monument to the chemical engineer. Without great engineering skill, as exhibited in the equipment used for making the flakes of metallic iron and nickel, in assembling the flakes in their containers, and finally in assembling the containers into the unit or plate, this battery would be economically impossible. It fits into the important field of transportation—the storage-battery automobile, the storage-battery locomotive and the like, as it is extremely rugged and non-sensitive to road shocks; it is not readily injured by over-charging or complete discharging, accidents often occurring in this type of service, where the unit may be called upon to deliver to its final limit before reaching the charging station.

Electrothermic Industries. Up to this point reference has been made only to those industries in which the electric current is really a chemical reagent. The current used must be uni-directional, or commonly called "direct," although in a few rare cases alternating current is superimposed upon a direct current for accomplishing certain objectives. A large part of electric energy consumed in the chemical industry is also used to furnish a convenient source of heat. Owing to the peculiar properties of the electric current, energy may be concentrated within a small space, and enormously high temperatures may be obtained on a scale limited by the power input only. The ease with which the electric current can be controlled through resistance, reactance, or voltage regulation also makes it a convenient source of energy for certain exacting heating operations, where high temperatures are not necessarily required. Furthermore, no byproducts are formed in the conversion of electrical energy into heat; this is extremely important as certain processes require definite temperatures and absence of gases of combustion. In fact, electric vacuum furnaces are operated in the complete absence of gases. As electrical energy can be produced from water power, this source of heat may be available in countries lacking fuel. The heat is furthermore produced in properly designed apparatus at the point of utilization, insuring a high degree of efficiency.

Calcium Carbide. Commercial production of calcium carbide is possible only in the electric furnace. This process was developed many years prior to the foundation of the Institute, although the furnaces used at that time were small, of a few hundred to a few thousand horsepower capacity. Charging of the raw materials, lime and coke, was done without extreme care, and the resulting product had to be carefully sorted to meet standard specifications. Today furnaces of 30,000 hp. capacity are in operation in several parts of the world. Elaborate preparatory treatment of all raw materials is now an important and universally applied practice, the consequence of which is the production of a carbide of practically unvarying quality. Handling the enormous amounts of molten carbide tapped from these large units, at a temperature close to 2,000 deg. C., presented a serious problem to the engineer.

The earliest use for carbide was in the production of acetylene, for lighting and later for welding. Today a large part of the carbide produced is converted into cyanamide, a raw material for the fertilizer and chemical industries, or into acetylene, which in turn is converted into acetaldehyde, acetic acid, and acetic anhydride.

The cyanamide industry, which today consumes over 500,000 hp., started commercial production about the time when the Institute was founded. The first plant, built in 1905, with an annual capacity of a few thousand tons has developed into about 35 plants with a capacity of 1,500,000 tons per year. Its development has been almost entirely in the hands of the chemical engineer, no new fundamental changes in general principle having taken place. Crushing carbide to impalpable powder without explosion; the handling of this powder without deterioration through the cyanamide furnace; and the final treatment for the preparation of fertilizer products or in the various chemical industries, are all problems calling for a highly developed engineering skill; these complicated operations had to be performed on a sufficiently large scale and at a cost low enough to compete with byproduct nitrogen and fixed nitrogen of natural origin.

Production of acetylene from carbide, although not a reaction involving the use of electric power, deserves a few words. In the early days the small generators dropped water onto carbide and furnished a satisfactory acetylene. With the enormous demands for acetylene created by the chemical industries and the welding technique, a different type of generator had to be provided, feeding carbide into water, according to the gas requirement. The hazards involved in generating and handling acetylene required observance of certain fundamental principles of design and construction before a satisfactory large generator was obtained.

Construction of containers for storage and transportation of acetylene under pressure, dissolved in acetone, also called for great engineering skill.

Conversion of acetylene into acetaldehyde, acetic acid, and acetone are problems outside the electrochemical field and will be dealt with in another chapter. Development of these chemical reactions has fortunately taken up the slack in carbide production brought about by the widespread distribution of electric power and replacement of the isolated lighting plants.

Abrasives. Although the fundamental principles underlying the production of artificial abrasives preceded the birth of the Institute, the development of the automobile industry brought about the greatest progress in this field. While originally confined to carborundum or silicon carbide, industry has now a wide range of abrasives and the related metallic carbides to choose from. By a better selection of the raw materials and more thorough preparation, control of the physical properties of the carborundum grain and improvement of its bonding characteristics have been made possible. The handling of the grain itself, after the furnace operation, has resulted in a better and more adaptable finished product.

Shortly after the founding of the Institute, fused alumina, essentially an artificial corundum was brought on the market. New types of furnaces had to be developed to meet the exacting requirements of this electrothermal operation; control was effected, making possible the production of alumina grains of different degrees of hardness and toughness for the specific applications. Treatment of the product from a furnace of this type is a complicated chemical problem, and great skill is required in the designing of the necessary equipment. Modern industry requires a large number of the different types of abrasives, which must be bonded and formed into innumerable types and grades of wheels. The equipment necessary for mixing, coating, baking, and finishing of these products has all been contributed by the chemical engineer, who likewise has been called upon to develop all types of non-rigid abrasives, and to furnish the many types of paper and cloth, both grease- and waterproof; development of equipment for proper application and testing has also been necessary.

Although unrelated in many respects, the products of these furnaces have also found a place in the refractory industry; carborundum and alumina refractories are now of vital importance to the combustion engineer.

Closely connected with the abrasive industry are the recent uses of tungsten carbide and boron carbide, which, owing to their extreme hardness have found application, not only in cutting tools, but in hardening metals to resist extreme wear. The advent of Carboloy, tungsten carbide cemented with metallic cobalt, has created a revolution in the art of cutting metals and the like, and other hard substances. Facing of bits with these carbides has been of great value to the prospector and well driller; as preservation of the form and cutting edge of the tool becomes extremely important with increasing depth of the hole. Pulling a string of tools from a well a mile deep to sharpen a bit is an expensive operation.

Phosphorus and Phosphoric Acid. In the early history of the electric furnace one of the first applications was the production of phosphorus by reduction of phosphate rock with carbon, using silica as flux. Phosphorus is expelled as vapor which subsequently must be condensed. Not only did the use of the electric furnace simplify the condensation by reducing to a minimum the quantity of gas passing through the condenser, but it removed the difficult maintenance problem in connection with the old fuel-fired retort.

Within the past decade the phosphorus furnace has been altered in design and so equipped that the phosphorus evolved is oxidized in the furnace and recovered as phosphoric acid by suitable scrubbing equipment, followed by electrostatic precipitation.

Recovery of phosphoric acid by this method is a difficult problem and involves the handling of the most corrosive of gases and liquids. The problem to be solved involved cooling the gases, scrubbing them in towers of acid-proof construction, usually of baked carbon, and finally the design of a special electrostatic precipitator in which the remainder of the acid is dropped out. Pumps and piping for circulating the acid offered a difficult problem to the engineer, but the use of some of the newer alloys reduced the corrosion difficulties to a minimum.

In Europe the problem of producing cheap phosphoric acid in electric furnaces, in competition with the ordinary acid phosphates of the fertilizer trade, has also been undertaken; in the largest installation phosphorus is condensed rather than oxidized in the furnace, later to be burned in a separate apparatus. The problem of burning large quantities of phosphorus is not simple, but the engineer solved the difficulty in two ways, by using a spray burner, or by dropping the liquid through a combustion tower. Ultimate recovery problem is the same as where phosphorus is burned in the furnace, but the operation is somewhat easier as some of the particularly vicious corroding agents, such as the fluorides, are absent. Recently the operation of the electric furnace has been duplicated in fuel-fired equipment, condensing all or part of the phosphorus as such, or burning it adjacent to the furnace, and collecting the phosphoric acid. The competitive situation of the fuel-fired versus the electric furnace is a matter of controversy; the third competitor, the old sulphuric acid treatment process, still remains the largest factor in the phosphoric acid industry.

Electrostatic Precipitation. While strictly speaking neither an electrochemical nor an electrothermic process, the recovery of dust, mist, and other fine material from gas streams by electrostatic methods belongs to the field of the chemical engineer. Many metallurgical and chemical processes have to contend with losses of volatilized products or with smoke and fume nuisances. The necessity of abating such nuisances called forth the development of the Cottrell precipitator, shortly before the founding of the Institute. Its first installation was the precipitation of sulphuric acid mist in California. This was quickly followed by a second installation for recovery of metallic fume, in this case a question of recovering values rather than nuisance abatement. Since then the application of such equipment has spread, until it has found a place throughout the chemical industry. Many installations were primarily based upon abatement of nuisance, but the products recovered were often found of great value; in some of the more complex installations the equipment has been designed and operated to afford differential separation of the valuable constituents and the less valuable dust. Electrostatic precipitation has also made its way into the gas industry for separating tar from gases; the engineering problems connected with this precipitation are of the most intricate and varying types. In smelter fumes containing arsenic and metal-bearing flue dusts, the unit is so constructed that the latter is separated at a temperature at which the arsenic is still in the vapor phase; by suitable cooling, arsenic is condensed and recovered in a second unit. In sulphuric acid production three different problems presented themselves to the chemical engineer: removal of dust from hot roaster gases; removal of mist from the sulphur dioxide gases ahead of the drying towers; and finally, recovery of acid mist from the exits of the absorption towers.

In sulphuric acid concentration the precipitator performs the function of a reflux condenser.

The chemical engineer has played an extremely important part not alone in meeting the problems of high temperature, corrosion, and abrasion, but has been forced to assist the electrical engineer in the development of insulating materials which enter into the electrical features of the precipitation process. A wholly new class of materials was demanded by the extreme conditions encountered. Intense application of engineering principles to this precipitation work has reduced the early qualitative theory to an exact science with workable equations and known constants, enabling the design of precipitation equipment to meet almost any requirement, the fundamentals of which can be quantitatively expressed.

Electro-Ionics and Photocells. While neither of these fields is essentially electrochemical, both involve the use of electricity for the control of chemical operations. The vacuum tube of the radio set is finding extended use in apparatus controlling chemical operations. It is capable of converting minute differences in voltage into energy sufficient to actuate switches for motors and other equipment. More and more this apparatus is coming into the market as the extended field is developed by the engineer.

The photoelectric cell with its auxiliary tubes is controlling a number of chemical operations. It warns of the discharge of smoke and fume, keeps densities of solutions to a desired value, and functions in automatic measuring apparatus. Although the bulk of its operations are at present confined to the mechanical arts, use of this equipment in the chemical industry is nevertheless on the increase. Such applications naturally fall within the sphere of the chemical engineer.

In a field as large as the one just covered contributions of the chemical engineer to the electrochemical field can only be touched upon. Industrial electrochemistry, as we know it today, received its largest development during the period represented by the life history of the Institute; examination of the membership of the Institute shows the important part which the chemical engineer plays in this industry. With the advent of cheaper power more and more applications of electricity will be made in fields of chemistry, not even touched upon in this brief summary and for purposes today served by perfectly good non-electrical equipment. The ease of control of the electric current makes it one of the most convenient tools of the chemical engineer; in consequence the next 25 years may be expected to result in far wider applications, at least in number and variety, if not in the amount of energy consumed.

CHAPTER VII

PROGRESS IN THE ELECTROMETALLURGICAL INDUSTRIES

By Francis C. Frary

Director, Aluminum Research Laboratories, Aluminum Company of America, New Kensington, Pa.

SINCE METALLURGY may logically be considered to be a branch of applied physical chemistry—the chemistry and physics of the metallic state—electrometallurgy becomes a part of electro-chemistry, and the division between them is necessarily an arbitrary one. For the purposes of this chapter, the electrometallurgical industries are considered to be those in which metals and alloys are reduced from their compounds at elevated temperatures by the aid of electricity, leaving to the chapter on electrochemical industries the discussion of all processes going on in aqueous solution. We shall therefore discuss the production of certain metals and alloys in the electric furnace, and the production of aluminum, magnesium, and sodium by the electrolysis of fused salt baths.

Ferro-Alloys and Alloying Metals, 1907-1932[1]

The movement to found the American Institute of Chemical Engineers gives notable importance to the year 1907. Moreover, to those who were then just entering the ferro-alloy industry, or, having served their apprenticeship, were appraising and directing the trends, the year is now marked by other occurrences that later contributed to the development of electrometallurgy and hence to the advancement of chemical engineering.

Two prominent engineering schools had recently graduated small, but enthusiastic classes, from their respective courses in electro-chemistry and electrometallurgy. The corporation now most prominent in the manufacture of ferro-alloys and in alloy research had just undertaken commercial production in the electric furnace. In that year the manufacture of ferrosilicon passed from a small, though

---

[1] Contributed by Harry R. Lee of Union Carbide and Carbon Research Laboratories.

continuous operation, to a tonnage industry using larger electric furnaces. At the same time the development of a sound technique and a steady demand permitted continuous production of low carbon ferrochromium on a substantial scale that has since never ceased to expand. Then also came the completion of three years of arduous experimentation and successful development on the part of one company in the electrometallurgy of ferrovanadium. Likewise in 1907 the producer now most prominent in vanadium alloys started a new plant on the present site, first using aluminothermic reduction, later the electric furnace. Also in that year the first commercial heat of chromium-vanadium steel for automotive construction was poured by a steel company that thenceforth played a leading part in the production of alloyed engineering steels.

All these works and signs of progress came to pass in a year now chiefly remembered for a financial embarrassment then heralded as "unprecedented in our national history"—again a familiar phrase. It is scarcely credible that the educational, technological, and industrial developments of major import just recounted, seven in all, happened to coincide in 1907. On the contrary, each in its field was a manifestation of the enterprise that makes the latest achievement a springboard for the next.

So continuous is the growth of invention and industry that the year 1907 should be recognized as a milestone, and not mistaken for a birthdate. To take an illustrious example, in the preceding decade Moissan and his collaborators had made a great many of the ferro-alloys or alloying metals now commercially known, although of qualities far from those now necessary for commercial utility. However, from 1907 the industry has grown steadily into larger commercial production, to an increased number of elements available in the form of metals and alloys, to an improvement in chemical purity, and to a wider variety of qualities devised and controlled in accordance with consuming requirements.

Many of these phases of commercial advance have been actuated and controlled by aggressive policies and programs of metallurgical research, largely directed to new uses for well-known alloys, but occasionally, as with zirconium, promoting an element from the chemical museum to the market place. Whether reaching toward solar temperatures or the absolute zero, chemical engineers all think in elements, and in that order may well be reviewed the ferro-alloys and alloying metals that have rendered exceptional service within the past 25 years.

Ferrosilicon. In 1907 the manufacture of 50 per cent ferro-silicon, theretofore conducted in small single-phase furnaces, was advancing toward three-phase units using thousands of horsepower. The problems met in this rapid expansion were principally those of electrical design appropriate to the use of very large currents without serious decrease in power factor. The principles thus developed raised electric furnace design to a new level, and they were soon applied with advantage to large furnaces for other products. The variety containing 50 per cent silicon is the electric furnace alloy of greatest tonnage and is the one most used for deoxidizing steel, offering in this field ample chemical activity together with low unit price. Well over three-fourths of the domestic steel production is treated with some form of silicon. Ferro-silicon containing 75 per cent silicon is used principally as an alloying addition, non-aging transformer steel forming the main outlet. The alloy containing slightly over 80 per cent silicon is preferred for generation of hydrogen, but this use is almost entirely limited to aeronautic balloons, and the peace-time need is slight. Manufacture of calcium-silicon on a commercial scale is more recent, and the demand is still relatively small. Although occasionally used as a deoxidizing scavenger for alloy steels, it is chiefly employed in iron castings of peculiar texture and high strength.

Silicon metal has extended the benefits of the element to some of the non-ferrous metals and alloys. About twelve years ago it was found that a large addition of silicon to aluminum—for example, 12-13 per cent—produced an alloy of high strength and superior casting properties. To meet the requirement, high-grade electric furnace silicon was soon produced, and for many years a standard product containing about 98 per cent silicon and less than 1 per cent iron has been available in carload quantities. Silicon is an active deoxidizer of copper, and silicon-copper has long been used for the treatment of copper and brass.

Ferromanganese. Even before 1907 the electric furnace production of high carbon ferromanganese was known to be possible, but then as now the method was economical only under some conditions. In 1915 heavy demand coincided with sudden shortage, and an important tonnage was for some months produced in a large electric furnace until the emergency had passed. The metallurgical operation was smooth, the product excellent, and the recovery of manganese superior to that of the blast furnace. In 1917 further electric furnace manufacture was begun in Alabama, and an appreciable production, extending to 1920, contributed much to the insufficient domestic supply. Ferromanganese enters almost all steel, and the high-carbon variety serves the largest tonnages. Practically all low-carbon ferromanganese is made in the electric furnace, and it has been currently available for over 20 years. It is used to introduce the fractional percentage of manganese desired in the well-known high-chromium stainless steels, and to a still greater extent in manganese rail steel and some automotive engineering steels. The alloy is probably destined to much larger use in the relatively new chromium-manganese stainless steels containing 8-9 per cent manganese. Metallic manganese has been produced for many years in the electric-furnace. With a manganese content of 96-97 per cent, and with down to one per cent iron, it deoxidizes and desulphurizes non-ferrous alloys, principally those of copper and nickel. Manganese-copper, providing manganese for the same use, has the advantage of a lower melting point. Silico-manganese and silico-spiegel contain manganese, silicon, and iron in various proportions, with moderate amounts of carbon. This country is witnessing a rapid increase in the proportion of the total steel output that is treated with these alloys and almost all of the domestic demand is being met by home production. From recent research in this country on the deoxidation of steel, silico-manganese promises to yield a product cleaner than present practice affords.

Ferrochrome. By 1907 the electric furnace manufacture of high-carbon ferrochromium had been continuous for ten years, and subsequent production has been unbroken. After the first large use in naval armor and projectiles the alloy entered the present wide field of engineering steels; it is limited to those varieties, the chromium and carbon contents of which do not require the low-carbon alloy. Even prior to 1907 low-carbon ferrochromium had become important to steel metallurgists, and the indispensability has never ceased. The first search for an electric furnace reduction method independent of carbon had begun in 1903, and was early rewarded by discovery of the principle of silicon reduction still in use. By 1907 the demand for the best quality then current warranted commencement of the process development that has since never ceased. Throughout the past 25 years the constant demand for a lower carbon content has presented a problem of cumulative difficulty, which, however, has always been met. In 1904 a maximum carbon content of one per cent was acceptable, but by 1909, 1913, 1920, and 1924 the respective limits had descended to 0.5, 0.2, 0.1, and 0.06 per cent, the latter figure governing much of the present production.

Naturally the low-carbon alloy permits manufacture of steels high in chromium and low in carbon, comprising chiefly those resistant to atmospheric oxidation at high temperatures, to chemical corrosion, and to atmospheric tarnish. The recent, but well-known chromium and chromium-nickel stainless steels, requiring alloy of the lowest carbon content, cause the largest single demand for low-carbon ferrochromium. For about 15 years the electric furnace manufacture of chromium metal has been continuous, and the present product contains up to 98 per cent chromium and less than one per cent iron. Its principal use is in the manufacture of the ductile nickel-chromium alloys, widely used for electric heating elements, and in Stellite, the metal-cutting tool alloy. Use in chromium bronzes promises to grow.

Ferrotungsten. By 1900 tungsten powder and ferrotungsten were produced commercially in this country, but even before 1907 there had been developed here an electric furnace process capable of the more economical production of very low carbon ferrotungsten from ores, of qualities quite diverse and often adverse. About 1910 the method was commercialized, and it has since been successfully employed. The major part of all ferrotungsten enters high speed tool steels, which typically contain 18 per cent tungsten together with significant amounts of chromium and vanadium.

Ferromolybdenum. Well in advance of 1907 there were devised in this country for the direct reduction of molybdenite two efficient processes—the lime-carbon and the silicon-reduction methods. However, commercial use had to await the development of molybdenum steels, and the earliest demand for ferromolybdenum came about 1916 from European governments. The present large American mine production of molybdenite had not then begun, so for some years thereafter the electric furnace dealt almost entirely with Western wulfenite, the lead-molybdate ore known for its numerous impurities. However, for a post-War period of many years the high-grade molybdenite flotation concentrates of Colorado were regularly smelted by one of the processes mentioned, and the resulting high quality ferromolybdenum has been widely used in molybdenum steels both here and abroad. Subsequently molybdate compounds for incorporation of molybdenum in steel were devised and successfully introduced. Whether applied as a ferro-alloy or molybdate, the element finds principal use in the chromium-molybdenum and other molybdenum steels. These engineering steels are prominent in automotive and aeronautic use, and are remarkable for their ready machinability and for excellent physical properties when heat-treated.

Ferrovanadium. In years preceding the electric furnace, silicon reduction of ferrovanadium was developed and applied to Colorado vanadiferous sandstone, to precipitated vanadates of calcium and of iron, and to the earliest arrivals of vanadium-sulphide ore from the great Peruvian deposit. This early production from Peruvian ore had a far-reaching effect on the metallurgy of alloy steel in this country, as it provided ferrovanadium for wide distribution to American steel makers then ambitious to enter the new field. In 1907 the present principal producer of vanadium alloys began making ferrovanadium by aluminothermic reduction. For a few years during the War period appreciable quantities of the electric furnace alloy were made from oxide recovered as a byproduct of Western radium ores. About 1920 South African complex ores of copper, lead, and zinc, rich in vanadium, were offered in commercial quantities; for a few years these were a source of electric-furnace ferrovanadium. About six years ago a Colorado deposit of vanadium-mica was brought to commercial production of vanadium oxide, from which considerable ferrovanadium is now produced. In addition to the important use in high-duty engineering steels, it is now usual to add one or two per cent vanadium to high-speed tool steels of the tungsten-chromium type. Moreover, recent extensive tests show that a vanadium content of about five per cent, with a correlative increase in the carbon content, economically prolongs the cutting life.

Ferrozirconium. Governmental need for zirconium steel in 1918 led to immediate and intensive experimentation toward the electric furnace production of zirconium alloys. Within that year ferrozirconium, silicon-zirconium, and zirconium-ferrosilicon were produced and shipped in considerable quantities. Although public demand did not follow at once, the producer of the alloys continued to conduct extensive research on the properties of zirconium-treated and zirconium-alloyed steels. Zirconium is unique in the metallurgy of steel, being a deoxidizer more potent than silicon and a corrective of the injurious effects of nitrogen, sulphur, and phosphorus. Silicon-zirconium and zirconium-ferrosilicon are currently produced and sold. Following initial large use in castings of carbon steel, application of the alloys has rapidly extended to rolled quality steels. Typical examples are found in free machining steels of the plain carbon, the low-alloyed and the stainless varieties, in low-alloyed automotive steels, in plain carbon and low-alloyed tool steels and in numerous high-alloyed specialty steels.

For the manufacture of ferro-alloys and alloying metals low in carbon, aluminothermic reduction has long been used and is still employed, having preceded the electric furnace in the production of chromium, manganese, and other alloying metals.

Beyond the enormous increase in output of ferro-alloys within the past 25 years, outstanding achievements of the industry are found in the attainment of increased energy yields and element recoveries from ore to alloy, in the advancement of many elements from rarity to the commercial status, and in the ability to meet analytical specifications that have become more and more exacting. Furthermore, for the past 15 years the principal alloy producers have pursued a policy of aggressive research, much of which is directed to the benefit of the consumer and to assistance in his problem.

Our fast-moving material world is literally dependent on ferro-alloys.

ALUMINUM

Twenty-five years ago the modern aluminum industry had existed for just 21 years, and its world production had grown from 16 metric tons in 1886 to 19,800 metric tons in 1907. More than half of that growth had occurred in the last three years of that period—an indication that real progress was about to be made. It is, therefore, not surprising to find that, in the 25 years that have elapsed, the world production (based on 1929 figures) has increased over 1,300 per cent, to an annual total of over 280,000 tons. For comparison, we may note that in the same period the production of iron increased about 60 per cent, that of lead less than 75 per cent, and that of zinc 100 per cent; while copper, the principal competitor of aluminum, made a gain of 170 per cent. Even so, in 1929 the world produced five times as much zinc as aluminum, and 350 times as much iron.

This great increase involved no fundamental change in production principles; the basic work had all been done in the early days. But there has been a continual refinement of methods and improvement in equipment and control of the process, resulting in marked improvements in quality and reduction in cost; an extensive development of new producing plants has also taken place. Thus, in the past 25 years five of the present Norwegian plants, all of the Italian and Russian plants, all German plants except one small one, two of the British plants, five French plants (including the largest one) and half of the plants in the United States and Canada were built, and most of the previously existing plants were enlarged.

One of the important limitations of the producing process has been the relatively small size of electrolytic cells which could be used; much effort has consequently been spent and many improvements have been made in the design of larger units. When we consider that 1,000 amps. will only produce about 16 lb. of aluminum per 24 hrs., at 90 per cent efficiency, we see the serious limitations of the 8,000-12,000 amp. cells in use 25 years ago. The electrical and mechanical difficulties involved in handling larger currents and correspondingly larger cells have gradually been overcome; at present the average current per cell is probably nearer 20,000 amps., with some lines of cells apparently carrying about twice this load.[1] Even a 40,000 amp. cell, producing about 600 lb. of metal per day and absorbing, say 250 kw., is a relatively small operating unit for an industry producing over 500,000,000 lb. of metal per year; so it would seem that there was still room for progress.

Commercial experience with the cells provided with a single, large Söderberg self-baking electrode instead of a group of smaller prebaked electrodes has shown them to be satisfactory and economical in operation, and to produce exceptionally high grade metal. By eliminating some of the mechanical difficulties involved in the operation of large multi-electrode cells, they may point the way to cells of still larger capacity.

Recently the practicability of electrolytically refining a metal in a fused salt bath has been proved by the Hoopes cell for the electrolytic refining of aluminum,[2] which has been developed to the point where it operates steadily and easily under works conditions. The very high purity aluminum thus produced has brought about important scientific and commercial advances.

One of the largest items in the cost of aluminum is the cost of the pure alumina used. Most of this is made by the Bayer (sodium-aluminate) process, which has been considerably improved in its details by chemical engineering work. Of the acid processes, the only one which has reached a commercial stage is the Blanc nitric-acid process for recovering alumina and potassium nitrate from leucite, upon which much effort has recently been expended in Italy. Electrothermal processes for producing fused alumina have received considerable attention, and much development work has been done upon them. The modified Hall dry process, in which bauxite and coke are smelted to produce molten alumina and a ferrosilicon aluminum-titanium alloy, has been operated commercially, as has the

1 Billiter, "Technische Elektrochemie" (1932), Vol. 3, p. 145.
2 Trans. Am. Electrochem. Soc., 47, 1 (1925).

Haglund process, which resembles the Hall process but adds a sulphide (pyrite) to the charge, producing an alumina slag containing aluminum sulphide. This slag is disintegrated with water, instead of being blown with air, as is the Hall process slag. The Pedersen process, involving furnacing bauxite and limestone to produce calcium aluminate, leaching with soda, and precipitation of the alumina with carbon dioxide, has also reached commercial operation.

Particular progress has been made along the line of new and improved products, especially alloys. Wilm discovered the heat-treatment of aluminum alloys about 25 years ago, and from that discovery has been worked out the commercial development of wrought and cast alloys of the Duralumin type, and several other varieties. Dirigibles and airplanes were the first users of these alloys, which now also are employed in trucks and passenger cars, railroad cars, and in a variety of other structures where high strength is required in combination with lightness. The problems involved in the fabrication of these alloys into the desired shapes, and the combination of such shapes into finished structures, have required large investments of time and money during the past 20 years. Their protection from corrosion in thin sections by very thin surface layers of pure aluminum or corrosion-resistant alloys has been worked out and commercialized.

Much progress has been made in the fabrication of pure aluminum and the older alloys. Aluminum pipe and foil, extruded shapes of a great variety, and sheet of much larger dimensions and higher quality have become common commercial articles, and the use of aluminum-bronze powder for general painting has become widespread.

Strong alloy forgings have become of commercial importance. Autogeneous welding has spread from the workshops of a few producers to the plants of many large consumers; and to the torch welding process have been successfully added electric spot and seam welding. Oxide-coating processes have been developed and commercialized; at first for electrical insulating purposes, and later for protection and beautification.

In the foundry, the quality of aluminum castings has been tremendously improved and their use very much extended. Permanent-mold casting and die casting have been developed commercially on a large scale, in addition to the older sand-casting process. The whole art of heat-treatment of aluminum-alloy castings has developed within the last ten years, and now some of the largest aluminum castings are successfully heat-treated. Introduction and use of silicon alloys for castings, either "modified" by the addition of a trace of sodium, or unmodified, has marked a decided step in advance in the casting field, particularly because of the excellent casting qualities of these alloys. Aluminum-base alloys of the magnalium type, introduced long ago, failed to make progress for many years owing to a lack of satisfactory casting and working technique. As a result of more modern information they are now being revived and show promise of great usefulness in certain fields.

All of these advances in what may well be called the art of use of the metal will be reflected in increased demand, which will give incentive and support for improvements in producing processes. In particular, modern investigation is increasing the demand for metal of the maximum purity commercially obtainable, and this will doubtless bring about further improvements in the operating process which will increase substantially the proportion of very high grade metal produced.

MAGNESIUM

Twenty-five years ago magnesium had a bright future, but not much past. Some metal was being made in Germany by electrolysis of the fused chloride, but the production was small and the uses few. In the interim, the development of new alloys and the technique of using them has largely increased the market, and the process of producing the metal has been improved and cheapened.

The difficulties and expense inherent in the production of fused anhydrous magnesium chloride, due to hydrolysis, and the problems involved in collecting and disposing of the chlorine evolved, when the electrolysis was carried out on a commercial scale (nearly three tons of chlorine being produced per ton of magnesium), made the costs high. To avoid these difficulties, a process of electrolyzing the native carbonate, or the oxide made from it by calcination, was developed [1] and commercially exploited. To purify the resulting metal for certain uses, a vacuum sublimation process was developed and commercialized.[2]

Meanwhile, the economical preparation of molten chloride from the natural brines was worked out by the Dow Company, where methods for adding the partially dehydrated salt directly to the bath were also developed. At the same time, foreign workers developed

---

[1] Harvey, Trans. Am. Electrochem. Soc., *47, 327* (1925).
[2] Bakken, U. S. Pat. 1,594,344.

the continuous production of the fused anhydrous chloride from magnesite[1] by the use of the chloride from the electrolytic cells, thus making most of the chlorine cyclic and affording an elegant simultaneous solution of both difficulties. The resultant lowering of costs and prices for very pure metal caused the abandonment of the oxide process, leaving the chlorine process in control of the field. The interesting story of the development of the chloride process in this country has recently been told by Gann.[2]

While some non-ferrous castings are made in permanent metal molds or in baked sand molds, most of the world's foundry industry is still based on the use of water-tempered sand as a mold material ("green sand molds"). When cast in ordinary green sand molds, such as are used for aluminum, magnesium catches fire and burns, on account of its reaction with water. Since the War, however, research has developed a variety of substances which can be added to the sand or to the water with which it is moistened, permitting the magnesium alloys to be cast satisfactorily with a technique which allows economical production of large tonnages of such castings. Permanent-mold and die-casting processes have been commercialized, and much of the increased demand for the metal is due to its use in the cast form. This has, of course, been facilitated by the development of better and more corrosion-resistant alloys. The aviation and automobile industries, where weight saving is of great importance, are naturally the principal consumers.

Magnesium rods also have found uses in various commercial fields, whereas the production of other wrought magnesium alloy articles has made slower progress. Sheet and forging sales up to the present time are limited to the aircraft field because the fabricating methods are still relatively expensive. Much remains for the next 25 years to accomplish in this field.

SODIUM [3]

The Castner process of producing electrolytic sodium from fused caustic soda was developed about 40 years ago, at the same time as the Hall-Heroult aluminum process; it was still the only one in use at the beginning of this 25 year period. The obvious disadvan-

---

[1] U. S. Patents 1,331,688, 1,702,301, 1,749,854.

[2] Metal Progress, *21*, 33 (April 1932); Mining and Metallurgy, *13*, 179 (April 1932); Metal Ind. (N.Y.), *30*, 235 (June 1932).

[3] I am indebted to Dr. W. F. Zimmerli of the Roessler & Hasslacher Chemical Company, Inc., for part of the information in this section.

tage of using caustic soda, however, led to investigations of the electrolysis of the fused chloride, which appears to have been first successfully accomplished commercially about 1913 by the Gesellschaft für Chemische Industrie in Basel[1]; their cell is understood to be still in commercial use, although only in the small plant of that company.

A more practical and satisfactory cell was later developed in the United States by Downs;[2] it has completely replaced the Castner cells in this country and in a large German plant. It is understood that the greater part of the world's supply of sodium is now produced by this process. Use of the chloride instead of the hydroxide not only reduces the cost of raw material and eliminates a noxious raw material from the process, but it doubles the current efficiency theoretically obtainable. Theoretical efficiency is, of course, not reached in practice, but a very substantial increase is obtained over that realized with the Castner process. Part of this advantage is, however, probably counterbalanced by a higher operating voltage. Recovery of high-grade chlorine as a byproduct also reduces the cost, as do improved labor conditions and the possibility of using larger cells than those employed in the Castner process. The Downs cell may be considered a major advance in sodium production.

Shipping methods have been developed and the metal can now be handled economically in carload lots, as 12-lb. bricks packed in airtight drums; at its present price of less than 20c. per pound, its low specific gravity makes sodium one of the cheapest of the pure metals per unit of volume. It has become an important raw material for the inorganic and organic chemical industries, and for certain metallurgical purposes. Not only is it necessary for the manufacture of sodium oxide and peroxide and of pure sodium cyanide, but it is of great importance in the production of lead tetraethyl and a variety of dyestuffs, synthetic perfumes and similar products.

Low specific gravity and low cost, combined with high thermal and electrical conductivity, high heat of vaporization (twice that of water), and the fact that it may be handled without difficulty in steel, point to interesting future possibilities in chemical engineering at high temperatures, for heat transmission and for temperature control.

---

[1] Ger. Pat. 236,804 (1909), Brit. Pat. 18,300 of 1910 and 17,047 of 1911; Billiter, Technische Elektrochemie, 2nd Ed., Vol. 3, p. 55 (1932).

[2] U. S. Pat. 1,501,756; Brit. Pat. 238,956; Billiter, loc. cit., p. 56.

Castner is said to have been bitterly disappointed when, after all his work in developing a process for making cheap sodium as a raw material in the production of aluminum, Hall's direct electrolytic process destroyed this market; but modern chemical industry appears to be developing other markets which should absorb large quantities of the metal, with the great advantage over most markets for metal that they do not involve the return of "secondary" metal to plague the producers of the primary or "virgin" metal.

CHAPTER VIII

ADVANCES IN PULP AND PAPER MANUFACTURE
1908-1933

By G. A. Richter and W. B. VanArsdel

Research Department, Brown Co., Berlin, N. H.

DURING the 25 years covered by this brief survey, the pulp and paper industries have experienced a remarkable growth. The main lines of development were already apparent at the beginning of the period, but the force of economic circumstance, leading as it did to important geographical shifts in the producing centers, provided an unusual incentive to engineers and designers to make use in their new mills of every advance in technique and apparatus. Unfortunately for the industry as a whole, however, these same circumstances led to over-optimistic building programs, with the result that in 1931, for instance, actual paper production was only at the rate of about 64 per cent of capacity. The situation in Canada was, if anything, even less satisfactory.

The total production of paper and paper products in the United States in 1908 was about 4,000,000 tons, or 90 lb. per capita, and its value was about $400,000,000. A peak of production was reached in 1929, the total output of that year being 13,400,000 tons, or 221 lb. per capita, and the total value was $1,892,000,000. Each of the two succeeding years saw a shrinkage of about 10 per cent in production. The increase from 1908 to 1929 was 235 per cent in tonnage and 370 per cent in value.

Wood has continued to be by far the largest single source of raw material. The wood-pulp mills, bound as they must be to nearby forests, have been the ones to feel the currents of economic geography. From the old producing centers in New England and New York the tide shifted first toward the northern Lake States and Canada, then toward the far South, and finally toward the Pacific coast. At the same time the proportions manufactured by the four most important processes were shifting, partly because of the changes in species of wood available, and partly because of technical advances in one field or the other. The production of wood-pulp in 1908 was about 2,120,000 tons, divided as follows: mechanical, 48 per cent; sulphite, 40 per cent; soda, 12 per cent. The kraft, or sulphate, process was just being introduced into America that same year. In 1929 the production was 4,860,000 tons, of which 34 per cent was mechanical, 36 per cent sulphite, 11 per cent soda and 19 per cent sulphate.

Fundamental Research. A characteristic feature of the period under discussion was the appearance of organized, continuous research into the materials, processes and products of the industry. In the United States the Forest Products Laboratory at Madison, Wis., and the Paper Division of the Bureau of Standards at Washington, were established with governmental funds. University schools of chemistry studied the structure of cellulose and of lignin, while schools of chemical engineering established the laws governing heat exchange, gas absorption and other industrial processes.

Pulp manufacture and paper making both originated in a day when secrecy was the rule, rather than the exception, and when free discussion of manufacturing problems was a thing unheard of. A very significant tendency away from secrecy has resulted in a remarkable approach toward standardization in equipment and process. It is realized more and more that the principles of filtration and evaporation, to take only two examples, apply just as truly in a pulp mill as in a sugar refinery; and to a large extent, process equipment is now purchased in some standard form.

MECHANICAL WOOD-PULP

"Groundwood," as mechanical wood-pulp is commonly known in the industry, is still being produced in fundamentally the same way as it was in 1908; the fibers are torn or ground from a debarked log of wood by means of an abrasive wheel and in the presence of a stream of water.

For most purposes, the value of groundwood depends upon the production of long, clean fibers, free from wood-flour and from large shives or splinters. Careful studies of pressure, temperature, operating speed and character of grinding surface have resulted in a distinctly improved pulp, and a definitely lowered power-consumption. Built-up grindstones, made from artificial silicon carbide, have supplanted the natural stone in many mills. Attempts have been made to utilize other varieties of wood besides the usual spruce and fir, but so far with no great degree of success.

Chemical Treatments. There has been great activity in the

investigation of pretreatments for wood, as for example by steaming or by soaking in salt solutions. None of these processes has been commercially important. The color of groundwood, on the other hand, has been distinctly improved, partly by better control of the grinding process, and in some cases by semi-bleaching with a reducing agent, such as a sulphite.

ALKALINE PROCESSES. (SULPHATE AND SODA)

Soda pulp was the first kind of chemical wood-pulp ever to be produced on a large scale. Briefly, the process consists in cooking suitable wood chips with a solution of caustic soda at elevated temperature and pressure. Its close relative, the sulphate process, differs chiefly in the substitution of sodium sulphide for part of the sodium hydroxide. The two processes may be conveniently considered together.

Wood Varieties. Poplar wood was originally considered to be best suited to the soda process, and is still the most commonly used variety; other deciduous woods, however, such as birch, maple, beech and chestnut, are now used successfully, and in fact with real economy because of the higher yield per cord. The sulphate process is applicable to almost any variety of wood, but has had its greatest successes with the highly resinous woods, like pine, spruce and fir, which are not easily pulped by the other processes. For this reason, pulp mills in the South, where pine is the leading commercial wood, almost without exception use the sulphate process.

Type of Pulp. Soda pulp, made from the short-fibered deciduous woods, has assumed a relatively minor place in papermaking since the advent of cheap, high-grade sulphite pulps. It will continue to be used as a constituent of certain papers where its valuable properties of imparting flatness, opaqueness and good formation make it almost indispensable; but it cannot any longer be considered as a low-cost filler.

Sulphate pulp, on the other hand, made from the long-fibered coniferous woods, has always been distinguished by its physical strength; in fact, it is commonly known as "kraft"pulp. As originally produced it was very dark brown in color and not particularly clean. Careful control of the process has resulted in a great improvement in color and cleanliness, and in enhanced strength. Originally confined to coarse wrapping paper, this type of pulp has won its way into many types of high-grade paper where color is not of primary importance.

Cooking. Important engineering advances have occurred in the digester rooms of soda and sulphate mills. The technique of welding has progressed so that today the welded steel digester may be said to be standard. There is still much to learn, however, about the corrosive attack of these alkaline liquors on boiler plate.

The idea of heating the digester charge indirectly is an old one, but simplicity and low initial cost have continued to be on the side of direct heating—heating, that is, by steam introduced directly into the charge. Indirect systems are in wide use, however, the successful principle being to remove liquor continuously through a strainer bottom in the digester, pass it through an external tubular heater, and return it to the top of the digester. Such a system undoubtedly permits a much more uniform digestion of the charge of chips, and of course obviates the dilution of cooking-liquor which is inseparable from the direct use of steam.

Liquor Recovery. The high usage of chemicals in alkaline pulping necessitates the use of a recovery process of some sort. Formerly it was thought sufficient to drain as much as possible of the liquor from the pulp at the end of the cook, but the design of washing systems, based upon fundamental chemical engineering research, has made possible a nearly complete recovery of alkali and a much lower chemical cost. These washing systems commonly employ the countercurrent principle, so as to deliver a strong waste liquor to the evaporators; in many plants the continuous vacuum filter, such as the Oliver filter, is employed as the thickening device.

Great strides have been taken in the design and construction of evaporators which will concentrate the waste liquor to the point at which it can be economically burned for recovery of the sodium compounds. Six- and eight-effect units are now in operation, with a marked saving in the heat required for this step.

The old-fashioned furnace in which the concentrated liquor was burned has been displaced almost entirely by furnaces designed on thermodynamic principles to burn the organic matter completely with little or no addition of extra fuel. Complete combustion makes it possible to dispense with the old step of leaching the ash; a simple dissolving process takes its place. In at least one plant, use is made of the high rate of heat transfer by radiation at high temperatures to complete the evaporation and combustion of atomized liquor particles during the short time they remain in the furnace. Construction of the furnace itself, exposed as it is to the destructive action of fused alkalies, has been greatly improved by the use of suitable refractories. In some mills the fine fume of volatilized sodium salts in the stack gases is recovered by the Cottrell electrical precipitation process.

Alkali Recovery. The smelt from the recovery furnace consists largely of sodium carbonate in the soda process, and a mixture of carbonate and sulphide in the sulphate process. In either case, the carbonate must be causticized before the liquor is reused. The causticizing step remains the same in principle as it has always been, but chemical engineering refinements have lowered its cost materially. The Dorr continuous system is in use in many mills, and in others the separation of sludge from solution is accomplished by modern filter presses, often with specially treated cloths to withstand the action of the alkali. In some places where lime is not cheap, the calcium carbonate sludge has been advantageously reburned in Wedge or Herreshoff types of continuous furnace.

BLEACHED KRAFT PRODUCTS

Until quite recently, kraft pulp was considered to be essentially a dark-colored stock, useful on account of its high strength, but limited to specific fields. It was bleachable, but only with the expenditure of huge quantities of bleach, and at the sacrifice of all of its exceptional strength. Within the past few years there has been a great advance in the production of strong, white pulp from a sulphate type of cook. The initial attempts were confined to a partial bleaching to a light tan or cream color, like that of manila stock, and so much was possible without a serious sacrifice in strength.

Further advances in this direction have followed partly by improvements in the cooking process itself, resulting in a pulp of lower lignin content but of the same high physical strength which has always been characteristic of the kraft type of pulp; and partly by radical changes in the bleaching operation. The latter invariably comprises several steps, rather than one drastic oxidation, and at least one of the steps utilizes a solution of free chlorine instead of the usual hypochlorite. The resulting pulp has the color of a bleached sulphite fiber, but still possesses the strength, tearing resistance and folding endurance which have been characteristic of brown kraft. This achievement suggests that a major change in the economics of white wood-pulp production may be under way.

SULPHITE PROCESS

There have been no basic changes in the chemical procedure of sulphite pulp production during this quarter-century; the fundamental principles were well understood by Ekman, Kellner and Mitscherlich. Changes have been mainly refinements in process and control, and marked improvements in plant design.

The first sulphite pulp was produced with a cooking liquor which was relatively high in combined sulphur dioxide (i.e., SO_2 equivalent to the Na_2SO_3 content); thus a common standard for sulphite acid in the early part of the century was 1.3 per cent combined SO_2 and 3 per cent free SO_2. Modern sulphite mills use an acid containing about 1 per cent combined SO_2 and 5 per cent free SO_2. In the days of Ekman, most sulphite cooks ran from fourteen to thirty hours at a relatively low temperature, while present-day practice has raised the temperature and shortened the time to only eight to eleven hours.

Wood Preparation. Spruce and balsam fir remain the standard wood varieties for sulphite pulping. Much work has been done on other varieties, notably the more resinous pines and western firs and hemlocks, and the latter have recently become of commercial importance in the Pacific Northwest.

Engineering developments have resulted in greatly improved barking and chipping processes. The barking is now accomplished almost exclusively by tumbling the logs in a rotating cylinder or drum, and in the presence of a shower of water. Careful control of chipping has also come to be recognized as of great importance; the chips must not only be as uniform in size as possible, but their dimensions must be chosen so as to facilitate diffusion of the cooking acid to the center of the chip without undue sacrifice of fiber length.

Acid Preparation. The production of cheap elemental sulphur by the Frasch process has led in this country to complete abandonment of pyrites as a raw material. Sulphur, of course, has the great advantages that the burner gas is markedly higher in SO_2 concentration, that there is no dust nuisance, and that SO_3 formation is minimized. There have been great strides in the chemical engineering of this department of a sulphite mill; rotary sulphur burners, automatic control of sulphur- and air-supply, and cooling by direct contact with water in a tower packed with extended-surface stoneware products, are typical examples.

The acid system has also undergone close technical scrutiny and has become much simpler and more efficient than its predecessors.

Absorption of SO_2 is facilitated by lowering the temperature by means of mechanical refrigeration, by operating under slight positive pressures instead of under vacuum, and in many cases by utilizing highly efficient packed absorption towers. The latter offer the important advantage of direct control of the rate of absorption, independent of the amount of basic material which is to be dissolved as a bisulphite.

The high concentration of free SO_2 which is desired in the cooking acid can only be attained by efficient utilization of the strong SO_2 gases which are liberated when the digester is "relieved" and when its contents are discharged, or "blown." Chemical engineering design of such recovery systems, which must include efficient coolers, operating under highly corrosive conditions, has progressed to a point where it is possible to produce a cooking acid considerably stronger than is needed for standard cooking.

Several systems for utilizing the heat in relief liquors and gases have recently attained some prominence. The Chemipulp system preheats the fresh charge of cooking acid, while maintaining it under pressure, with a material saving in steam, shortening of the cooking time, and improvement in acid penetration into the chips.

The first investigators of the sulphite process realized that any soluble bisulphite could be used, but for economic reasons, the industry standardized on that of calcium—sometimes on a mixture of calcium and magnesium. In recent years it has appeared that for some purposes, a sodium base may be used advantageously, particularly where high strength and unusually good color are important. Such a cooking liquor offers the possibility of a recovery process analogous to that used in a sulphate mill, but apparently there has been no commercial exploitation as yet of such a process.

Sulphite Cooking. Sulphite digesters are now much larger on the average than they were 25 years ago. The increase in size has carried with it some danger of non-uniform cooking of the charge of chips, and largely for that reason there has been much study of indirect heating systems, with forced circulation of the acid through the chips. The commercial production of the 18-8 type of chrome-nickel alloy has apparently brought this desirable development within the bounds of practicability, for there are several such systems now in successful use. The avoidance of dilution by condensed steam not only gives better control of the acid concentration, but also simplifies the recovery system for relief gas.

The steam requirements of a sulphite mill are so variable, and rise to such high occasional peaks, that economical boiler operation is difficult. A number of mills have installed the Ruths steam accumulator and have realized considerable savings in boiler-house equipment.

Finishing Sulphite Fiber. The demand for a high degree of cleanliness has necessitated careful attention to the screening system. While the principles involved were well understood 25 years ago, there have been notable advances in the design and construction of screening and riffling systems, and in the recovery of good fiber from the "white water" from washers. One development which has grown out of the study of the screening process is a method of "classifying" the fiber into long-fibered and short-fibered fractions, and utilizing the fractions separately where their distinct characteristics will be most useful.

As in the case of kraft pulp, there has been great activity in the study of bleaching systems. In general, the tendency has been to operate at ever higher stock densities, in order to intensify the effect of the hypochlorite and economize in the use of both chemicals and steam. It is also becoming common practice to bleach in two or three steps, with intermediate washings, and one or more of these steps is frequently a treatment with a solution of free chlorine. Large-scale operations with the very corrosive chlorine solutions have challenged the skill of the chemical engineer, and called for the use of unusual materials of construction. The result has been, however, to improve the color and strength of sulphite wood-pulp vastly over what was possible in 1908, and also to attain a much needed flexibility in the characteristics of a product which has to serve as raw material for such totally different manufactures as book-paper, glassine or grease-proof paper and rayon.

In the early days of the industry, the pulp was usually prepared in the form of compressed wet laps. At the present time it is practically all dried in sheet form, and there have been important engineering developments in the construction of suitable dryers; comparatively recent accomplishments are the Minton vacuum dryer, which minimizes the damage caused by overheating of the partly-dried pulp, and the Fidalgo tunnel-dryer for shredded pulp. There have also been some installations of a waste-heat economizer which diminishes steam-consumption at this point by preheating the air which carries off the moisture evaporated from the pulp.

Waste Liquor Utilization. The tremendous loss of dissolved wood-substance and of sulphur compounds in the sulphite waste-liquor has evidently struck almost every chemist connected with the industry as being a shame; the patent literature on projects for waste-liquor utilization is voluminous. Except for a few minor uses, especially in tanning leather, nothing has come of these projects. For a time there was great activity, especially in Europe, in the production of alcohol from the fermentable sugar present in the liquor, but it has been reported that none of these plants is now operating. It now appears that an economic utilization of the liquor waits for the development of a chemical recovery process, based upon a sodium-bisulphite acid, and possibly correlated with the similar recovery process of 'a nearby kraft pulp-mill.

RAG AND COTTON PULPS

Rags in the form of cotton or linen have been used for papermaking since the earliest days of that art, and the processes now in use differ only in degree and closeness of chemical control from those used a century ago. The early rag pulps were not subjected to any bleaching action; conclusions based on the splendid state of preservation of old rag papers do not always take this fact into account. The commercial demand for some time, however, has been for a bright, white paper, such as may be produced only by bleaching. Careful control of the purification and bleaching is essential if the valuable property of permanence is not to be sacrificed.

Recent developments in the textile industry have caused the papermaker some trouble, because of the tremendous quantity of rayon which is now incorporated in many varieties of cloth; rayon has no papermaking value. The use of mixtures of silk or wool with cotton has also increased the rag mill's difficulties. Great efforts have been made to introduce suitably processed cotton linters as a "rag" constituent, but so far linters have found their chief use as a filler in absorbent papers.

Some controversy has existed regarding the relative merits of lime, sodium carbonate, caustic soda, and various combinations of the three, for boiling rags. The best treatment undoubtedly depends upon the type of product desired; for instance a rag stock which has been given a rather severe treatment with caustic soda alone would appear to be a suitable furnish for a very soft paper.

MISCELLANEOUS PULPS

The number of distinct types of papermaking pulp is constantly increasing. A catalog of the present-day uses for cellulose and paper products would reach into practically every field of human activity, and the industry has been versatile enough to supply products to meet the most diverse requirements.

Semi-Pulps. Many efforts have been made to produce a semi-cooked wood-pulp which would be satisfactory for cheap wrapping paper and similar uses where the requirements are not severe. The aim, of course, is to raise the yield of pulp from the 45-50 per cent characteristic of the chemical processes, to 60 per cent or 70 per cent of the weight of wood used. The most successful efforts in this line so far have utilized a mild treatment of chips or wood waste with a cheap alkali such as milk of lime or lime and sulphur, followed by maceration or grinding of the softened wood in a kollergang or rod-mill. In spite of the facts that the cost is low and the resulting product sufficiently strong for the desired purpose, no great expansion has taken place in this process; the pulp is always dark-colored and is usually dirty.

Chlorine Pulping. Following out the process worked out in the laboratory many years ago for isolating cellulose from wood, several inventors have exploited the successive treatment of wood and papermaking grasses with chlorine and dilute alkalies. The process has received the most attention in Europe, where the names of Pomilio, Cataldi and de Vains have won recognition. Up to the present time no important development has occurred in this country.

Straw Pulp and Strawboard. It has long been the dream of the pulp producer to make available for papermaking the huge quantities of such waste vegetable material as corn-stalks, straw and bagasse. A very large tonnage of straw is, of course, now utilized for straw-board, and the rapid growth in use of fiber packing-cases has made this production of "boards" the largest single tonnage and value item in the census reports for the industry. A mild soda cook is standard for this type of cheap pulp, and the fundamentals of the process have undergone little change with the expansion in business.

Much vegetable waste is still being burned on the farms, largely because of the economic difficulty of collecting a sufficient supply of a low-valued raw material. Chemical engineering studies have continued to progress, however, particularly in Iowa, where Sweeney and his co-workers have succeeded in producing from cornstalks a high-grade wall-board and a saleable cellulose pulp. The latter is handicapped for use in papermaking by its short and weak fiber, but it seems entirely possible that these annual crops will some time supply a cellulose entirely suitable for conversion into rayon or cellulose esters.

Sodium Sulphite Pulp. Neutral or alkaline sodium sulphite has long been recognized as a mild delignifying agent, and within the past 15 years much experimental work has been done in an effort to commercialize the process. Like the kraft or sulphate procedure, this type of cook makes a difficultly bleachable pulp; its future undoubtedly depends upon the perfecting of an economical cycle for recovery of the sodium and sulphur, and also to a certain extent upon the use of multiple-step bleaching processes.

Purified Wood Fibers. The producer of wood-pulp has never been content to regard his product as a fundamentally inferior raw material for high-grade papers, but until quite recently he has been unable to make a wood fiber possessing at the same time the desirable papermaking qualities and the high degree of permanence characteristic of fiber made from new white rags. During the past decade he has measurably succeeded in his object of supplementing rags with a purified wood cellulose. His product possesses the physical strength, flexibility and toughness of rag fiber, and according to a variety of accelerated aging tests, appears to have a stability equal to that of high-grade cotton papers. This represents a great advance over any type of wood-fiber heretofore known, and the product has found a very large market in the various pulp-using industries. The appearance of this new papermaking fiber is undoubtedly one of the most significant achievements of the period under discussion.

The purification of wood fibers involves elimination from the fiber of minor proportions of lignin, hemi-cellulose, pentosan, resin and ash, which exert an influence in papermaking out of all relation to the quantities present. Chemical and chemical engineering research on a very large scale were necessary before the difficulties inherent in the project were overcome.

PAPERMAKING

New pulps and new uses for paper have compelled the papermaker to improve his technique and apparatus greatly during the 25 years. Although the basic principles of fourdrinier and cylinder paper machines have remained unchanged, there have been significant advances in design, construction and operation.

Beaters. The first step in papermaking is always a "hydration," or mechanical working of the pulp in the presence of water. The familiar hollander type of beater has been gradually increased in capacity, and improvements in design have made it possible to decrease the power consumption while bettering the rate of actual hydration, as opposed to cutting or shortening of the fiber. Beaters now operate with a thicker pulp suspension and a greater rate of circulation than formerly. Some new types of hydrating engine, modeled after the colloid mill, give promise of great savings in power. The development of new control devices has made possible a far better degree of uniformity in the beaten pulp.

The theory of beating has been studied in many laboratories, but as yet there is no general agreement on the fundamentals of what is evidently a very complicated colloidal process. It remains quite probable that the effect termed "hydration" is a combination of a fraying of the fibers into their much finer constituent fibrils, and a sorption of water, accompanied by reversible swelling. Various attempts have been made to produce the same effect chemically, but so far without important success.

It has been known for some time that hydration is promoted by low temperatures in beating, and there has been some practical use of a system which removes water continuously from the circulating stock, cools it in an external heat exchanger, and returns it to the beater.

Sizing. Writing papers are invariably sized to give a surface which will resist ink. Rosin in some form is still employed for most papers of this type. The problems encountered in rosin sizing have been attacked both by the chemist, with a study of the colloid chemistry of the process, and by the engineer, with new procedures for making the size. Rosin size is commonly made by boiling rosin with an alkaline solution and dispersing the resulting soap in water; various combinations of free and combined rosin are applied to specific paper requirements. The dispersion of the soap has been greatly improved by the use of specially designed mixing-nozzles. A cold process of dissolving the rosin in alkali, characterized by simplicity of operation and ease of control, has recently been installed in many paper mills.

Starch and wax emulsions have received much attention for special sizing problems. It is recognized that by proper selection of materials the strength, stiffness, water-resistance and stability of paper may all be substantially improved. The colloid mill has played a large part in the successful dispersion of many of the water-insoluble sizes.

The emphasis which has recently been placed on the permanence of paper has directed special attention to the harmful effect of acidic constituents, such as alum. Excess of these materials is now rigidly avoided, many paper mills making routine use of hydrogen-ion control at all stages of the stock preparation.

Papermaking Machinery. Designers and builders of paper machines have increased the tonnage capacity of a single unit remarkably during the past 25 years; whereas in 1908 the largest machines in existence made a sheet about 150 in. wide, and operated at not over 400 ft. per minute, some modern newsprint machines are over 200 in. wide and run at speeds of over 1,000 ft. per minute.

Engineering improvements incorporated in modern paper machines include such features as the following: (a), New methods for controlling the flow of stock onto the machine. Control at this point is obviously the basis of uniformity in the sheet. (b). Improvements in suction boxes and suction rolls which dewater the stock as rapidly and completely as possible before it reaches the press-rolls. (c). Development of smoother and more effective lateral shaking of the fourdrinier wire, to improve the formation or texture of the sheet. (d). Perfection of the vacuum dryer. This significant advance in papermaking is the result of painstaking calculation and skill in mechanical design. (e). Better and more flexible drives for the paper machine. The synchronization of the various units in such a way as to allow for the shrinkage of the sheet is a difficult problem, which has been solved by cooperation between the papermaker and the electrical engineer. (f). Centrifugal refiners placed at the wet end of the paper machine have accomplished a remarkable improvement in the cleanliness of the sheet.

MISCELLANEOUS PRODUCTS

New uses for paper and other cellulose products continue to appear. For instance, a very large business has been built up in vegetable parchment, and another in vulcanized fiber products. A comparative newcomer is an impregnated porous cellulose web which closely simulates leather. Impregnation of suitable paper sheets with varnish resins, Bakelite, rubber latex and the like is an essential step in the manufacture of many mechanical and electrical appliances.

An interesting new use for pure cellulose is as a reinforcing agent and filler in plastics and rubber, under conditions which exclude the use of wood flour or groundwood. The pulverization of a semiplastic material, such as cellulose, without undue contamination, has been a difficult mechanical problem.

Cellulose is perhaps the most versatile raw material known to mankind. The pulp and paper industries are continually extending the field of its usefulness, and in this absorbing enterprise the chemical engineer will continue to play a major rôle.

CHAPTER IX

COAL PROCESSING—ITS PROGRESS SINCE 1908

By Horace C. Porter

Consulting Chemical Engineer, Philadelphia, Pa.

TWENTY-FIVE years ago coal processing loomed big for the future, with bright prospects based on its expected production of raw materials for chemical manufacture. There was no sound basis for such optimism, as the demand for such raw materials was overestimated. It is true that much chemical manufacture—dyes, pharmaceuticals, and other, for which this country at one time depended upon Germany, has been taken over by our own industries, and that new products such as synthetic plastics have added to the demand. For these the phenols, benzene, toluene, naphthalene, and other products, from the light oil and tar of coal carbonization, make up an important part of the basic material required, and we are now producing practically all of it ourselves. But the amount needed to fill domestic requirement is scarcely one-tenth of the capacity of our byproduct ovens alone. Other factors offer more encouraging prospects, such as a rapidly growing use of coke-oven gas in city distribution, growth of creosoting of timber, and increasing popularity of coke as a domestic fuel.

Coal processing has developed greatly in 25 years along engineering and technical lines. Efficiencies have been greatly improved, whereas costs, both for plant and for operation have been much reduced.

To the writer, one of the brightest spots in the horizon, although it may at first appear to the carbonization industry an obstacle, is the competition of the newer, cleaner, "convenience fuels." There is a fast-growing demand for the fuels that make a minimum of dust and dirt and which are adapted to automatic control. Coal processing can make such fuels in the shape of gas, coke, and semi-coke, and others may possibly be developed in the future. It is necessary, however, to bring down conversion costs, and the engineers and chemists will have to do this if processing is to survive and grow.

The treatment of the subject in this chapter will, therefore, to a large extent be devoted to improvements in equipment design and developments in application of the products. Inasmuch as engineering developments depend upon the economics of the situation in respect to costs and returns, supply and demand, competing products, and foreign developments, it is necessary to give some attention to this phase of the subject in order to make a well-rounded and intelligent presentation.

Scope. The following are the main uses for coal processing in modern civilization: (1) To make coal gas, for public distribution or for steel plants or other industrial use in connected projects. (2) For metallurgical coke, for blast furnace or foundry use. (3) For coke, for domestic and general industrial use, a smokeless, clean fuel. (4) To make byproducts, such as oils, tar, ammonia, and secondary derivatives of these products. (5) For special smokeless or improved solid fuel of a character somewhat different from that of the usual hard coke.

In all these uses, the principal object is to give a greater "form-value" to the coal products than that of the original raw coal.

There are other phases of coal processing which appear to have future possibilities and which to some extent have been developed in America, although they cannot yet be classed as important industrial developments. They will be given very brief notice in this chapter. Among these are briquetting, low-temperature carbonization, pre-treatment of power-plant fuel, "colloidal fuel" (intimate mixtures of powdered coal and oil), specially processed lignite (by steam drying), "activated" carbon materials obtained from anthracite and other types of coal.

It is thought best to include some reference to failures of processes that have been proposed and tried. Several of these have occurred during the last quarter of a century and have cost their backers much money. Full publicity as to these no doubt will be of assistance in preventing similar losses in the future.

The chapter will, where possible, give credit to those individuals who have done much to promote progress in the field. Some of these individuals belong to big industrial organizations and the credit for advancement is due in some measure to such corporations and their executives. Laboratory and small-scale research in the field, while not covered completely or in detail, is given attention as it deserves, although briefly.

Economic Considerations. The last 25 years' accomplishment in this field must be regarded chiefly as the rationalizing of the industry—putting byproduct coking and other high-temperature carbonization on an orderly engineering basis, to bring about the attainment of uniform heats, rapid coking rates (when required), a high-grade metallurgical coke universally accepted as such, and a uniform quality of gas, satisfactory for public distribution. Preparation of coals by cleaning, their selection for a given purpose, suitable size reduction and blending, have during these years brought a much higher standard of quality and regularity of products.

The chimera of low-temperature carbonization has been brought down to earth and analyzed thoroughly on a business basis. The necessity for making this form of coal processing practical, based on the balance-sheet, has been demonstrated and accepted.

Owing to increasing competition, arising from the rapid growth in distribution of natural gas and falling prices of fuel oils (used in industry and in house-heating, as well as in the manufacture of carburetted water gas), it is vital to the continued progress of coal carbonization or processing, as emphasized before, to reduce costs. Much progress has been made along this line, but it must be continued if the industry is to grow in the future.

TABLE I.—Gas Sold for Public Distribution in the United States, 1918 to 1931

(Billions of Cubic Feet)

Year	Natural Gas (Domestic and Commercial)[1]	Coke Oven and Retort Coal Gas[2]	All Other Gas
1918	271	82	190
1919	256	94	206
1920	286	94	235
1921	248	100	232
1922	255	106	248
1923	277	125	255
1924	285	124	264
1925	272	140	261
1926	289	155	282
1927	296	173	273
1928	321	187	273
1929	360	213	258
1930	376	211	233
1931	372 (preliminary)	205	209

[1] Not including industrial consumption for field purposes, in carbon black manufacture, power plant, petroleum-refinery and other miscellaneous uses, outside of public distribution. (From Mineral Resources of U. S., II, 27, p. 464, Chapter on Natural Gas in 1930, Bureau of Mines. 1932).

[2] Not including sales to steel plants, etc., outside of public distribution.

The figures in Table I show the growth in consumption of different types of gas for public distribution. Up to 1929 there has been a considerable increase in coke-oven gas, used for this purpose. But in 1927, natural gas (for public distribution) showed a faster rate of growth, which is continuing steadily. There are many localities, however, where natural gas cannot be distributed at a price at which it is able to compete with coke-oven gas at present prices, and if costs of the latter can be still further reduced, the number of such localities should increase. Costs of distributing natural gas mount rapidly as the distance from the wells increases.

In this connection it is necessary to plan for disposal of the products other than gas on a satisfactory average-load basis. Without this the net cost of gas cannot be kept down. In times of industrial depression, the disposal of coke, tar, and other products is difficult. Outlets must be found which are not seriously affected by the ups and downs of industry and whereby the products may be stored or accumulated advantageously through the periods of low demand.

There has been an increasing demand for domestic coke, including all coke used in the heating of buildings. The figures in Table II illustrate this trend. Here again it is a question of competition with anthracite coal, oil, and natural gas, and unfortunately, to some

TABLE II.—Coke and Other Solid Fuels Used for Domestic and Miscellaneous Industrial Purposes in the United States, 1918 to 1931

(Not including furnace and foundry coke[1]).

(Thousands of Net Tons)

Year	By-Product Coke	Bee-hive Coke	Gas-house Coke[2]	Total Coke	Bri-quets	Anthra-cite Coal[4]	Bitu-minous Coal
1918........	2,537	211	1,400	4,148	..	56,000[2]	..
1921........	1,680	57	1,400	3,137	..	58,000[2]	..
1923........	4,276	742	1,400	6,418	..	60,500[2]	..
1924........	4,860	720	1,400	4,353	581	55,500	3
1925........	6,158	966	1,400	8,524	840	37,500	3
1926........	6,719	1,350	1,400	9,469	995	53,000	3
1927........	6,725	681	1,500	8,906	971	48,600	3
1928........	7,573	524	1,450	9,547	948	45,800	3
1929........	9,070	776	1,400	11,246	1,213	45,300	3
1930........	9,436	621	1,300	11,357	1,029	42,750	3
1931........	9,928	406	1,200	11,534	698	36,000[2]	3

[1] From Mineral Resources of United States, II:28, (for 1930), Bureau of Mines, 1932, p. 537.
[2] Partly estimated.
[3] Estimated as between 56,000,000 and 77,000,000 tons per year.
[4] Not including "steam sizes," except about ¼ of the No. 1 Buckwheat, estimated as applied to domestic and other heating purposes.

extent, with the gas produced by the coke manufacturers themselves. Engineering progress has helped to reduce costs in the production of both coke and coke-oven gas, but in order to meet competition in the future, it will be necessary to continue efforts along this line and reduce still further the outlay for plant, the overhead, and the operating cost per unit of output.

Coal processing, in other words, gives us products that are desirable, due to convenience and cleanliness in use, and to certain requirements in chemical manufacture. But the demand that can be set up in the face of competition, by such improvement of the raw coal, is what determines the growth of the industry and the prices obtainable for its products. These prices must bear a favorable relationship to the costs of manufacture.

Early in our 25 year period carbonization cost, including conversion, fixed charges, and overhead, amounted to from 50 to 60 per cent of the price of the coal, not including a loss and consumption at the plant of 20 per cent of the energy in the coal. Now, under normal good operation, these costs are less, about 40 to 50 per cent, and the loss of energy about 15 per cent.

This represents an advance, but even now it is necessary to sell coke—uniformly and regularly—at a price 50 per cent higher per ton than that of the coal, if the price of gas is to be kept down to a competing figure. Conversely, it is necessary to obtain for the byproduct gas, at the works, a price close to that of other competing gases—water gas and long-distance natural gas—if coke is to be sold at a price making competition with anthracite coal or oil possible.

Keen competition in coal processing is therefore still with us except in the limited fields of metallurgical coke and certain raw materials for dyes and chemical manufactures. Continuous research and engineering progress are required to improve methods and lower the costs and the losses.

Byproducts are frequently held up as big profit-makers in coal processing. This is a false hope. Although it may be figured, on the basis of retail prices and consumers' rates for gas, that "fifteen dollars' worth of byproducts come out of a ton of coal," the fifteen dwindles to about three dollars when prices obtainable at the works are considered, and this is in large part balanced by the costs of conversion and losses in the coking process. Tar and light-oil markets are decidedly limited and byproduct ammonia suffers tremendous competition from synthetic ammonia and from low-priced foreign products.

Much attention has during the last few years in England, and to some extent in other foreign countries, been given to development of coal processing for the increase of a domestic supply of motor spirit and fuel oil, incidentally producing a smokeless solid fuel for house heating. Hydrogenation of the coal itself or of tar and tar oils derived from it, has been proposed and developed with great thoroughness. In 1931 Dr. W. R. Ormandy discussed this subject from a national viewpoint before the Institution of Chemical Engineers and presented valuable figures of costs and yields. Although a yield of 160 gals. refined motor spirit per ton of coal treated has been shown to be possible by direct hydrogenation, at a cost of eight pence per gallon, more favor appears to be given to low-temperature carbonization followed by hydrogenation of the tar, a process which results in a yield of 15 gals. refined motor spirit, together with 6.6 gals. of diesel oil. Industrial hydrogen is said to be possible on a large scale in England and Germany at a cost of about one shilling per 1,000 cu. ft., this being sufficient to produce, by direct hydrogenation of coal, 8.8 gals. of motor spirit. Such costs, it is admitted by those who have carefully investigated the problem in England, are prohibitive in competition with the present price of motor spirit, and it is a fact that no producing plant on any considerable commercial scale has so far been put into operation. Claims are made, however, by well informed British experts, that the present situation cannot last and that the government should, as a measure of political economy, undertake extensive experiments along these lines in commercial plants.

Technical Progress. The greatest progress in this field has come through improved design of high-temperature carbonizing equipment —coke ovens and vertical gas ovens—and in organization of the industry on a strong, systematized basis of good engineering and salesmanship. The best of the European developments were taken over and advanced by American enterprise and skill. New features of design, resulting in much greater uniformity of heats and improved quality of coke, and greater facilities for increase of production rate per unit of investment were worked out here in America during our 25 year period of progress. Development of silica refractories capable of standing up under load at high temperatures has been a feature of this period. Steaming of the charge toward the end of the coking period, especially in vertical gas ovens and retorts, has added to the efficiency and economy of gas manufacture by carbonization.

Coke-Oven Design. Just prior to the beginning of the 25 year period U. S. Steel Corp. became thoroughly converted to byproduct coking and its possibilities for advance, both technical and commercial. After investigations abroad, they announced their decision to build large byproduct coke plants and utilize both the coke and gas in their operations. This gave impetus to an upturn in the carbonization industry which a little later was followed by rapid growth in the public distribution of coke-oven gas.

At this time, about 25 years ago, large amounts of American capital was enlisted for development of byproduct coking, and The Koppers Co. was organized in this country to build plants, some of which later were operated and owned by subsidiaries. The Koppers oven, a German invention, was developed and improved by American engineers. This development, supplementing the earlier pioneer work of the Semet-Solvay Co. in this country (since 1893), put the industry on a firm foundation, and both steel companies and gas utilities soon accepted the products as satisfactory or even superior for their use. Production of byproduct coke was trebled in the 8 years from 1909 to 1916.

Becker Coke Oven. Outstanding among the engineering developments of the period is the invention of the Becker oven. To Joseph Becker, chemical engineer, now president of The Koppers Research Corp., of Pittsburgh, and formerly vice-president of The Koppers Construction Co., ably assisted by J. Van Ackeren and other engineers of The Koppers Co., belongs the credit for this important step toward higher efficiencies and capacities in coke-oven design. The first Becker ovens were built about 1922.

Before this invention some improvement in coke-oven design had been accomplished in America such as greater uniformity of heats in the oven walls; use of silica high-temperature refractories; tighter walls and door jambs, and mechanical devices for oven door handling and coke pushing. Byproduct recovery had been made more efficient. But there were shortcomings in the Koppers heating system for the oven walls that limited the height and length of the oven. The entire amount of gases of combustion at the tops of the vertical heating flues had to be carried along through a horizontal flue and then down another row of vertical flues in the other half of the heating wall. This required a large flue, weakening the structure and limiting the height of oven. It made difficult the attainment of uniform heats in the wall from bottom to top. Becker overcame this difficulty largely by arranging the vertical flues in groups of five or six and passing the combustion gases from each group through a cross-over flue and down on the other side of the oven. This made possible greater height and length of the oven as the horizontal flue could be smaller, and the vertical flues longer, without building up too great a volume of combustion gases. Furthermore, as the cross-over flue is small and well insulated by brickwork, the temperature is not too high in the oven tops and is kept more uniform in the wall.

Through Becker's invention, ovens can be built higher and longer; which together with the increase in the uniformity and regularity of heating makes greater capacities obtainable. The modern oven (of about 17-in. average width) often makes 25-26 tons of coke per day, compared to 5-8 in the old types of 25 years ago. Although the oven unit costs somewhat more, quadrupling of the capacity has brought a marked reduction in unit costs of products under normal operating rate. The quality of coke also has been improved by virtue of the greater uniformity in heating conditions.

Another advantage gained by this design lies in facilitating the use of producer gas and blast-furnace gas in the heating flues. These gases, by reason of their high content of inerts, are characterized by a long flame and a large volume of products of combustion. The Becker design can take care of this type of flame very much better than the older types and give uniform heats thereby. Most of the byproduct ovens of recent installation are built for the use of one or the other of these heating gases so that the entire make of oven gas may be utilized for more remunerative purposes.

Vertical Gas Ovens and Retorts. To meet the requirements of the small city gas plant, and to afford a design better suited to the steaming process, which assists in lowering gas-making costs, the United Gas Improvement Co. of Philadelphia has developed its intermittent vertical gas oven, and the Glover-West and Woodall Duckham Companies have further improved and developed their continuous vertical gas retorts during the 25-year period under consideration. These types make possible a favorable cost figure for the labor of operation, owing to their vertical position and gravity discharge; as stated, they also facilitate the steaming of the charge in the oven during the latter part of the coking period. Steaming materially increases the yield of gas without a corresponding decrease in the yield of coke; to some extent it also utilizes the sensible heat of the coke before it is discharged and wasted.

Improvement of this type of coal carbonizing equipment has

brought economies such that in the modern plants where steaming is used, only 240-300 lbs. of coke is required in the gas producers per ton of dry coal carbonized, and the yield of gas formed in regular operation has reached as high a figure as 4,000 B.t.u.'s per pound of dry coal. Such figures speak well for the success of engineering research, in improving yields and lowering costs. As the steam used is ordinarily produced in waste-heat boilers, and as the yield of marketable coke is not materially reduced by the steaming process these figures show an increase of over-all efficiency of probably 3 to 5 per cent. The gain in dollar return by producer-gas heating and by use of the steaming process is proportionately greater by reason of the relatively higher form-value of B.t.u.'s in gas, compared with coke. Daily gas-making capacity of each investment unit, compared with other carbonization systems, has to be studied here, and account taken of any particular demands of the coke market for quality, before the process best suited to any locality can be determined. But, in any case, the developments above noted have resulted in an essential gain in manufacturing economy during recent years.

Plant Operation. It is impossible to cover in detail all the advances that have been made during this period in operating methods for coal carbonizing plants. Some of the outstanding ones should be mentioned. Chief among these, as stated in earlier paragraphs, has been the attainment of greater regularity of operation and uniformity of heats; these factors, together with a considerable increase in heat economy by control of draft conditions, pre-heating of air and producer gas, and minimizing of leakage in oven walls and doors, have probably contributed far more than any other single factor to improved practice and lower costs.

In addition should, however, be mentioned:

(a) Increasing use of blast-furnace gas for oven heating. This cheap and low-heat-value gas has required careful engineering for its successful application; it is now being successfully used at two or more large plants in this country, permitting disposal of all oven gas and coke.

(b) Re-charging of coke dust and fine coke breeze (under ¼ in. size), in amounts up to 5 per cent, intimately mixed in the coal charge, thereby improving the blockiness and strength of the coke and giving this formerly wasted material a value greater than that of the raw coal.

(c) "Self-sealing doors" for coke ovens, a device obviating the costly and troublesome clay-luting process.

(d) "Dry quenching" of coke, a process whereby the sensible heat of the discharged coke—3-4 per cent of the total heat in the coal as charged or about one-third of all the heat consumed in the coking process—is to a large extent recovered by transfer in a circulating inert gas stream to boilers, or recently by circulation of producer gas which is thereby preheated and enriched.

(e) The "coke oven tar still," utilizing the sensible heat in the coal-gas leaving the ovens for fractional distillation of the tar sprayed back into it at suitable points near the oven off-takes.

Byproducts of Carbonization. While efficiency in byproduct recovery has been advanced during the last 25 years, the commercial demand for byproducts has not increased correspondingly; financial returns, on all products except gas, have therefore suffered.

Gas must now be considered the principal byproduct. Ammonia has fallen off greatly owing to competition from the synthetic product and from low-priced foreign products. Tar and light oil, although now recovered more efficiently and in many ways utilized for new chemical applications, are at present over-produced and possess little more than the fuel value.

Creosote oil, for timber preservation, is increasing in use. This product makes up 40 per cent or more of the weight of coal tar produced by carbonization and commands a price nearly three times that of the raw tar; it therefore offers a promising field for increased returns on byproducts, provided the other products of tar refining, notably pitch, can be advantageously sold. There is a widening market for creosote oil. Domestic production trebled itself in the six years from 1924 to 1930, while imports during the same period decreased somewhat.

In recent years pitch coke has been produced by improved processes; in one of these the molten pitch is sprayed on the inner walls of a hot oven. This material is finding increased application as a high-grade ashless fuel offering considerable promise of larger financial returns from tar distillation. Pitch makes up more than half of the raw tar recovered in high-temperature carbonization.

Other recent developments in byproducts which seem to offer good possibilities, although extensive commercial manufacture has not yet taken place, include recovery of sulphur from the gas, in a finely divided form which is found especially suitable for agricultural purposes; ammonium thiocyanate, which is finding application in agriculture as a weed-killer and for other purposes; and urea, a new concentrated fertilizing material made from ammonia.

Although many secondary, refined products are now obtainable from the byproducts of coal, and many recognized uses have established a demand that in some cases brings very favorable prices, the cost of preparation and of selling the relatively small tonnage required has prevented coal processing from gaining any great advance by this means. The mainstays of the industry are still found in the improved solid fuel, coke, for industrial and domestic use, and in the byproduct gas, which has a large and growing market, well established over a long period.

Power Plant Pretreatment of Coal. The large consumption of raw coal for production of steam power, which is showing an increasing trend toward concentration in large central stations, has stimulated efforts to achieve successful pretreatment and byproduct recovery from power plant fuel. But the lack of any encouraging prospect for the marketing of oils and tars, which would be the principal byproducts in the low-temperature carbonizing processes suitable in this connection, has militated against industrial progress in this field. Another deterrent has been the difficulty of the variable load problem on direct-connected pre-carbonization plants, as such plants can only be run profitably on a good load factor.

Notwithstanding these difficulties, a few European plants of this type are reported to operate successfully on a small scale. One at the Langerbrugge Central Station in Belgium has used the Salermo process of low-temperature carbonization with retorts in the shape of parallel inclined troughs, on English and Polish coals of only a moderate caking quality, chosen so as to avoid troublesome sticking of the stirring apparatus. This plant, it is claimed, makes profits when the tar is worked into motor fuel and other products by cracking treatment, and when there is a steady market for such products.

The Pintsch process has been used at a number of power stations in Germany on non-coking and brown coals, the coal being carbonized by internal heating with part of the hot combustion gases from the furnace, a short vertical retort being placed just in front of the stoker, onto which the semi-coke is delivered hot.

In America no developments of this type have led to industrial application.

Low-Temperature Carbonization. Although this field of coal processing has attracted a great deal of attention, owing to the extravagant claims made regarding yields and profits, it is a fact that in America no such process has yet been able to establish itself on a successful commercial basis. At least 25 years of effort have been given to it, in this country, and more than that in Germany and in England.

It will not be attempted here to describe or mention all of the low-temperature carbonization processes that have been tried on a commercial scale. Large amounts of capital have been invested in some of these experiments without practical result. In Germany and in England several processes have been placed on a semi-commercial scale and, under the market conditions for oils and semi-coke prevailing in those countries, have continued to operate with some success.

These processes have been of various design, some of them of the continuous type with rotating cylinders, externally heated, and others of the narrow vertical retort type, intermittently charged. One plant (McLaurin retorts) in Scotland has operated on the internal heating principle, with partial gasification as in a gas producer, and carbonization by the hot producer gas.

In America, there have been notable instances of large-scale trials of low-temperature carbonization which have failed commercially. Just following the World War, a large plant at Clinchfield, Va., operating on the so-called Carbo-Coal Process, was given a thorough trial on a scale of 575 tons per day. This was a two-stage process, the first stage being low-temperature carbonization in horizontal cylindrical retorts, stirred by rotating paddles, the solid residue being briquetted and then carbonized at high temperatures. The briquets were of good quality, but the high cost of operation made the plant unprofitable.

In 1924-25, two large plants of the Piron-Caracristi Process were built by the Ford Motor Company at River Rouge, Mich., and Walkerville, Ont. This process used a thin traveling layer of coal on a heated lead bath. Neither plant operated successfully for any considerable length of time. The process was not adapted to steady, low-cost operation.

In 1928, large investment was made in a plant at New Brunswick, N. J., by the International Coal Carbonization Company, a subsidiary of International Combustion Engineering Corporation, to use the German "K.S.G." Process. This used large rotating steel cylinders, externally heated, with an inner concentric cylinder serving as a preheater for the coal. This project failed, owing to its very large plant investment per unit of output and certain difficulties in securing steady operation. The yields of products were, in many respects, satisfactory. Markets for the special grades of coke and tar produced were, however, not found as favorable as expected.

The McEwen-Runge Process for carbonizing powdered coal in suspension in hot gases was given thorough trial on a commercial scale about 1926-27 at the Lakeside power station of Milwaukee Electric Railway and Light Company. While the powdered semi-coke produced gave good results, in steam-making capacities, the returns from byproducts were not sufficient to balance costs and losses, and the plant has been abandoned.

Recently a plant has been installed by an American company in Porto Alegre, Brazil, to utilize the native Brazilian coal for producing gas for public distribution, recovering byproducts, and utilizing the solid residue as boiler fuel for electrical power production. The coal is not of a coking type and the char recovered from the retorts, in finely divided form, is mixed with washed coal for burning on the grates. The plant consists of two Reed-Lamie retorts, each with a capacity of 30 tons coal per day. They are cylindrical rotating retorts, of relatively simple and inexpensive construction, heated externally by producer gas. The byproduct gas from the retorts is diluted with producer gas before distribution.

Probably the most recent development in low-temperature carbonizing processes is the new Salerni rotating drum retort built in England in 1931-32. The units are horizontal cylinders, 70 ft. long and 4 ft.-8 in. in diameter, with a daily capacity of 100 tons of coal, and planned particularly to operate on a mixture of raw coal and recharged pulverized semi-coke. This last feature gives a product of much better quality than the usual semi-coke,—stronger and of greater density. This retort is claimed to be frictionless; a special arrangement of circulating the cooling gases to distribute the heat properly in the system, largely prevents distortion of the metal parts.

The lack of important commercial progress in low-temperature carbonization may be set down as due largely to insufficient revenue from the oils, tars, and semi-coke to counterbalance greater operating costs per unit of capacity and very much reduced yield of salable gas. The problem may be said to be one of future development of new and profitable uses for the tars and oils and of securing steadier and faster operation per unit of plant investment. So far these conditions have not been met satisfactorily on a commercial basis in the United States.

Briquetting. There has been considerable progress in the briquetting of coal and mixtures of coal with other materials during the last

25 years. The product made at American briquetting plants in recent years has, in many cases, been of excellent quality and has been favorably received in competition with anthracite coal and domestic coke.

To the American Briquet Co., with plants at Lykens, Pa., and Charlestown, Mass., must be given credit for having promoted most successfully in this period the briquetting of anthracite culm into a satisfactory and marketable product at reasonable cost. They have used a patented starch-asphalt binder and a process of baking the briquets so as to harden but not carbonize them after they are made.

Through chemical engineering research, introducing suitable blending and mixing of the raw materials and treatment of the briquets after manufacture, there has been accomplished in recent years a great improvement in the burning qualities and weathering resistance of this type of processed fuel.

In the eight years from 1922 to 1930, the production of fuel briquets in this country increased from 619,000 to 1,029,000 tons yearly.

Special Kinds of Coal Processing. Hydrogenation of coal (Bergius Process) has been developed abroad on a commercial scale. Pulverized coal suspended in oil is treated with hydrogen under high pressure and elevated temperature; in this way a product is made which can be fractionally distilled to produce high yields of oil (about 50-60 per cent of the coal). The rights to this process in America have been acquired by the Standard Oil Company of New Jersey but no commercial plant to treat coal has, as yet, been built in this country. Colloidal fuel, a mixture of finely pulverized coal and fuel oil, was developed during the World War and used to some extent on naval vessels. It can be atomized under the boilers as a liquid fuel of high calorific value and gives great economy in bunkering space. Steam drying of lignite, of which vast deposits in the West await development when economic conditions permit, has been brought out by researches at the University of North Dakota. A very much improved fuel is thus obtained, higher in calorific value and of greater economy in transportation and handling. Activated carbon, as a product of anthracite coal, was developed to some extent during the World War and efforts have recently been made to revive this process due to the increasing use of such material in industry at an advantageous price.

Research. It is impossible, in a review of this nature, to mention all of the important lines of research work—in laboratory or in plant—that have been carried on for the betterment of the industry.

A few of the outstanding workers in the field should, however, be mentioned.

Professor S. W. Parr, pioneer worker in the chemistry of coal and its carbonization, who died in 1931, devoted almost his entire career to research in this field, always directing it toward practical application. He completed much fundamental research on the nature of the coking process, particularly as applied to high oxygen coals; on the effects of oxidation and weathering on coal; and on the utilization of the high-oxygen types for coke and gas manufacture.

Various workers at the U. S. Bureau of Mines have advanced the knowledge of coking and byproduct making with all types of coal. J. D. Davis and A. C. Fieldner, especially, deserve credit in this field for excellent researches on a testing method for coke and gas-making properties of coal, and the correlation of chemical and physical properties, determined in the laboratory, with practical results in carbonization on a commercial scale.

In England, many investigators have been at work in this field, notably R. V. Wheeler and associates at the Government Fuel Research Laboratories. They have accomplished a thorough and valuable study of low-temperature carbonization in its scientific and practical aspects, have developed evaluation of coals by means of the proximate separation of their constituents, have given much attention to the hydrogenation of coal for production of oils and for converting non-coking coals into products having greatly improved coking quality, and to other important investigations in coal processing.

Dr. Franz Fischer and his co-workers in Germany at The Institute Mühlheim for Coal Research, have carried on a great variety of exceedingly valuable researches in this field, both in regard to processes for treating coal and for utilization of the products.

Dr. Kurt Baum at Essen has made a special study of industrial coal carbonization, developing valuable methods for determining temperature relationships in ovens and retorts, together with the effect of these upon operating results.

The great value of scientific research in this field must be realized by all who have given attention to either the commercial or technical problems involved. New ways of utilizing the products in order to bring higher revenue, particularly the oils and tars, will have great influence on future expansion of coal processing. Investigations looking toward improved and simplified operation so as to lower costs have been cited in earlier paragraphs as essential. While it may be that coal processing, during the last few years of our period, has developed commercially somewhat faster than economic conditions warranted, still there can be no question that its future is assured, since the products in important and growing measure are necessary to our modern civilization.

CHAPTER X

THE SUGAR INDUSTRIES

(A). Progress in Cane-Sugar Manufacture and Refining

By George P. Meade
Manager, Colonial Sugars Co., Gramercy, La.

SUGAR REFINING is of particular interest to the chemical engineer. Not only does it employ a great number of the unit operations of chemical engineering but the apparatus for carrying out many of these operations was first devised especially for sugar work. Prominent among these are the vacuum pan and the multiple-effect evaporator. The vacuum pan, which was first used in English sugar refineries about 1820, was invented by Howard whose name is also associated with the invention of the filter press. Norbert Rillieux, of Louisiana, stated the principles of vacuum multiple-effect evaporation in 1834 and later built double-effect evaporators for the concentration of cane juice. The first suspended centrifugal was developed by Weston for cane sugar work and was introduced in Hawaii in 1852. Crushing and grinding have been carried to a high degree of perfection for the milling of cane since the first three roller steam-driven mills were put into use in Jamaica in the latter part of the eighteenth century. Steam production on a large scale with a wet fuel was probably first made possible by the invention of green bagasse furnaces about 1890 by Fiske in Louisiana and Cook in Cuba. Bone-black filtration owes its use and development to the refining branch of the industry, where it was first employed in England about 1825.

Raw-Sugar Manufacture

The manufacture of raw cane sugar has seen little change in fundamentals in the last quarter century. Extraction of the juice by crushing and grinding in mills; treatment with lime and heat; removal of the precipitate by sedimentation; evaporation in multiple effect; boiling to grain in vacuum pans with further crystallization in motion; and separating the crystals and molasses in centrifugal machines are still the same process steps that were used at the beginning of the century. There have been great changes, however, in the capacity and design of the machinery used and in the application of scientific methods.

Milling the Cane. In milling machinery the increase in the size, strength, power and capacity is illustrative of the changes that have taken place in the industry. Twenty-five years ago the usual mill train consisted of a crusher (two deeply grooved rolls for breaking up the cane) and two or three sets of mills of three rollers each. The capacity of such a combination was 50 or 60 tons of cane an hour. Today, the larger factories have several trains of 18 or 21 rollers, preceded by double crushers or shredders and knives for cutting the cane into chips, and with capacities of 250 tons per hour. The extraction of the sucrose from the cane has increased from an average of 90 per cent in the older installations to 96 per cent and above in the modern plants. The modern train of mills, with crushers, carriers, driving mechanism and accessories, is one of the largest machinery combinations in use in any industry, and a mill room with three such trains in full operation is a truly impressive sight.

A very recent method for the preparation of cane for the mills which is in use in only a few factories is the Morgan cane disintegrator which takes the place of the crusher. The cane is first cut into chips by rapidly revolving knives, similar to those used in ordinary milling installations, and then fed into the disintegrator which is in effect a large centrifugal pump with a solid steel impeller revolving at a speed of 600 r.p.m. The cane is torn into a fluffy mass by the impact between the vanes of the impeller and the casing, no juice being extracted by the process, after which the disintegrated cane goes through the regular milling process.

It has long been the practice to spray water on the partly extracted bagasse before it enters the last set of mills in order to increase the extraction of sugar. This process, known as simple maceration, was later extended to double maceration by having the thin juice from the last mills returned to the bagasse on the carriers entering the previous set of mills. With the increase in the number of sets of mills, "compound maceration" was developed in which the juices from two or more sets of mills were returned separately to the carriers of preceding mills. This was a logical procedure but it multiplied accessory apparatus such as juice strainers, juice tanks, pumps and piping under the mills to such a point that the increased extraction was offset by increased sugar losses, due to souring and fermentation. During the past few years the introduction of strainerless

juice pumps such as are used for sewage and dredging work has
made it possible to pump juices back to the mills without straining,
resulting in great improvement in sucrose extraction and in sanitation
around the mills.

Bacteriologic studies of sanitary conditions in and around mills
have shown that large losses in sugar have occurred at this point
in the process. Since the technical control of the factory starts after
the juice has been extracted, sugar losses at the mills are not deter-
minable by the ordinary control methods. Mills are now designed
for easy cleaning, free flow of juice and the avoidance of projections
and moving parts in such accessories as intermediate conveyors, juice
strainers, troughs and pumps. Bacteriology has undoubtedly made a
large contribution to raw-sugar manufacture through these improvements.

Bagasse Utilization. The electrification of milling machinery, improved bagasse furnaces, scientific power plant control, together with
steam economies in the factory itself, particularly at the evaporator
station, have resulted in many factories having an excess of bagasse
(or cane residue from the mills) for fuel, where not many years ago
it was always necessary to use some purchased fuel in addition to
the bagasse. The excess bagasse may prove to have considerable
money value as the cellulose is of use in the making of explosives
and rayon.

For many years attempts have been made to use bagasse commercially for paper but without great success. Recently in Louisiana
bagasse has been successfully employed in the manufacture of "Celo-
tex," a fiber-board. The process consists of weathering the bagasse
for several months, then feeding it into cookers to remove the waxes
and resins, after which a waterproofing material is added. The fiber
goes to the machine forming the board and thence to very long dryers.

A more ambitious process which is still in the experimental stage
aims at the simultaneous manufacture of sugar and fiber-board from
cane. The cane is disintegrated by shredding it against an abrasive
wheel after which it is put through a regular counter-current diffusion
process, the extraction being better than 99 per cent, leaving the cane
fiber so pure that it goes direct to the manufacture of the fiber-board.
The juice to process has a dilution of about 30 per cent, the same as
that obtained by the regular milling process. This is a return to
diffusion, abandoned in the cane industry some 25 years ago because
of the high cost of excess fuel, now made practicable because of a
more valuable use for the bagasse.

Clarification of Juice.   The raw juice is now weighed in tank scales as it comes from the mills, a great improvement in control methods over the older practice of measuring and calculating the weight.   Heat and lime continue to be the universal clarifying agents, followed by sedimentation of the precipitated impurities and decantation of the clear juice.   The addition of a small amount of soluble phosphate to increase the precipitate is a recent improvement in use where juices are difficult to clarify.

The technology of clarification has been profoundly altered by two contributions of pure science, the use of pH control and the application of colloid chemistry.   Practically all factories now control the addition of the lime at the clarification station by colorimetric pH tests and many of the larger plants have automatic electrical recording apparatus to determine pH continuously.   A few factories are actually carrying out the addition of the lime automatically by electrical devices operated by pH recorders.   The literature of clarification has been greatly increased by members of the Carbohydrate Division of the Bureau of Chemistry at Washington and others who have studied colloid elimination and its effect on subsequent steps in the process and the final quality of the raw sugar.

Continuous settling devices such as the Deming system were tried out many years ago but were never entirely successful because of fermentation and frequent running of cloudy juice.   The open defecator with intermittent settling retained its popularity until about 1920 when the clarifier patented by J. V. N. Dorr was introduced.   It is similar to the Dorr thickener used in hydrometallurgy and has resulted in large fuel economies, less mud draw-off, and reduced juice in process.   A continuous flow of clear juice and the avoidance of fermentation are other advantages.

The removal of the mud from the scum waters in the defecation process is still generally carried out on plate-and-frame filter presses although suction filters of the vacuum type have been successfully used in a few factories during recent years.   A clarification system which completely eliminates the filter station is the Petree-Dorr process which uses a double set of Dorr clarifiers, the heavier juices from the first mills being defecated in the primary clarifier and the scums from this system together with the thin juices re-defecated in a secondary clarifier.   The scums from the secondary clarifier are sprayed on the mills, the blanket of bagasse acting as a filter, while the mud goes to the boilers with the bagasse.   The Petree-Dorr system has the advantage of simplicity but requires a complete change of control methods since the cold juice cannot be weighed and tested as in the ordinary defecation system.

Evaporation of Juice. The clarified juice containing from 12 to 18 per cent of solids is evaporated to a heavy syrup of 60 deg. Brix or above in multiple-effect evaporators, usually of the "standard" type in quadruple effect. Great changes in practice at this station have come about by the introduction of steam economy methods which "rob" some of the vapors from the first effects and use these for juice heating, thereby giving double-effect results in the heating of the juices. An elaboration of this idea is the addition of a vapor cell ahead of the effects in which the juice is heated by exhaust steam, all the vapors from this cell being used in juice heating. This has been carried still farther by having a double-effect dead-end vapor cell ahead of the evaporator. The Pauly-Greiner pre-evaporator uses live steam at about 40 lb. pressure, the vapors in this case being sent to the exhaust steam system of the factory. The "Pauly" acts substantially as a reducing valve and is not in general favor in raw-sugar houses.

Crystallization. The evaporated syrup goes to single-effect vacuum pans for concentration to a massecuite, the calandria pan having superseded the coal pan in raw-sugar factory work during the past ten years. Notable studies by A. L. Webre have shown the necessity for artificial circulation and he has designed vacuum pans with stirring devices which have been introduced in some of the newer installations.

Great changes in pan boiling practice have taken place in the re-boiling of molasses. Elaborate and apparently complicated systems of handling the various grades of massecuites have been worked out in order that the factory may turn out one grade of sugar only, which is of good refining quality. The older methods of producing two or even three grades of sugar and the use of hot room cars for crystallization of "string-proof" sugars disappeared about 20 years ago in the more progressive cane producing countries. The low grade massecuites are now sent to crystallizers where the grain is kept in motion and the exhaustion of the molasses facilitated.

Improvements in crystallizers have been noteworthy during the past decade, the primary idea being to speed up the cooling of the massecuite by artificial means. The Kopke cooling coils, one of the first of these, are stationary coils between the rotating arms of the crystallizer through which cool water is circulated. A similar idea which is said to be still more effective is in use in many South African factories and consists of substituting coils for the rotating arms. The coils are made of heavy curved piping connected to a hollow rotating shaft and the cooling surface of the coils is thereby brought in closer contact with all parts of the massecuite. The LaFeuille rotary crystallizer is a longitudinally rotating drum, slowly turning on rollers and equipped with cooling pipes extending lengthwise. The rotary motion gives more effective cooling and the exhaustion of the molasses is about six times as fast as in the ordinary crystallizer. Experiments in Java indicate that with this apparatus it may be possible to reduce molasses purities of high test massecuites to such an extent that one re-boiling may be avoided.

Separation of crystals and syrup in the massecuite is universally done in the sugar industry by means of the centrifugal. The introduction of electric drives and the invention of the self-discharging centrifugal with bottomless basket are improvements during the past 20 years which have more than doubled the capacity of these machines. Accessories such as automatic washing devices and automatic starting and stopping arrangements are more generally used in refining than in factory work.

Quality Control. Twenty-five years ago loss of polarization in raw sugars during storage was considered a necessary evil and the money so lost each year amounted to hundreds of thousands of dollars. Studies by bacteriologists showed that these losses were due to various forms of micro-organisms (bacteria, yeasts and molds) some of which could be eliminated by proper factory sanitation and others prevented from propagating by regulating the density of the molasses film on the raw sugar crystal. This latter is now measured by a so-called "safety factor" in which the percentage of moisture is less than one-fourth of the non-sucrose, or expressed mathematically:

$$\frac{\text{Per cent moisture}}{100 - \text{Polarization}} = 0.25 \text{ or less}$$

Raw sugars conforming to these standards and stored with proper protection against moisture absorption now keep for many months with little or no loss in polarization.

The demand by refiners for a better quality raw sugar has been so insistent during the past 10 or 15 years that much attention has been given to this point by the factories. So-called molasses sugars and other low polarizing raws are no longer produced to any extent and there has been a steady increase in the polarization of all raw sugars produced. The average polarization of sugars entering the port of New York is now about 96.5 where formerly it was 94.5.[1] Hawaiian factories produce a sugar of still higher test, close to 98 polarization. The size and character of the grain, the color and colloid content of the molasses film and the filtrability of the sugar are all factors which are closely watched by both manufacturer and refiner.

Sugar Refining

Sugar refiners have been traditionally conservative in the interchange of ideas and the publication of their investigations; because of this policy the literature on sugar refining up to recent years has been scant. Fortunately, a more liberal tendency has developed during the past decade so that publications by refinery technologists are now fairly numerous. Investigations by outsiders on the subject of decolorizing carbons have had their effect on the theory and practice of bone-black filtration and many published articles on mechanical filtration and the use of filter-aids by the manufacturers of these products have also tended to enrich the literature of refining.

The refining process begins with the removal of the film of molasses from the crystal of raw sugar. The raw sugar is "washed" by mingling with a heavy syrup, centrifuging and spraying with water. Self-discharging centrifugals with automatic water sprays and automatic timing devices are now general for wash plant work.

Defecation and Filtration. The washed sugar dissolved in hot water or high test sweet waters must undergo some form of defecation and filtration before it is sent to the char filters. A complete revolution at these stations has taken place since 1915. The Taylor bag filter, formerly universally used, has almost entirely disappeared, being generally replaced by pressure filters of the Sweetland or Vallez type. The preparation of the liquor for filtration has also changed markedly, the majority of refineries replacing the old phosphoric acid-lime treatment with kieselguhr, an inert filter-aid. This is put on the market in several grades of different filtration rates, the practice being to add sufficient lime to the liquor to bring the reaction to neutrality, after which from 4 to 7 lb. of filter-aid per ton of solids are added and the treated liquor sent through the presses. Regeneration of the kieselguhr by heating in Wedge furnaces is practiced in a few of the larger refineries. Some few plants use paper pulp as the filter-aid in conjunction with the Vallez rotary press, the paper

---

[1] See annual reports by F. W. Zerban, chemist-in-charge, New York Sugar Trade Laboratory.

pulp being recovered for reuse by sending the press cake through counter-current pulp washing systems. Small amounts of phosphoric acid or some form of soluble phosphate are used in certain refineries in conjunction with paper pulp or mineral filter-aids.

The most recent variation in technique is heavy density pressure filtration which works with liquors of 67-68 deg. Brix instead of the lower density of 62-64 deg. Brix more generally employed. Fuel savings, greater clarity of char-filtered liquors, and reduction in the quantity of filter-aid are some of the advantages claimed for this heavy density filtration.

The Williamson defecation system in use in one or two refineries was patented by George B. Williamson of Louisiana about 12 years ago. This does not depend on filtration, but is in effect an air-flotation system. The washed sugar liquor at about 160 deg. F. is treated with phosphoric acid and lime as in the old bag-filter days, then impregnated with air by forcing it through siphon jets, after which it is allowed to flow into shallow tanks having steam tubes in the bottom. As the air-charged liquor flows continuously over the heating surface the temperature is raised to 210 deg. F. and the air bubbles rise carrying the flocs of tricalcium phosphate precipitate with them, entrapping the colloidal and suspensoid impurities. A heavy blanket of scum is thus formed which is pulled over a lip at the end of the tank by a slowly moving roller, the clarified liquor being drawn off from the body of the defecator. The scums are diluted and filtered through plate-and-frame presses.

It will be seen from the above that very few plants in the United States employ identical defecation technique or have the same apparatus at the filtration station. This wide divergence in defecation and filtration practice possibly indicates a transitional stage from which may emerge a more uniform procedure embodying the advantages of several of the systems.

Char Filtration. During the hundred or more years that bone black or "char" has been in use in refining, char filtration has developed into a highly specialized industrial art. The general design of filters, dryers and kilns is much the same as it was 30 years ago but a great deal has been added to the scientific knowledge of bone black within that period. Investigations in the comparative values of bone black and vegetable decolorizing carbons and the application of the principles of colloid chemistry have shown that bone black acts by absorption according to Freundlich's equation. Determination of reactions by pH methods both on liquors and on the bone black itself has not only been used in these investigations but has also become an indispensable part of routine control practice. Another analytical aid to the development of the knowledge of bone black has been the introduction of spectrophotometric methods of color analysis. Investigations made previous to the introduction of scientific color analysis and of pH determination were of doubtful value.

One of the difficulties long recognized in filling char filters was the "channeling" of liquors through the poor distribution of the coarse particles and the fines in the cistern. Many methods have been suggested to avoid this, among which was simultaneous filling of the char and the liquor. A practical method for accomplishing this "wet filling," developed at the California & Hawaiian Refinery, consists of a set of staggered funnels hung in the top of the filter by which the char and the liquor are intimately mixed. This practical advance in char filter technique has improved decolorization, reduced the quantities of sweetwater, and added to the active time that the filter is running liquor.

Vegetable carbons were suggested as decolorants for sugar liquor even before animal charcoal was adopted. Recently the vegetable carbons have come back into some favor in small refineries located in the tropics. Considerable work has been done by Professor Charles E. Coates and associates in the Audubon Sugar School of the Louisiana State University looking toward the use of these decolorants for "direct consumption sugars." These carbons are in the form of an amorphous powder and are added directly to the liquors in relatively small proportions as compared to bone black, after which they are filtered out in filter presses. The advantages are low initial cost of investment, much less carbon and liquor in process, and less water for washing. The disadvantages, which up to the present have outweighed the advantages, are the high cost of the carbon, the difficulty of revivification, and the fact that special sugars such as confectioners' sugars, soft sugars and the like have not been successfully made by the carbon processes. For these reasons, no bone black refinery on this continent has yet adopted the use of carbons even as an adjunct to bone black.

Other Improvements. Coil pans are largely used in white sugar boiling with calandria pans in favor for remelts and soft sugars. The Webre calandria pan which has internal paddles for forced circulation and specially designed down-take is in use for soft sugar work in certain refineries. Boiling temperatures as low as 110 deg. F are recorded with it. Shock seeding with powdered sugar is generally practiced in all refinery pan boiling. Crystallizers and centrifugals follow the same trend in refineries as in the raw house. A suction filter of the continuous vacuum type is reported to have been successfully developed in one refinery for purging white massecuites of their syrups.

Rotary drum dryers or "granulators" have been employed for drying sugar crystals for half a century but certain changes such as saw-toothed flights for even distribution of the falling sugar have increased capacity in the past 25 years. Dust collecting systems of the "cyclone" type have replaced the old dust-box and a more recent form is the "vorticose" dust collector in which the dust is caught by a series of staggered vertical baffles.

The dried refined sugar from the granulators was formerly passed through reel bolters to remove lumps but vibrating screens of the Hummer and the Newaygo types have now largely replaced these. A recent powder mill, called the "Mikro" pulverizer, claims a finer powdered sugar, greater capacity and less power than the older swing hammer types.

As in all other phases of food manufacture, automatic packaging has become an important part of the sugar refining industry. Because of the multiplicity of grades of sugar and kinds of packages and the automatic machinery necessary, the packing department of a modern sugar refiner is an elaborate institution.

An ever-present problem in the warehousing of refined sugars in moist climates has been the caking and hardening due to moisture absorption and subsequent chilling or drying out. This has been solved in certain refineries in the past 5 years by the installation of air conditioning systems in refined sugar warehouses. Heated air is circulated through the warehouse so that the relative humidity inside is always lower than that of the outside atmosphere.

THE SUGAR INDUSTRIES (*Continued*)

(B) Developments in Beet-Sugar Processing

By R. W. Shafor

Chemical Engineer, The Dorr Co., Inc., New York, N. Y.

ONE MUST, in reviewing the advances made in the processing end of America's beet sugar industry, definitely bear in mind that the annual period of operation is limited to approximately 100 days. Only those plant and process improvement projects which promise a satisfactory economic return under these conditions can be considered or given a trial.

Under this stringent limiting condition however, some astonishing and many noteworthy advances have been realized during the past 25 years. They have resulted, as has been aptly said, "from the close attention of many men to many things," from an economic necessity and a management policy calling for a better job than has been done previously with the means already available. No revolutionary invention has been forthcoming during the last quarter of a century. Technically the flowsheet remains essentially as it was imported from Europe some fifty years ago.

An outstanding achievement lies in the astonishing increase in equipment capacities—astonishing because the process had already passed through 50 years of prior operation and development. Entire factories which in 1908 were treating 800 tons of beets daily have been "stepped up," with only relatively minor changes in the installed equipment, so that they are now treating 3,000 to 3,500 tons. The average increase is probably approximately 200 per cent.

Sucrose recovery—in terms of "sugar packed for market," per cent on sugar in beets introduced into the process—has likewise been increased materially. Dependable statistics are not available but it seems safe to say that while in 1908 an average recovery of approximately 80 per cent was obtained, a like figure at this time would lie between 90 and 95 per cent. A material portion of this increase must be credited to increased use of and advancement in methods for recovering sucrose from molasses.

Sucrose recovery—in terms of sugar in beets introduced into processing, per cent on sugar on sugar in beets harvested—has likewise been increased through improvement in harvesting, beet storage and beet handling methods due in part to a better utilization of knowledge concerning the loss of sucrose through respiration in the harvested root.

A quarter of a century ago the consumption of factory operating labor probably amounted to 2.5 to 3.5 man hours per bag (100 lb.) of sugar produced. Today the comparable figure would lie between 0.5 and 1.0 man hour. Increases in equipment capacities, the installation of labor saving equipment, and the change from the 12-hour to the 8-hour shift have each contributed to this result. The consumption of operating supplies including coal (for power and evaporation), filter media, and limestone, have also been reduced to a noteworthy extent.

In reviewing these general developments the thought occurs that no small portion of the accomplishment must be credited to the highly developed, comprehensive system of technical accounting almost universally employed throughout the industry in an increasing degree during the years under consideration. Also it is the writer's belief that this development (described by H. E. Zitkowski in Trans. A. I. Ch. E. 1924) might profitably be studied by other branches of chemical industry.

Improvement in Unit Operations. From a more detailed viewpoint, many of the improvements leading to the general achievement are of interest. That the technical process has not been basically changed has previously been pointed out. The type of equipment and its operation have undergone material change in several of the unit operations involved. For consideration herein the process may be divided into seven groups of unit operations under the following general headings: (a) The extraction of sucrose from the beet root. (b) The purification of the solution resulting from the extraction steps. (c) The concentration of the purified solution, together with steam utilization in general. (d) The crystallization of the sucrose from the concentrated solution. (e) The storage of refined sugar. (f) The treatment of molasses for the recovery of sucrose. (g) The recovery of byproducts.

The Roberts diffusion process (invented in 1848 and imported with the industry) for extracting the sucrose from the plant cell of the beet root remains basically unchanged both as to equipment and method. Its application involves the use of steps for separating the beet from foreign materials, the slicing of the root into "cossettes" and the subsequent treatment of the cossettes in a battery of "cells" (closed tanks) in a semi-continuous counter-current manner.

In the achievement of "stepping-up" capacity, the period of cossette detention in the battery cell has been reduced from approximately 2 hours to as little as 40 minutes or less. Contributing factors include a more complete separation of foreign materials prior to slicing, an increase in cossette area per unit of weight, a better distribution of the weight of the charge together with avoidance of short-circuiting of the extracting solution through the incorporation of chain baskets in the battery cell, improved apparatus and methods for discharging the exhausted cossette from the cell and improved control of temperatures. The only disadvantageous feature of this "stepping-up" has been an increased dilution ranging from 10 to 25 per cent.

Means for converting the operation from semi-continuous to a continuous basis capable of meeting American economic requirements have not been found. Efforts of European contemporaries directed toward a similar end are said to have met with some success.

Purification of Solutions. The solution-purification operations have been quite generally converted from intermittent to continuous methods. The first steps in these operations (first carbonation) involve the mixing of the "raw juice" with milk of lime, and the treating of the mixture with CO_2 gas to produce a precipitate which contains impurities together with calcium carbonate. The solution phase contains .07 to .10 gms. of CaO per 100 cc. and is subsequently separated from the precipitate by filtration.

Pressure filters of the plate-and-frame type were in universal use in 1908. Their operation was relatively costly and with the development of the Kelly and Sweetland pressure filters several of the larger plate-and-frame installations were replaced. Later an effort to employ the continuous features inherent in the thickener-vacuum-filter combination promised satisfactory results if fluctuations in the character of the precipitate could be reduced.

This effort led to the development of a process method in which the purifying reaction is carried on continuously with the end-point automatically maintained by electrical means for controlling the admission of the CO_2 gas. This process [1] produces a precipitate having not only more uniform characteristics but with material improvement in those characteristics affecting sedimentation and filtration rates. It is being generally adopted in the industry at this time. In addition to rendering usable thickeners of the sedimentation type it pre-

---

[1] See article by George M. Darby, *Chem. & Met. Eng.*, Vol. 36, No. 4, pp. 211-13 (1929).

sents the added advantages of increasing filter capacities in general and of increasing the ease of separating the solution from the precipitate to the end that sugar losses in the discarded filter cake are reduced.

The investigation led to a second development—that of the vacuum filtration thickener of the Oliver-Borden type for use in connection with the vacuum type filter. Several installations of this combination are in use. The contribution of these developments to labor saving and lower consumption of filter media was appreciable.

In the second steps of the purification group (second carbonation) the alkalinity of the solution resulting from the preceding operations is reduced from approximately .08 gm. CaO per 100 cc. to a point below 0.01 gm. per 100 cc. employing CO_2 gas as a precipitant and the resulting precipitate is separated from the solution. The change from intermittent to continuous methods of precipitation was effected in a simple manner early in the period and the development of the vacuum type thickener has led to several successful installations employing apparatus for continuous separation.

The third steps in the group provide only for the final adjustment of the solution alkalinity by the use of SO_2. Formerly this reaction was controlled by titration but with the development of plant methods for determining pH, titration has been supplanted. This resulted in an appreciable improvement in the uniformity of results obtained in the subsequent evaporation and sugar crystallizing operations. Pressure filters are still employed for clarifying the adjusted solution, the amount of the precipitate being very small.

In the third group of operations, namely those involving concentration of purified solution together with general steam economy, attention should be drawn to the high state of development attained in the employment of evaporator vapors for various purposes with the advantages not only of fuel economy but also of temperature control; to the nicely drawn balance between high pressure steam utilized for producing power and the exhaust steam required for evaporation and to methods developed for cleaning evaporator heating surfaces by chemical means with minimum loss of operating capacity.

Evaporation is usually effected in quintuple effect apparatus with concurrent flow of vapors and solution. The vapor produced in the first body has a temperature of about 108 deg. C. It is being used successfully to replace exhaust steam in the calandria type of vacuum pans employed for crystallizing raw (second boiling) sugars as well as for the customary purpose of preheating solutions entering the evaporator. Vapors produced in the second body have a temperature of approximately 100 deg. C and are obviously well suited for heating solutions to maintain a temperature of 90 deg. C especially where it is advantageous to avoid boiling. Third body vapor presents similar advantages. The chemical engineer who is interested in balancing the process steam and power requirements of a process may well study closely the developments made in the beet sugar industry.

In the fourth group of operations—those dealing with the crystallization and separation of sucrose from the concentrated solution—numerous improvements have been made. Although these have been of small magnitude, as a group they are worthy of note.

Crystallization is usually effected in two steps, the first producing the marketable refined sugar, the second (operated on the syrup produced from the first), producing a raw sugar (to be redissolved and refined) and a molasses of minimum sucrose content.

A continually increasing emphasis upon recovery and improved quality of finished product has been experienced during the past twenty-five years. This has led to at least two noteworthy achievements.

Increased Recovery From Molasses. The molasses produced at the beginning of the period probably contained sucrose in the ratio of 160 to 175 parts per 100 parts of non-sucrose impurities. A comparable ratio in molasses produced in recent years falls between 125 and 140 indicating a reduction in this "loss" of some 25 per cent which has been realized largely through improved methods of operation.

In recent years the trend has been away from the two-step system toward a three-step operation with an improvement in results. The first step is employed to produce the marketable refined sugar, the second a relatively high quality of "raw" sugar and the third a lower grade of "raw" together with a well-exhausted molasses. Both "raw" sugars are dissolved and reintroduced into the refining process.

Two equipment changes are worthy of mention. In the interest of fuel economy the calandria type of vacuum pan has largely replaced other types for effecting the crystallization of raw sugars. Quality of finished product and capacity demands have resulted in the adoption of automatic devices for washing the sugar charge in the centrifugal basket, replacing manual methods and yielding a product of more uniform quality.

Better Storage Practice. It is still customary practice through the industry to "bag" the refined sugar as it is produced and to store it thus ready for the market.   In some localities such storage buildings have been equipped with means for humidity control for purposes of reducing the costs of reconditioning due to caking.

Recently one large producer has installed and successfully operated a plant, similar in appearance and construction to large grain storage silos in which the product is stored in bulk to be packed when and as the market demands.   This improvement promises lower handling charges, eliminates almost entirely the necessity for reconditioning due to caking in storage and repackaging with attendant charges, lessens first cost of storage facilities and utilizes labor during the "intercampaign" period in a way to lessen the seasonal demands of the industry.

The solution to this problem involved, among other factors, a selection of materials of construction so as to avoid contamination, a design which would provide what amounts to a hermetically sealed storage space with a minimum of temperature fluctuations therein and a close control over the temperature, moisture content and crystal "surface film" purity of the sugar sent to storage.

Steffen Process.   In the sixth group of operations, two processes are in use for desugarizing beet molasses.   Of these the Steffen process, employing quick-lime as a precipitant, has the wider application.   In fact, the use of the second process, commonly termed the "Barium process" and employing barium hydrate as a precipitant, is limited to the treatment of molasses which cannot be economically treated by the former.

The Steffen process for desugarizing beet molasses was imported from continental Europe although it had never met with wide application there.   The process provides for the treatment of diluted beet molasses with finely divided quick-lime at temperatures of from 5 to 15 deg. C to precipitate 85-90 per cent of the sucrose as tri-calcium saccharate, $3CaO - C_{12}H_{22}O_{11}$, and the separation of this precipitate from the solution and the subsequent heating of the latter to approximately 85 deg. C to effect the precipitation of from 75-100 per cent of its sucrose content, possibly as tetra-calcium saccharate—the necessary lime being present in the solution leaving the cold separation.   The precipitates are mixed, the mixture heated and added to the "beet juice" in the first carbonation station where its lime content may serve as a purifying agent to displace completely the milk of lime employed when no molasses treatment is practiced.

The early installations used tube mills for grinding the lime, batch reaction vessels in both steps of the process and plate-and-frame filters for the separation steps. The displacement of the tube mill with the Raymond Bros. pulverizer employing closed circuit grinding with air classification marked, early in the period, the first big improvement in the American development of the process and may possibly have spelled the difference between its success and failure. Uniformly fine ground lime is essential and the tube mill is not at its best when grinding batches of quick-lime.

The replacement of the plate-and-frame filters with those of the continuous rotary vacuum type on the cold reaction precipitate and with the combination of Dorr thickeners and Oliver type filters on the hot precipitate followed. These changes resulted in improved cake washing and marked lowering of operating charges for labor, filter cloth and maintenance.

Trend to Continuous Operations. Batch precipitation originally employed in both reaction steps, first gave way to continuous operation in the case of the hot reaction. The primary difficulty encountered in the transition was the production of a precipitate which could be filtered as readily as the batch product. The ultimate result was a product which filtered much more easily and which in fact materially increased the attractiveness of the thickener-vacuum filter combination.

Equipment and methods for effecting the cold reaction on a continuous basis were installed and successfully operated in two factories in recent years. This change completed the transformation of the original wholly batch flowsheet to one entirely continuous. There is some question as to the economic ability of this improvement to replace the batch system in existing installations but it seems certain that new applications of the process will employ it.

A novel feature of this improvement lies in the employment of a series of 16 (preferably more in installations of larger capacities) reaction vessels with the addition of the powdered lime precipitant to all except the latter two or three.

From the viewpoint of process efficiencies, that of the precipitation has been increased from approximately 90 per cent to an efficiency approaching 97 or 98 per cent.

On the whole it is probable that the amount of sugar actually recovered in marketable form (per cent on sugar in molasses treated by the process) has been increased by 10 to 15 per cent or in other words that the sugar recoverable for packaging per ton of sugar in molasses treated, is from 115 to 125 per cent of that recoverable with methods in use 25 years ago.

Barium Process. The crystallizable portion of the precipitated sugar varies appreciably with the locality in which the beets are grown due to the presence of variable amounts of precipitable non-sucrose impurities in the molasses. The re-introduction of these impurities into the purification step of the beet treating process causes them to become entrapped in the cycle so that their concentration in the circuit must be held at or below a workable maximum by means of continuous or periodic discarding of molasses. This byproduct molasses was formerly sold for producing alcohol and yeast and for feeding cattle. By means of a recent development it is being treated successfully for the recovery of about 75 per cent of its sucrose content. This is the so-called Barium Desugarizing Process which employs barium hydrate as a precipitant.

A primary requirement in the application of the Barium Process under American conditions was a process for reconverting barium carbonate, a byproduct, to barium hydrate at a permissible cost. Neither the processes employed in the barium chemicals industry nor those developed in the European sugar industry promised to meet this need. The answer was found in the relatively undeveloped DeGuide process in which the barium carbonate is mixed with mono-barium silicate, the mixture furnaced in a rotary kiln and the resulting clinker leached to produce a solution of barium hydrate and an insoluble mono-barium silicate suitable for reuse in the furnacing operation. Elimination of sulphates, which tend to accumulate in the mono-barium silicate circuit, necessitated the development of a secondary furnacing operation on the product. The barium hydrate is continuously crystallized from the solution by cooling and the mother liquor is returned to the leaching system.

In the molasses treatment process some novel features of minor importance developed, among which the continuous precipitation of the barium saccharate and the subsequent separation of the precipitate on vacuum (batch) filters may well be mentioned.

Byproducts. In the last group of processes the exhausted cossette or beet pulp constitutes a byproduct of the industry wherever it operates. Its use has, thus far, been limited to stock feeding, especially for fattening, and in its wet state transportation costs limit its distribution to territories adjacent to the point of production. This limitation has lead to successful efforts directed toward partial dewatering by pressing and the application of methods and equipment for drying. The latter employ dryers of the rotary drum type heated by gases from fuel burned for the specific operation or the waste flue gases from power plants.

A second group of byproducts may, at some future time, be developed through treatment of wastes arising from molasses desugarizing operations and containing potassium and nitrogenous compounds. Market conditions during 1915-18 led to an appreciable production of potassium salts from this source but this market disappeared with the return of lower prices.

"The attention of many men to many points" has produced steady rather than revolutionary improvement in the beet sugar process.

CHAPTER XI

HIGH PRESSURE SYNTHESIS—BASIS OF NEW CHEMICAL ENGINEERING INDUSTRIES

By Charles O. Brown,

Vice-President, Chemical Engineering Corporation, New York, N. Y.

I. Status of High Pressure Synthesis in 1933

O UR PRESENT KNOWLEDGE of the important field of high pressure synthesis, as is always the case, came from very remote and humble starts in the field of pure science in the latter part of the last century. In 1897 the brilliant work of Sabatier [1] set forth the conditions whereby hydrogen, with the aid of a catalyst, may be added to unsaturated organic compounds, to produce "synthetic" edible fats and soap fats of higher melting points. The present industrial development of these and other researches, three decades later, uses pressures of several hundred atmospheres for the hydrogenation of oils and the production of various materials. Haber's early work on the ammonia equilibrium in 1904 [2] was done at atmospheric pressure and it was Nernst in 1907 [3] who experimented on this same subject at 72 atmospheres, starting a controversy with Haber, who in 1908,[4] working at 30 atmospheres, fixed the values of the ammonia equilibrium constant and called attention to the great advantage gained by synthesis of ammonia at high pressures. In 1908 Dr. P. W. Bridgman, in the United States,[5] published the first of his classic researches on the development and measuring of high pressures up to 7,000 atmospheres per sq. in. The technique of Bridgman has since permitted him to study hydrostatic pressures of many times these values.

The commercial development of high pressure synthesis started, more directly, from the work of Haber, through his connection with the progressive and resourceful German firm, the Badische Anilin

---

[1] *Bull. de la Societe Chimique de France,* 1897.

[2] Haber-Van Oordt, *Zeit. Anorg. Chem.,* 43, 111 (1904).

[3] Nernst, *Z. fur Elektrochemie* 13, 521 (1907).

[4] Haber-Le Rossignol, *Zeit. fur Elektrochemie* 14, 181 (1908).

[5] *Proc. Am. Acad. of A. & S.,* 44, 201-17 (1908).

und Soda Fabrik. Although at that time thermal data and physical data were meager and rough, Dr. Carl Bosch of this firm completed the first commercial synthetic ammonia plant in 1913. There are those who believe, with good reason, that this accomplishment is directly responsible for the greatest World War, followed by a world chaos that has ruined the economic structure and position of nations, and two decades which have passed have not as yet produced a new and stabilized order.

The commercial development of high pressure synthesis has been largely "hydrogenation," whether of nitrogen to produce ammonia, or of carbon monoxide to produce methanol, or of various hydrocarbons to produce more valuable products. In this latter field, by high pressure synthesis, it is now possible for the first time to change or control the ratio of hydrogen to carbon atoms in any hydrocarbon, and even to change aliphatic compounds to naphthenic and aromatic bodies. Aldehydes, ketones and acids are produced by methods of high pressure synthesis, but are of lesser commercial importance.

As one could easily predict, this epoch making development unchecked through 20 years, led to the usual reaction—over production. This is today manifest, both in the birth of too many "processes," as well as in too many individual plants. The year 1932 completed a program of more than $137,000,000 of invested capital, whose annual products are valued at over $56,000,000. During this period there has been a break in the prices of synthetic ammonia and of methanol to a steady level of one-sixth to one-quarter of their former quotations, and all prices, formerly subject to wide and ruinous fluctuations, are now quite steady from season to season and year to year. But the bottom has probably not been reached. These changes in basic commodities have also rearranged the importance of their compounds and changed the financial stability of nations, particularly of Chile. Germany was the first to demonstrate that, through high pressure synthesis, it was possible to feed a nation and carry on a major war, without outside help. Today finds a relatively large number of countries independent of nitrate supplies from without their boundaries—having developed atmospheric nitrogen fixation through high pressure synthesis.

Until 1922 the world's supply of the "methyl" radical in chemicals came from natural sources, more or less as a related product, produced only in proportion as other materials were produced. This condition led to serious fluctuations in the supply and, having no connection with the demand for methyl compounds, the price changes in a single year were often unreasonable. High pressure synthesis has now changed and stabilized this condition so that former ranges of $0.50 to $1.50 per gal. of methanol are now steady at $0.35 per gal. and methanol consumption has doubled—as much due to reliability of supply as to the lower price. The production capacity of the United States is now over 10,000,000 gal. per year of synthetic methanol, and each year finds this steadily and cheaply produced high purity alcohol reaching out into and supplying the fields of ethyl alcohol and other solvents.

II. FUNDAMENTAL PRINCIPLES

All processes of high pressure synthesis involve the use of one or more of the common gases and, therefore, the most fundamental and useful tools for theoretical studies are the gas laws and the thermal and physical data pertaining to gases. There is not sufficient space in this chapter, to review them in detail, and the excellent publications of theoretical work make it unnecessary. Members of the Fixed Nitrogen Research Laboratory have contributed in a very large measure to the progress made in fundamentals, and important papers are still appearing from the pens of these able scientists who have left the Fixed Nitrogen Laboratory for other positions. Our recent knowledge of the order and mechanism of all chemical reactions has come largely from observations of homogeneous and gas phase systems, and the studies of low pressure reactions, notably by Langmuir, in a field sometimes called "surface chemistry." Kunsman [6] has summarized data on active gases, catalytic surfaces, heterogeneous surface reactions, thermionic properties of surfaces and X-rays.

For experimental studies, certain other tools are necessary which were not in common use before the days of high pressure synthesis. To measure the pressures commonly used, up to 1,500 atmospheres, the old Bourdon coil type of gage, with a metal tube coil, has been found unreliable. It can only be used for approximate work after frequent calibration, using both increasing and decreasing pressures, and shortly becomes useless, because of mechanical hysteresis and "set." The mercury column is impractical for any but ordinary pressures. The problem has been solved by the use of a special dead weight gage, made by Olsen or the American Instrument Co. A description of the gage and methods of calibration have been given

---

[6] See A. C. S. Monograph, "Fixed Nitrogen," edited by Harry A. Curtis, Chemical Catalog Co., 1932.

by Keyes.[7] The dead weight gage picks up the pressure to be measured by oil in a cylinder with a carefully measured and accurately fitted piston. The movement of the piston is balanced through a moment arm with known weights. When the piston is oscillated mechanically or revolved completely in its packing, and equilibrium has been established with a sensitive electric device, this gage has research precision.

Volume measurements at high pressures are difficult to make accurately, but the method used is to combine physical measurements of the apparent volume with calculations of the variation due to stretch and elasticity of the metal under pressure, and expansion of the metal due to temperature changes, and permanent creep. The physical measurements are made with special instruments. Methods of calculation of volume and design are given by Keyes.[8]

Temperature measurements of the reacting gases, or in many cases, of the catalyst used, are most important, as the volume of the reacting gas and also the value of the reaction equilibrium are dependent on the temperature, and the precision of temperature measurements must equal the precision of pressure measurements, not an easy task. The Beckmann type of mercury thermometer may be depended upon up to 200 deg. C., but any glass-mercury thermometer is difficult to apply to the exact zone in high pressure work. Special wells and a correction factor are necessary. In research work the platinum resistance thermometer is a most satisfactory instrument. It has been used with success at temperature of — 200 deg. C. to 550 deg. C. with an accuracy of 0.001 deg. C. The design and operation has been described by Beatie.[9]

In plant work the platinum resistance thermometer is not used because of the skill required to manipulate it and such accuracy of measurements is not needed. Commercial thermocouples, when built with care, are quite satisfactory. It is common practice to procure carefully calibrated and matched alloy wire and to have the entire amount tested by the Bureau of Standards, and then made into thermocouples. Such couples are interchangeable on the job, without further calibration, and when a constant temperature cold junction and potentiometer are used the reading is within 0.1 deg. C. of the true temperature.

The viscosity of hydrogen, nitrogen, methane, carbon dioxide,

[7] *Ind. & Eng. Chemistry,* 23, 1375 (1931).

[8] *Ind. & Eng. Chemistry,* 23, 1378 (1931).

[9] Beatie, Jacobus & Gaines, *Proc. Am. Acad. A. & S.,* 66, 167 (1930).

carbon monoxide and ammonia have been determined at 25 deg. C., 50 deg. C. and 75 deg. C. and up to 1,000 atmospheres [10] and this physical property now is conveniently available to the designer and engineer.

Recently an excellent piece of work on the compressibility of the common gases has been completed and put into the form of tables, by Dr. E. P. Bartlett. These tables consist of compressibility factors for each temperature and pressure, and the use of the data requires that one know the volume occupied by that particular gas or mixture at 0 deg. C. and 1 atmosphere, and then the factor is applied for the desired condition. This work of Bartlett has permitted Deming and Shupe[11] to develop new values for the constants in the Beatie-Bridgman equation of state for hydrogen and nitrogen. Pickering [12] has corrected the critical constants for the six common gases. During the last few years great improvement and advances have been made in the thermodynamic treatment of chemical equilibria at high pressures. The variation of the ammonia equilibrium constant with pressure [13] has been determined and Gillespie,[14] Keyes,[15] and Beatie [16] have given an equation of mass action for real gases, which agrees very well with the values of the ammonia equilibrium constant determined experimentally.

The molal heat capacities of the common gases have also received attention. Eastman [17] has made a summary of the existing data at ordinary pressure, and has published a table of constants for the calculation of Molal Heat Capacities at constant pressure over a wide temperature range.[18] Equations of state have been used to calculate the change in Cp with pressure. The Bureau of Standards has published a large Mollier diagram for super-saturated ammonia vapor, and Plank and Kuprianoff have extended the data for a similar diagram for carbon dioxide.

The data for the heat conductivity of the common gases have been collected in a table by Curtis [19] and the vapor content of several

---

[10] Michels and Gibson, *Proc. Roy. Soc.*, 134, 288 (1931).

[11] *J. Am. Chem. Soc.*, 53, 843 (1931).

[12] *J. Phys. Chem.*, 28, 97-124 (1924).

[13] Larson-Dodge, *J. Am. Chem. Soc.*, 45 (2918-30), 1923; 46 (367-72), 1924.

[14] Gillespie, *J. Am. Chem. Soc.*, 48, 28 (1926).

[15] Keyes, *J. Am. Chem. Soc.*, 49, 1393 (1927).

[16] Beatie, *Physics Review*, 32, 691 (1928).

[17] Eastman, Bureau of Mines, Tech. Paper No. 445 (1929).

[18] Eastman, Bureau of Mines, Tech. Paper No. 445 (1929).

[19] Curtis, Fixed Nitrogen, p. 264.

compressed gases has been studied by Pollitzer, Strebel, Larson, Black and Bartlett.[20] All this fundamental data makes it easier to design equipment and predict operating conditions for the many reactions carried out at the highest pressures.

III. Catalysis and Catalysts

The commercial advance of high pressure synthesis methods and processes has been absolutely dependent upon the development of suitable catalysts. Not always has the most active catalyst for a reaction been adopted, as the most active catalyst is also the most sensitive toward poisons, and the catalyst of most importance is a compromise between activity and ruggedness.

After forty years of research and fundamental studies the mechanism of contact catalysis is unknown and it is not possible to predict in general what material or compounds should catalyze any given reaction. Catalysts are still developed by experiment and trial and error. To be sure, the amount of work to the desired goal is shortened if done by an able, experienced catalyst student.

There is abundant evidence that the explanation of the mechanism of all contact catalysis lies in the field of absorption and "surface chemistry," but just how little of definite value this statement carries may be realized by the conclusions reached by the Committee on Contact Catalysis [21] which are, briefly:

1. Is catalysis effected by the formation of intermediate compounds, and, if so, what ones?
2. When adsorption takes place on a catalytic surface, what bonds or contra valaces are broken or opened up?

These conclusions leave much to be explained.

Research to solve this question has been extensive, clever and widely distributed over all fields of pure science. The electric arc has been used as a tool in this quest by Kunsman [22] who attempted to apply the conditions existing in the arc, where electrons, positive ions, normal and excited gas molecules, normal and excited atoms, energy transfers, dissociation and combination are all found, to an explanation of catalysis. Compton and Langmuir [23] studied thermal

---

[20] Curtis, Fixed Nitrogen, p. 265-266.

[21] Bancroft, *J. Ind. Eng. Chem.*, 326, 444, 545-642 (1922). A better reference to the present status of our knowledge of contact catalysis is: Frankenburger, *Zeit für Elektrochem, und Angew. Phys. Chem.*, 39, 45 (1933).—Editor.

[22] Curtis, Fixed Nitrogen, p. 92.

[23] Compton and Langmuir, *Rev. Mod. Phys.*, 2, 124 (1930).

ionization, thermionic emission of electrons and ions, photo-electric emission of electrons, chemical emission of electrons and many comparisons of classical kinetic theory with experimental data from several systems.

Chemical reactions favored by the Glow Discharge,[24] activation of gases, particularly of nitrogen by the low pressure corona, and studies of molecular spectra have all been recorded. Decomposition of chemicals on various hot surfaces have contributed kinetic data. Crystal structures of known catalyst molecules have been studied by means of the X-rays, and photo-electric methods have been applied to studies of catalytic action.

In commercial work many types of catalysts are recognized, such as oxidation catalysts and dehydrogenation catalysts; reducing or hydrogenating catalysts. The early art used the noble metals, later it has been found that the same work can be better done by oxides of the base metals. The preferred sulphuric-acid catalyst has changed from metallic platinum to an oxygen containing vanadium compound.* Ammonia is made by pure reduced iron containing small amounts of aluminum and potassium as oxides. Methanol is made from carbon dioxide and hydrogen with an oxide catalyst containing iron as a complex cyanide, while from carbon monoxide and hydrogen high purity methanol is only obtained when using oxide catalysts of copper, zinc and chromium and most carefully excluding iron from the catalyst and also from the materials of the system in contact with the gas. Hydrogenation of edible and soap oils is carried out with metallic nickel reduced from the formate, while hydrogen is added to petroleum oils with the aid of a promoted iron oxide catalyst only partially reduced.

Research on catalysts is taking the form of developing materials for our commercial processes, which are more rugged toward the prevalent impurities in the reacting gases, therefore requiring less costly purification and catalysts which will operate satisfactorily at lower temperatures or pressures.

IV. EQUIPMENT DESIGN

Proper design and construction of high pressure vessels is an art in itself. Every high pressure synthesis process contains both moving machinery, compressors, pumps and moving control devices, and dor-

---

[24] Brewer and Westhaver, *J. Phys. Chem.*, 33, 883 (1929) ; 34, 554 (1930).
* For an interesting account of this controversy see paper by A. P. Thompson and related discussion in *Trans. Am. Inst. Chem. Engrs.* (1931).—EDITOR.

mant reacting vessels. Usually a "unit" will consist of one compressor, piping and small pressure vessels, and one very large reaction chamber. All must be designed to do the work properly and still contain unusual safety factors.

The proper working pressure for any process is that pressure which produces the largest net profits from the product. To determine this is not simple. As the operating pressure is increased, a unit of product may be produced from high pressure apparatus having a smaller volume, and, although not in direct proportion, a lower weight. Since cost is a function of weight, increased pressures result in decreased equipment costs. At the very high pressures more costly alloys must be used, thus losing some of the savings. In moving compressors, the weight, power absorbed, and cost increase as the working pressure increases, but not in direct proportion. The cost of a compressor is roughly proportional to the power absorbed, and power to compress gases increases in proportion to the logarithm of the absolute discharge pressure. The power to compress a unit volume of gas at 1 atmosphere to 250 lb. per sq. in. (17 atmospheres per sq. in.) is about equal to the power required to compress this same volume of gas from 250 lb. per square in. to 4,400 lb. per sq. in. (17 atmospheres to 300 atmospheres). Piping weight, cost and cost of supports decreases with increased pressure, and the same is true of valves. The purely chemical phases of all processes, where a reduction in volume takes place, as between unconverted gas and product, are favored by higher pressures, although the advantage usually is not in direct proportion. At the higher pressures the efficiency of the catalyst to approach equilibrium values decreases somewhat. The net yield of product per unit volume of purified gas supplied is slightly lower at higher working pressures, as gas lost, in leaks and by solubility in liquids to be discharged from the system, is greater. Upkeep and repairs are proportionately greater on moving equipment at higher pressures, and, while more on stationary equipment, they are not in direct proportion to the increased pressure. The total productive time of a plant at 300 atmospheres is appreciably more each year than a plant using 1,000 atmospheres, which has an important rôle in reducing indirect charges against the product.

One is apt to forget such charges as overhead on branch offices in distant cities, on ships, docks and railroad facilities, when selecting a working pressure for a process, but they play an important part by indicating a working pressure, which will give the largest value of product each year from the allowable investment. As an example, one process operates at 1,000 atmospheres and changes catalyst each 18 days. Only three-quarters of a day is required to make the change, because of the relatively small head to be opened and closed, and this plant, therefore, gets 350½ operating days, or 96 per cent load factor. Gas utilization is 78 per cent (not alone due to the operating pressure of 1,000 atmospheres). In a plant using 300 atmospheres, the large catalyst vessel opening requires 2 full days to unmake and close, but it is only necessary to do this once in 2 years, so that this plant enjoys 364 operating days per year, or 99.7 per cent load factor, and at 300 atmospheres the gas utilization is 96 per cent. The increased production of this later plant so favorably affects a large indirect overload as to outweigh the advantages of a lower cost 1,000 atmosphere converter forging, a relatively small part of plant costs.

After selecting the working pressure for the process, the discharge pressure of the compressor is fixed, but there are many other points about a compressor which may be varied with advantage, or otherwise. For a complete discussion of compressors, the reader is referred to J. M. Ford, Compressor Theory and Practice.[25]

When a gas is compressed adiabatically, its temperature rises, and, since there is a limiting temperature beyond which we must not go, the compressing must be interrupted, the gas removed from the cylinder into a cooler and cooled, ordinarily with water, sometimes with air. This is termed one stage of compression. The allowable temperature is governed by such factors as the danger of thermal decomposition of the gas, decomposition of the lubricating oil into products absorbed by or reacting with the synthesis gas, loss of lubricating properties, and the economic amount of power required to compress a unit volume of gas. If one is required to specify compressors for high pressure synthesis frequently, it is convenient to construct a pound-molecule temperature-entropy diagram, with squares between the temperature-entropy lines equal to 50 B.t.u. per square and 12.5 B.t.u. per sq. in. The uses of this chart are many.

In any compressor where the gas passes through several cylinders in series, there are several possible arrangements of the cylinders. The industries favor horizontal machines, although the better oiling and more uniform wearing characteristics of vertical machines are recognized. One of the assemblies used is shown in the sketch Fig. I for a six stage steam or gas engine driven tandem horizontal compressor. This machine has a double acting first stage, com-

---

[25] Published by D. Van Nostrand Co., 1924.

pressing gas both on the forward stroke and on the back stroke. From the first stage the gas passes through a tubular intercooler to the double acting second stage, then through a second tubular intercooler to the third stage, and so on until the discharge of the fifth stage is reached, which has a coiled seamless tube intercooler, and a similar cooler after the sixth stage, this type of cooler being cheaper and mechanically better at high pressures. In this arrangement it is noticed that the gas crosses from one side of the machine *B* to the other side *A* between each stage. This distance is always conveniently greater than the length of any cylinder, and better coincides with the desired length of the intercoolers.

If the first, second and third stages were on side *B* and the fourth, fifth and sixth stages were on side *A*, the interstage coolers could con-

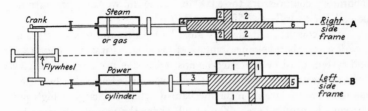

Sketch of Six-Stage Tandem Horizontal Compressor

veniently be only the length of the cylinders. Further, in the arrangement of Fig. I the highest pressures which must be packed against atmosphere are the third and fourth stages, while, in the second arrangement, the fifth stage must be packed to atmospheres. The leakage of gas past the rings from the fifth stage to the first and from the sixth stage to the second, has been found in practice to be slight and causes no trouble. It is easily detected by increase in the lower stage pressures. The pistons may be removed by removing the fifth and sixth cylinders, and these machines are considered easily accessible. The heavy weight of the three piston assembly, supported by a special anti-friction shoe, has proved no disadvantage. The selection of cylinder dimensions, roughly proportional to the decreasing volume of gas to be handled, should be carefully adjusted so that the work done by each side of the frame is equal; and the work done by the pistons going forward is about the same as the work done by the pistons going back. When this is accomplished, the machine is "balanced" and the crank effort diagram is satisfactory. A machine using this arrangement can be driven by a direct connected synchronous motor. A conservative and desirable speed for any large machine is about 100 r.p.m.

A peculiar arrangement is used in some compressors for even the highest pressures, where the final stage is packed to atmosphere, sometimes it is a separate machine, but, in general, it seems best to keep to an arrangement whereby all packing to atmosphere is under as low a differential as possible. Due to the necessity of delivering as pure a gas as possible, these high pressure gas compressors must be lubricated carefully and sparingly; no excess oil may be used. Since the gas passes through the stages in series, most of the oil is carefully and regularly measured to the first stage, and decreasing amounts fed to the succeeding stages. It may be that the fifth and sixth stages will not require oil from the lubricator, but will be sufficiently oiled by the gas from lower stages. Compressors are now built up to capacities of over 16,000 cu. ft. per min. intake, and laboratory compressors for 5,000 lb. per sq. in. working pressure may be had for as little as $550.

After compression, the gas must be led through pipes, valves and reaction vessels involving joints and packing. First, the compressor and system must be protected against excessive pressures, and it was found necessary to develop a special type of safety valve because of the most severe strain on the mechanism when discharging high pressure gas to atmosphere. The metal where the gas passes from high pressure to no pressure must be exceedingly tough to prevent being cut and distorted by the gas. An excellent valve has been described by Ernst [26] and Reed. The guiding theory in the design of high pressure joints, which must occasionally be broken and remade, is to provide that the metal of one part contacts with the metal of the second part by a narrow continuous area—termed "line contact"—as near as possible. This permits of some flexibility in the joint and the possibility of easily developing contact surface pressures several times the working pressure. The use of a lens gasket in such work has been tested by Baxter and the application of line contact cone to cone joints has been described by Ernst, Reed and Edwards [27] together with the design of valves, couplings and insulated electrical lead wires. In high pressure research work, gas pressure is usually regulated by an electrically operated valve, whose contact points are operated by a satisfactory pressure gage.[28] In commercial work, system pressures are adjusted by hand control of the speed of the compressors, by clearance pockets on the compressor, with "by-

---

[26] *Mechanical Engineering,* June, 1926.
[27] *Ind. & Eng. Chemistry,* 17, 775 (1925).
[28] Larson, *J. Ind. & Eng. Chemistry,* 14, 1012 (1922).

passing" of the gas or by slowing up the rate of the reaction until pressure builds up.

The design of reaction vessels has been treated by Curtis and various publications of the workers of the Fixed Nitrogen Research Laboratory. The vessels are forgings, often open at both ends, and usually closed by a bolted-on head, using a completely enclosed gasket, on which pressure in excess of the working pressure is developed by the cover bolts. A complete working drawing of a converter and catalyst basket suitable for ammonia production is shown by Ernst, Reed and Edwards [27] which, with slight modifications and a suitable catalyst, could be used for methanol. A better design provides for the head moving out slightly, against a completely enclosed gasket, held by an external ring, where the gasket pressure is developed by the interior gas working pressure pushing against the entire cross section of the head.[29] This closure, although a little more expensive than a simple bolted-on head, is applicable to a wide variety and size of vessels and remains tight, without tedious sledging of large bolts through a wide range of temperatures.

The wall thickness of pressure vessels required for various pressures may be determined from the formulae of Lame, Clavarino or Bach, all of which are in close agreement.[30] These formulae have been thoroughly proved. Full-sized steel vessels have been fabricated, and tested to destruction, both in the United States and England [31] and the correctness of the formulae proved. The design of flat plates for high pressures, both solid and those having an opening in the center, offer more difficulties. The formula of Fish [32] is recommended for both these cases. This problem is met, not only in the heads of pressure vessels, but also in pipe flanges. Pressure vessel design has been treated by Krase [30] in a very complete manner.

When a vessel operates at about uniform atmospheric temperatures welded steel vessels may be used in place of forgings with satisfactory results if economy is thereby obtained, but forgings are better for high gas pressures at higher, or varying temperatures. When a high pressure vessel is to serve as a scrubbing tower, with the interior wetted with some scrubbing liquid, such as water or oil, it may even be of riveted construction, since small, minute leaks will pass only the scrubbing liquid and not the valuable reaction gases.

29 P. W. Bridgman, *Proc. Am. Acad. Arts & Sciences,* 49, 627.

30 Krase, *Chem. & Met. Eng.,* 37, 540 (1930).

31 Catalog of John Thompson, Ltd., London.

32 Soc. of Mech. Eng. Paper, 1805 (1921).

The "creep" of steels is at present receiving a great deal of attention and, of course, plays an important part in the safe life of a large pressure vessel. At higher temperatures, creep is more serious, and sometimes a policy of regular inspections is used, and the time elapsed when 5 per cent loss of strength takes place is considered half the useful life of the vessel.[33] High pressure piping is assembled in as long lengths as possible and with as few joints as possible. All piping is thoroughly braced to avoid vibration.[34] This is accomplished by skillful bends in the tubing, usually made and fitted on the job. Some engineers most carefully anneal all tubing after bending it, and the completely erected and fully connected plant is given a true pressure test before operation, and preliminary operation consists of a test under working conditions with full gas pressure. The catalyst is prepared for operation during this period.

As most high pressure synthesis processes are conducted at high temperatures, as well as pressures, it becomes necessary to have a safe and yet economical "heater." This equipment has taken two forms. One widely used is a pipe heater, where the pipes are grouped into several parallel paths, joined into a common header. This assembly is then mounted in a furnace where design provides for uniform, even heating and careful temperature control. The heat transfer capacity of the assembly is increased by extended surface on the pipes. The second form of heater is smaller and more compact, using an electrical resistance element, in direct contact with the gas, to raise the gas temperature, recent practice being to build electrical heaters outside of the catalyst vessel and not inside as was formerly done. The space inside the catalyst vessel is too useful for added product capacity, to be occupied with a heating unit which is only used a small portion of the time during starting. If the heater is inside the converter forging, any little trouble from it will shut down this part of the plant. Therefore, both types of heaters are now outside units, and heat is transferred to the reaction catalyst and system by circulation of the heated reaction gases.

Usually it is necessary to pass the reaction gases over the catalyst several times before reaction is completed and, to avoid loss of pressure, the gases are pumped around the system and over the catalyst by a special compressor, or "circulating pump." This is a compressor having a very low compression ratio, for example 4,350 lb.

[33] F. H. Norton, Creep of Steels at High Temperature, McGraw-Hill Book Co., 1929.

[34] C. T. Mitchell, Trans., A.S.M.E., F.S.P., 52-25, p. 167.

intake and 4,500 lb. discharge. In this apparatus it is usually necessary to pack the piston from full working pressure to atmospheric, and certain precautions and aids in the care of this packing have been given by Sommers.[35] Since the compression ratio is so nearly 1 to 1, the work done pushing the piston rod into the gas with the friction of the machine is many times greater than the real work of the pump moving the gas, so that, to balance such a machine, it is better to have a rod and packing to atmosphere on both ends of the cylinder. A generous fly-wheel is always necessary.

V. RESEARCH APPLIED TO HIGH PRESSURE SYNTHESIS

The commercial results obtained in the field of high pressure synthesis in less than three decades has been due to research. This new field of industrial endeavor took research seriously, and it is proper to mention here briefly the research program and comment on the speed and swiftness with which results were obtained. In 1909 the Germans, characteristically, put the entire resources of the Badische company back of Dr. Carl Bosch, whose job it was to build the first Haber plant. The research program touched nearly everything. The well-known water-gas process for preparation of hydrogen, inorganic processes of purifying the gases, the difficult problem of developing catalysts, an enormous amount of work was done on corrosion, selection of metals, development of many new alloys, thousands of new designs of equipment and parts for this unknown high pressure field, and invention and development of most of the meters and instruments used, were some of the problems research solved to the end that the first plant was completed and successful by 1913.

In the United States both private corporations and the Ordnance Office of the War Department, and later the Department of Agriculture of the U. S. Government, carried on wonderfully profitable contributions to high pressure synthesis. The Government program has been carried out in the justly famous Fixed Nitrogen Research Laboratory, now completing its fourteenth year. This laboratory has had most gifted and able directors. The fruits of its mellow years of activity have been of two kinds. First, the technical knowledge, data and designs, which have been made available are unsurpassed by any source in the world; and, furthermore, the skill and ingenuity of its staff have produced contributions to the field of pure science and of practical application, not exceeded by the research efforts of our

---

[35] *Chem. & Met. Eng.*, 37, 575 (1930).

largest corporations. Second, this laboratory has produced technical personnel and executives, young men trained in this difficult field by the distinguished scientists who have directed the laboratory since 1919, who now have passed on to every fixed nitrogen plant in the United States and to some of our leading universities—where the ever-widening research program is being carried forward.[36] Research on the synthesis of methanol from different gaseous combinations has been ably pioneered by the Pittsburgh Station of the Bureau of Mines.

In the background of all the development programs of the United States, constantly watchful, active and helpful in advancing the cause of American chemistry, is the Chemical Foundation. The industries have been aided and encouraged by this worthy organization. Individual high pressure laboratories are now being ably conducted by Yale University, the University of Illinois, and Massachusetts Institute of Technology, and, of course, each of the industrial companies using high pressure synthesis processes, in nitrogen fixation, synthetic methanol, hydrogenation of oils or in the production of synthetic organic chemicals have their own research laboratory and staff. A brief but valuable account of the important contributions to theoretical high pressure synthesis has been given by *Chemical & Metallurgical Engineering,* in a symposium number on High Pressures and Temperatures.[37] There are still many theoretical and many practical problems to be solved.

The results of research by American chemists have placed our country on a footing of independence for fertilizer and explosive nitrogen. The War Department has several years ago definitely stated it has no further interest in Muscle Shoals since the industries are sufficiently and better equipped to supply all our country's needs in times of war, as well as peace. American research has developed a superior technique to handle the work of high pressure synthesis processes. One major company in this field went abroad to purchase foreign rights and the results have not been outstanding. The foreign process was at once made over and improved. A second foreign process had a short and unsuccessful life, ended many years ago. Against this American chemical engineering methods and designs have won important places in many plants abroad.

---

[36] Krase, N. W., *Chem. & Met. Eng.,* Vol. 37, 530-3 (Sept., 1930).
[37] *Chem. & Met. Eng.,* Vol. 37, No. 9, 534-7 (1930).

VI. Commercial Developments

It is not possible in this chapter to describe the plants, processes and products related to high pressure synthesis, and it is not necessary. Complete descriptions can be found in the technical journals. Synthetic ammonia is the youngest branch of an old nitrogen industry. There are, according to some classifications, as many as six distinct types of foreign processes, but regardless of process (all of which have been patterned rather closely on the Haber-Bosch Process, so closely that the differences are, in general, those required because of the different sources for obtaining hydrogen), the steps necessary to produce synthetic ammonia are relatively simple. The developments can be followed by the use of simple diagrams from the published literature.[38]

The development and purification of the hydrogen is still the outstanding feature of cost and extensiveness of plant equipment. The synthesis equipment is obviously a smaller and less expensive part, this being one of the advantages of the use of high pressure synthesis. A German plant, using the standard water gas method of synthesis, has been described by Ellis and others.[39]

Coke oven gas is another important source of hydrogen for high pressure synthesis purposes, and a description of a large plant at Sluiskil in Holland has been given by E. Borelli.[40]

A description of a large synthetic ammonia plant, using water gas hydrogen, in the United States has been given by Tour [41] and of another plant in the United States by *Chemical & Metallurgical Engineering*.[42]

A plant, using coke oven gas as a source of hydrogen, but having special methods of purification, as applied at Ostend, has been described by Pallemaerts.[43]

A plant, using electrolytic hydrogen, operating on a large scale in Canada, has been described by Kirkpatrick.[44]

Natural gas has also been used as a source of hydrogen, but no important articles describing these developments have appeared. The process is much the same as the process using coke oven gas, whereby

---

[38] *Refrigerating Engineering,* January, 1926.
[39] Trans. Am. Inst. Chem. Eng., Vol. 25 (1930).
[40] *Chem. & Met. Eng.,* 39, 126 (1932).
[41] *Chem. & Met. Eng.,* 26, Feb. 8 and 15, 1922, March 1 and 8, 1922.
[42] *Chem. & Met. Eng.,* 37, No. 9 (Sept., 1930).
[43] *Ind. & Eng. Chem.,* p. 22 of 1929.
[44] *Chem. & Met. Eng.,* 38, 626 (1931).

the natural gas is decomposed at high temperatures into hydrogen and, if steam is used during the pyrolysis, oxides of carbon are also obtained, which can be converted into hydrogen with more steam in the usual manner with the usual catalyst, a promoted iron oxide.

Methanol plants have been described by Patart, a distinguished name in the contributions to synthetic methanol.[45] A large and most successful plant operating in the United States has been described by Woodruff [46] and another plant is described by *Chemical & Metallurgical Engineering.*[47]

In addition to synthetic ammonia and synthetic methanol by high pressure synthesis methods, a great deal of capital has been invested in the commercial production of special fuels and lubricants by the process of hydrogenating certain petroleum oils. This work has been extensively developed by large commercial plants in Germany and in the United States. The plant of the Standard Oil Development at Bayway has been described by Haslam and Russell.[48]

The lesser development of other organic compounds by high synthesis methods has been described by Ellis [49] and consists principally of hydrogenated naphthalene producing various compounds valuable as solvents and thinners.

---

[45] *Chimie et Ind.,* 1925, Vol. 13, 179.

[46] *Ind. & Eng. Chem.,* 1927, Vol. 19, 1147.

[47] *Chem. & Met.,* 1927, p. 265.

[48] *Ind. & Eng. Chem.,* Vol. 22, p. 1030 (1930) ; *Ind. & Eng. Chem.,* News Edition, Vol. 10, 16 (Aug., 1932).

[49] Hydrogenation of Organic Substances, D. Van Nostrand.

CHAPTER XII

SOAP AND GLYCERINE INDUSTRIES ADVANCE THEIR TECHNOLOGY

By Martin Hill Ittner
Chief Chemist, Colgate-Palmolive-Peet Co., Jersey City, N. J.

SOAP manufacture is one of the oldest chemical industries while glycerine recovery is a development of only the last hundred years. Advances and improvements in these fields have been so gradual that some people in looking backward have viewed the modern industry almost as one that has always existed. This is not a correct view, however, as improvements have constantly been made and will continue to be made.

Chemical engineering achievements in this field have not been spectacular. This is due to two causes: the gradual improvements that are being made by all the successful manufacturers, and the fact that the business is highly competitive and is protected by a quasi-secrecy more than by patents. The most successful improvements in soap and glycerine manufacture in recent years have not been so much through the discovery of new chemical or mechanical principles, as in the adaptation of useful principles, both new and old, to large scale economical production.

Mutual Dependence. Glycerine production is inextricably tied up with soap manufacture. The cost of one cannot be calculated without reckoning the cost of the other. A superficial view once considered the return from glycerine sales as so much profit. This was undoubtedly true in the case of a few manufacturers who were the first to recover glycerine while the great majority still threw it away in their lyes or left it in their soap, but in these days when no manufacturer can prosper or even hope to survive in the competitive field without recovering his glycerine, soap and glycerine cannot be looked upon independently.

Soap consumers (which include the entire American public) receive better and more uniform value in their soap purchases than in almost any commodity they are forced to buy. This is due to strong competition in the field and to the fact that the return from glycerine recovery is credited toward lowering the cost of soap. During the war, soap-making fats rose to three or four times their pre-war prices and glycerine, which was in great demand as a necessary war material, gradually rose in price until large quantities sold as high as 65 cents a pound. Every manufacturer in buying his fats and oils was forced to credit the expected glycerine return to the cost of his fats, thus enabling him to pay more than he otherwise could, and to price his soap low because of the glycerine credit. No manufacturer could make any considerable amount of glycerine without making and selling a large amount of soap. Supply and demand of fats, glycerine and soap controlled the whole situation and neither the soap-consuming public nor the consumers of glycerine had any cause for complaint. An arbitrary artificial control would have been far less satisfactory from every point of view. It is thus apparent that improvements in either soap or glycerine production have been an aid to the other.

Glycerine Recovery. There has been no replacement of the general methods of glycerine recovery. The chief one of these consists in alkaline saponification and in washing out the glycerine thus formed with the lyes that are used to salt out the soap, resulting in the so-called "soap-lye crude." Another method still largely used employs some type of aqueous saponification which gives an aqueous solution of glycerine practically free of salt and with a relatively small amount of impurities. This latter method of saponification leads to the production of fatty acids and the so-called "saponification crude glycerine." This aqueous saponification is carried out either at atmospheric pressure with boiling water and a catalyzer, as in the Twitchell process, or in autoclaves with steam and water under pressure, in a manner long known but gradually improved upon along with improvements in engineering materials. Most of the stearic acid and candle material is produced in autoclaves.

All modern methods of glycerine refining are prepared to handle either soap-lye crude or saponification crude. An increased amount of chemical engineering technique involving neutralization, precipitation of impurities, filtration and evaporation has gradually been employed to better advantage in preparing these crudes themselves so that the refining process will have a minimum of purification to accomplish, thus lessening the cost, and improving the quality of the final product.

The clarified, chemically treated lyes and glycerine solutions are evaporated to produce the crude glycerine. A great variety of evaporators is employed in this process. Practically all of these employ diminished pressure for the evaporation and some of them have more than one stage of heating.

Refining Methods. Practically all glycerine refining is now accomplished by distillation with steam in stills under diminished pressure. There are several methods which are being or have been used which do not differ greatly from one another. They all depend on the fact that at the temperature that may be obtained with ordinary boiler pressure of about 150 lb. gage pressure, glycerine will volatilize readily, with the aid of open jet steam, under diminished pressure. The rate of distillation is so rapid under these conditions even with a so-called 28-in. vacuum, or at a pressure of two inches of mercury, that it is common practice not to resort to a much better vacuum. The glycerine is condensed in concentrated form in condensers that are cooled by air or hot water. The vacuum is ordinarily obtained by a one or two-stage dry vacuum pump working on the line after a surface condenser which condenses the jet steam and a small percentage of glycerine which has passed through the various glycerine condensers. Steam aspirators in conjunction with water jet condensers have been employed much less generally for this purpose.

No one type of glycerine still has come into general vogue, except that practically all systems in use resort to steam heating, open jet steam and diminished pressure. The systems which have been used the most are those of Van Ruymbeke, Garrigue, Wood, and Scott. Some of these systems have effected greater economy of steam than others, mainly through conservation of the latent heat of much of the steam used. The systems that effect the greatest steam economy sometimes give a product that is less highly refined than that which is made by the use of a little more steam.

Soap Processes. The greatest tonnage of soap is still made by saponifying fats and oils in open pans or "kettles" with alkali and open jet steam. A number of small foreign manufacturers have experimented with alkaline pressure saponification but it is hard to believe that any method of saponification now in regular use can compare either in simplicity, economy, or satisfactory results with alkaline saponification, with steam, in open pans.

Fatty acid distillation has been in more or less regular use for many years as a means of utilizing low grade fats too poor to make good soap by direct saponification methods. Distillation methods have improved in line with general improvements in the industry so as to give better acids and to realize increased economies. Practically all fatty acid distillation now utilizes good vacuum which is employed with open steam.

At times in the past there has been a great preponderance of soft oils over hard fats and for many years soap-makers and candle-makers looked upon the conversion of soft oils into hard fats or soft fatty acids into hard acids as their chief research aim. For a while, following the introduction of hydrogenation, which solved this problem, considerable advantage was derived from the use of hydrogenated oils in soap-making.

This has all changed due to the economic situation. Cottonseed oil, the chief domestic soft oil, has gradually come to be used almost exclusively for edible purposes and is no longer available in any considerable quantity for soap-making either directly or after hydrogenation. Foreign soft oils that were once used for hydrogenation are no longer available as they are charged with an import duty that is practically prohibitive even though they are not competitive with any domestic oil.

Although hydrogenated vegetable oils and hydrogenated whale oil are still used in some edible fats, these hydrogenated oils have certain defects for soap-making purposes that are not so evident in natural fats. Soaps made from hydrogenated fats are very appreciably less soluble than soaps from natural fats so that soaps containing any considerable amount of the former possess decidedly inferior lathering properties.

Fatty Acids From Petroleum. A sketch of this kind would be quite incomplete if it made no mention of the oxidation of petroleum hydrocarbons to obtain acids for soap-making purposes. The scientific literature and the patent literature during the last twenty years have been replete with descriptions of efforts to make commercial soap-making material from petroleum hydrocarbons. There is an element of sameness about all this work. Practically all of it involves (intentionally or unintentionally) a preliminary cracking followed by oxidation at the point of weakness. Some of the operators have oxidized in the presence of alkalies and others in such a way as to get free acids. It is apparent that practically no one has failed to get abundant oxidation. All oxidation of this type is undirected and results not only in the formation of fatty acids but also in many other oxidation products, some of which possess an extremely objectionable odor, while others give very dark and persistent colors. These acids do not yield readily to purification by known methods that are applicable to natural fatty acids.

Chemists have long known that the oxidation of a methyl group to a carboxyl group will give an organic acid. Many instances are known where this has been done in other hydrocarbons. A controlled oxidation of a terminal methyl group in a petroleum hydrocarbon has long been a great desideratum and still is. Natural fats are now very cheap and make good soap and glycerine. It is impossible to predict when satisfactory fatty acids from petroleum hydrocarbons will be able to compete with natural fats. Despite all the progress that has been made such economical production of competitive material still appears to be a matter for the future.

Soap Substitutes. Another type of detersive which is used some as a soap substitute has come into the public eye during the last few years. This group includes sulphates of some alcohols, and certain organic sulphonates and their salts. They have some desirable "wetting" and detersive properties in acid or neutral solution and are claimed to work well in the cleansing of some fabrics where an acid condition is desirable. They are being introduced by rather extravagant propaganda which would lead one (not knowing better) to conclude that soap as we have known it will soon be relegated to the past. The evidence is still lacking that would lead to such a conclusion. Incidentally it may be mentioned that certain sulphates and sulphonates have long been known to possess cleansing properties, notably the Twitchell reagents and the "Kontact" reagent and some of their salts. It is not unlikely that soaps will always be appreciably cheaper than these sulphates and sulphonates. If these latter find additional uses and do their work satisfactorily they will certainly be welcomed into the detersive field. If we assume that they displace any appreciable amount of soap, this cannot help causing some fat to go begging with the result that the cost of fats would drop and soap would become cheaper.

Soap has been a good and satisfactory detergent for hundreds of years. It is hard to believe that we shall now suddenly discover that this fact is not still a fact.

Chemical Engineering Contributors. During the last 25 years a considerable number of members of the Institute have taken and are still taking leading rôles in every phase of the soap and glycerine field. Some of them have been busied mainly in construction of evaporators, stills, and other equipment, some have made notable improvements in processes, and others have guided production. Institute members have occupied and are still occupying important posts with all the larger manufacturers, while others have been independent consultants to the industry.

CHAPTER XIII

CHEMICAL AND ENGINEERING ADVANCES IN THE RUBBER INDUSTRY

By GEORGE OENSLAGER

The B. F. Goodrich Co., Akron, Ohio

ONE OF THE EARLIEST to investigate the commercial possibilities of rubber was Thomas Hancock, who started his work in England in 1820. During several years of study he investigated and rejected latex for commercial use and devised ingenious methods for masticating and calendering crude rubber and for the spreading of rubber solutions—methods which have survived to this day as fundamental processes of the industry. Unfortunately, goods prepared from crude rubber, although they had excellent waterproofing qualities, became soft and tacky in warm weather, causing them to stick together and hold dirt on the surface; in winter they became hard and stiff and unfit for service. These and other shortcomings of rubber were overcome by the process of vulcanization with sulphur discovered by Charles Goodyear in 1839. Without the changes in its properties produced by this treatment rubber could never have attained its present commercial importance. To these two pioneers of the rubber industry the world is indebted for most of the processes commonly used today for the manufacture of rubber goods.

From the time of their discoveries until the beginning of the present century few additional fundamental discoveries were made. The requirements of the growing automobile industry for large numbers of tires, tubes, and other rubber articles presented to manufacturers of rubber goods not only the need of mechanizing their manufacturing operations but also of reducing costs and improving the quality of their products by the discovery and use of new raw materials. Under this stimulus during the past quarter century significant advances in the industry have been made and the scientific processing and use of materials have gradually replaced empirical methods.

CRUDE RUBBER

The first systematic attempt to obtain rubber by cultivation of rubber-bearing trees was made in 1876; in that year the English planted in the Botanical Gardens in Ceylon seedlings grown at Kew Gardens, in England, from seeds which had been obtained by Wickham in Brazil. It was not, however, until the beginning of this century that rubber plantations were developed on a large commercial scale. In 1904, there were 11,000 acres of plantation rubber trees in the Island of Ceylon. The production of rubber under carefully

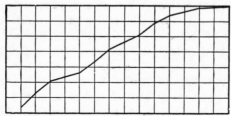

FIG. 1—AREA OF RUBBER PLANTATIONS IN THE
YEARS 1900 TO 1930

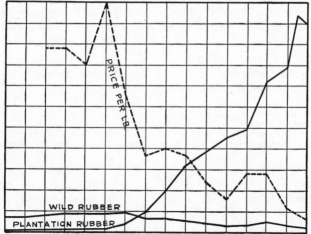

FIG. 2—WORLD'S PRODUCTION, IN TONS, OF WILD AND PLANTATION RUBBER
DURING THE YEARS 1900 TO 1930

regulated conditions proved to be profitable. Hence, until recent times the area brought under cultivation increased rapidly. As a result of the decrease in the cost of rubber from plantations the commercial production of rubber from trees growing wild in the forests of South America and Africa has practically ceased. At the present time about 93 per cent of the world's supply of rubber is obtained from plantations in Malaya, Java, and Sumatra. The development of the plantation industry is illustrated in Figs. 1 and 2.

Scientists in the employ of the English and the Dutch governments at the experimental stations in Kuala Lumpur, Federated Malay States, and in Buitenzorg, Java, have studied intensively the problems involved in the commercial production of rubber, giving special attention in recent years to the subject of plant breeding. Inasmuch as the annual yield of rubber from individual mature trees varies between 3 and 20 lb., it became the custom when starting new plantations to use only seeds selected from trees which had given high yields. About 14 years ago a further advance was made; it was believed that buds taken from trees giving a high yield of rubber would retain these characteristics when grafted upon trees grown from selected seeds. Preliminary studies on a commercial scale have proved this to be true, and many thousands of acres of budded trees have been planted. It is still too early to judge how important will be the effect of planting budded trees. However, the results so far have been most gratifying. The yield of rubber from such trees is claimed to be between 800 and 1,000 lb. per acre per annum, a large increase over the average production of 300 lb. per acre from trees grown from seeds in the usual manner. It is very likely that in the future trees will be grown only from budded stock.

The following data apply to a first class rubber plantation with selected, but not budded, trees:

Trees per acre	80 to 125
Rubber produced per acre per year	400 lb. (181 kg.)
Rubber produced per tree per year	4 lb. (1.81 kg.)
Rubber produced per tree per day	0.17 oz. (5.0 grams)

The number of employees on the plantations of the Far East during normal times is around 800,000, of whom only a few are "whites." Prior to 1930 the cost of bringing a plantation into bearing was approximately 400 U. S. dollars per acre.

Rubber is obtained from the tree in the form of a milk or so-called latex holding in suspension one-third of its weight of rubber dispersed as particles of an average diameter of about two microns. Upon the addition of a dilute solution of acetic or of formic acid, coagulation takes place. The resulting coagulum is squeezed between corrugated iron rolls and at the same time is washed by means of a spray of water. It is thus formed into a rough-surfaced sheet of about one-eighth inch in thickness, containing about 20 per cent of water, and this rubber after drying is known as "pale crepe." The greater part of the plantation rubber, however, is converted into "smoked sheets." In the manufacture of this type the rubber is coagulated in slabs

12 x 24 x 1 in. in dimensions; these slabs are squeezed between rolls for the removal of the serum and free acid. Both of these types of rubber are dried in lofts of simple construction. The sheets are dried and smoked in lofts heated by a slow-burning wood fire for about seven days, and the pale crepe with air under atmospheric conditions for a period of 14 to 21 days.

Probably three-fourths of the rubber as delivered from the plantation is sufficiently clean for immediate use in the manufacture of rubber goods. For special uses, however, such as automobile inner tubes, it is still necessary to wash about one-fourth of the total rubber consumed. Twenty-five years ago it was customary to dry the washed rubber either in lofts or in vacuum dryers; with loft drying under atmospheric conditions, the time varied between 14 and 28 days, depending upon the type of rubber and the humidity and temperature of the air. Later, forced drying in lofts was adopted, that is, the washed sheets of rubber were hung in lofts through which heated, clean air was continuously circulated at a temperature of 120 deg. F. Under these conditions the time of drying was between two and four days. The time required for vacuum drying was between three and four hours with a steam pressure of 10 to 40 lb. per sq. in. in the heating plates. Some 12 years ago a great advance in the drying of rubber was achieved by the adoption of the novel principle of drying in partially humidified air. In the Hunter, and later in the Carrier dryer, in which this principle is embodied, the rubber placed in trays is heated by circulated air automatically maintained at a temperature of 170 deg. F. and a relative humidity of about 33 per cent. The moisture taken up by the air during circulation over the wet rubber is removed by cooling and the air is recirculated after being restored to its original temperature and humidity. The cost of drying rubber by this method is extremely low. A Carrier dryer with a drying chamber 27 x 50 x 8.75 ft. will take care of three charges of washed plantation rubber per day of 24 hrs., or a total weight of approximately 100,000 lb.

The relative cost for drying rubber, smoked sheets for example, is approximately as follows:

Carrier dryer 1.0
Forced dryer 1.8
Vacuum dryer 2.1

It is not to be assumed, however, that because of the lower cost of drying, the Carrier dryer is eliminating the forced dryer and the vacuum dryer. As some of the physical characteristics of crude rubber, principally its plasticity, are influenced by the method of dry-ing, these characteristics will often determine which process shall be used.

For washing rubber the mills used are still essentially of the same design as those of 25 years ago; they consist of two corrugated rolls revolving at different peripheral speeds between which the rubber is squeezed and torn apart in the presence of a spray of water.

ACCELERATORS OF VULCANIZATION

Until 25 years ago the crude rubbers appearing in the world's markets might be divided roughly into two classes: those which cured relatively slowly, and those which cured rapidly when mixed accord-ing to any standard formula containing the usual compounding ingredients such as sulphur, zinc, oxide, litharge, lime, white lead, et cetera. Not only did the one class of rubber cure slowly, but the physical properties developed were relatively inferior. Hence, this type of rubber could be used only in conjunction with higher grades of rubber in the manufacture of goods of high quality, such as pneu-matic tires and inner tubes. The use of this type of rubber, there-fore, was confined largely to the manufacture of belting, hose, bicycle tires, matting, and similar products, where the highest quality was not a matter of great importance. The market value of this type of rub-ber, therefore, was much lower than that of the other type.

Believing that it should be possible to improve the quality of low-grade rubbers upon vulcanization, Marks and Oenslager of the Diamond Rubber Co. made a detailed study of the effect of a great variety of inorganic and organic compounds on the rate of vulcaniza-tion and on the physical properties of vulcanized rubber. It was found that a few inorganic compounds and many organic bases and derivatives thereof when used in a rubber mix even in small quantities not only accelerated the rate of cure but greatly improved the quality of the cured product. They also found that these materials had a similar beneficial effect on high-grade rubbers. This discovery was put into use on a large scale by the Diamond Rubber Co. in 1906, aniline and, shortly afterwards, sulphocarbanilide being the organic materials used. About 1911 the many desirable properties of para-amino-dimethylaniline were discovered by Spence, also of the same rubber company. In the course of a few years knowledge of this work, which had been carried out with great secrecy and great finan-cial profit, gradually spread throughout the industry. These organic compounds, now called organic accelerators of vulcanization, have largely replaced the inorganic accelerators such as lime, magnesia, litharge, and white lead, which were first used by Charles Goodyear.

In 1912, while working on a synthetic rubber Hofmann and Gottlob, of the Bayer Co., in Germany, discovered that not only did piperidine prevent the rapid oxidation of synthetic rubber but greatly improved its quality after vulcanization. On applying this knowledge to natural rubber they concluded after lengthy experimental work that any organic compound having an electrolyte dissociation constant greater than 10^{-8} would have practical value as an accelerator of the vulcanization of rubber. In 1913 they took out a German patent embodying this generalization. A United States patent covering this discovery was declared invalid in our courts in 1928.

Most organic accelerators are either oils or solids melting below 150 deg. C. They are easily incorporated into rubber and are preferably soluble in rubber, non-toxic, and non-staining to the finished product. The amount used is between 0.25 per cent and 2.0 per cent on the weight of the rubber. About 4,000 tons having a value of approximately $3,000,000 are consumed annually throughout the world.

When it was later found that the variation in the rate of cure of different types of plantation rubber was due to a difference in the amount of organic acids, such as stearic, oleic, and linoleic, occurring naturally in the rubber, the beneficial effect of organic accelerators was further increased. As a result of the work of Russell, Spence, Bedford, and Winkelmann, this variability was overcome by adding to the rubber mix stearic acid to the extent of 0.5 to 3.0 per cent of the rubber present. During the past five years stearic acid has been in part replaced by crude lauric acid manufactured from coconut oil.

Fig. 3, comparing the results obtained with rubber and sulphur alone, and rubber and sulphur with the addition of several organic and one inorganic accelerator, indicates the effects of accelerators in increasing the rate of vulcanization and the tensile strength.

Among the hundreds of organic compounds discovered to have an accelerating power, only a few are in common use in the rubber industry throughout the world, as follows:

Mercaptobenzothiazole (Captax); used in large quantities in the rubber industry, especially in the manufacture of pneumatic tires.

Aldehyde amines; poly butyraldehyde aniline is the most widely used accelerator of this type. Others of less importance are aldehyde ammonia, hexamethylenetetramine, heptaldehyde aniline, and tri-ethyl tri-methylene triamine (Trimene Base).

Guanidines; di-orthotolylguanidine and diphenylguanidine.

Tetra methyl thiuram monosulphide (Thionex and Monex), also Tetra methyl thiuram disulphide (Tuads); commonly known as ultra-accelerators, because of their effectiveness at temperatures between 100 and 170 deg. C.; used where very rapid vulcanization at a low temperature is desired.

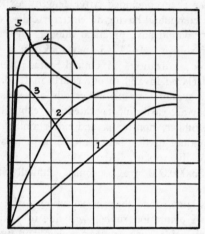

FIG. 3—ULTIMATE TENSILE STRENGTH OF FINE PARA RUBBER VULCANIZED AT 141 DEG. C. DURING VARIOUS PERIODS OF TIME

	1	2	3	4	5
Para rubber	100.0	100.0	100.0	100.0	100.0
Sulphur	10.0	10.0	6.0	6.0	6.0
Diphenylguanidine	—	—	—	0.75	—
Tetra methyl Thiuram disulphide	—	—	—	—	0.125
Zinc oxide	—	10.0	—	10.0	10.0
Litharge	—	—	10.0	—	—
Total	110.0	120.0	116.0	116.75	116.125

By the introduction of organic accelerators material costs and time of vulcanization of rubber goods, especially pneumatic tires and tubes, were greatly decreased, from which it follows that the cost of manufacturing was also greatly decreased; what is more important, however, the quality of the manufactured goods was greatly improved.

AGE RESISTERS IN VULCANIZED RUBBER

As rubber, whether in its crude state or soft vulcanized state, is a chemically unsaturated material, it tends to become hard and brittle on prolonged exposure to air, especially in the presence of light, mainly due to oxidation. To overcome this deterioration, materials known as anti-agers, age resisters, or anti-oxidants are now incorporated into commercial rubber mixtures. During the past few years rubber chemists have given much attention to developing synthetic materials as anti-oxidants for certain specific purposes; these chemicals may be classified as follows:

1. Compounds containing an hydroxyl group bound to an aromatic nucleus; for example, hydroquinone.
2. Compounds containing a primary amino group bound to an aromatic nucleus; for example, 2, 4-diamino toluene.
3. Compounds containing a secondary amino group; for example, phenyl-beta-naphthylamine, diphenylethylenediamine.
4. Aldehyde amine reaction products; for example, aldol-alpha-naphthylamine.

Among the anti-oxidants now commonly used are the following:

Trade Name	Chemical Composition
AgeRite Resin	Aldol-alpha-naphthylamine
AgeRite Powder and Neozone D	Phenyl-beta-naphthylamine
AgeRite White	Di-beta-naphthyl-para-phenylenediamine
Neozone	A mixture of phenyl-alpha-naphthylamine, stearic acid and 2, 4-diaminotoluene
Neozone A	Phenyl-alpha-naphthylamine
BLE	An amine reaction mixture
Resistox	
Stabilite	
VGB	

Most of these materials are either viscous liquids, powders, or resins, easily incorporated into rubber during the mixing operation. The amount required to produce the desired results varies with the nature of the compounding ingredients; it is usually between 0.5 and 2.0 per cent of the weight of the rubber. During the past ten years the use of anti-oxidants, especially in tire treads, has become common practice throughout the world. The amount of these materials used annually probably is about 2,000 tons, having a market value of approximately $2,000,000.

Additional advantages resulting from the use of anti-oxidants are the prevention by certain properly selected anti-oxidants of the development of surface cracking due to repeated flexure, as, for example, in the case of the side wall and tread of a pneumatic tire; also the effective retarding of the perishing of rubber which has been accidentally overcured in manufacture. No commercial anti-oxidant yet discovered, however, will prolong the life of rubber indefinitely.

As the natural aging of rubber goods of good quality is a slow process, sometimes requiring several years to become noticeable, it has been found necessary to develop accelerated aging tests. Two methods of testing are now in common use—one developed by Geer and Evans, and the other by Bierer and Davis. Test strips of rubber are either exposed to constantly renewed air from 7 to 21 days in an oven maintained at 70 deg. C., or are exposed to oxygen at 300 lb. per sq. in. pressure and at a temperature of 50, 60 or 70 deg. C. during a period of 1 to 14 days. The effect upon the rubber of exposure to hot air or to hot compressed oxygen is determined by changes in tensile strength, elongation, tear, and other physical properties. Attempts to correlate these two methods with natural aging, that is, exposure to air at ordinary temperatures in diffused daylight, have been only partially successful; but by properly interpreting the effects of these two rapid methods of aging, the manufacturer can now design compounds which will have prolonged life in service.

The following example shows the beneficial effects of an antioxidant in a typical tire tread.

AGING RESULTS: TIRE TREAD COMPOUND

	Pounds	Pounds
Smoked sheet rubber	55.20	55.20
Sulphur	2.25	2.25
Zinc oxide	15.00	15.00
Carbon black	20.00	20.00
Mineral rubber	5.00	5.00
Palm oil	2.00	2.00
Hexamethylenetetramine	0.55	0.55
Phenyl-beta-naphthylamine	0.00	0.50
	100.00	100.50

	Tensile Strength Lb./Sq. In.	Elongation, Per cent	Tensile Strength Lb./Sq. In.	Elongation, Per cent
Original	4,000	680	3,950	680
Oven Aging				
7 Day	2,300	500	3,000	590
14 Day	1,250	310	2,550	510
Bomb aging				
48 Hour	1,350	460	2,900	590
72 Hour	750	320	2,700	590

COTTON FABRIC

The rubber industry is a large consumer of cotton fabrics; for example, a pneumatic tire contains approximately, by weight, one-third rubber, one-third cotton, and one-third pigments and other materials; garden hose, boots and shoes, and belts contain, respectively, one-third, one-third, and three-fourths their weight of cotton fiber. It is estimated that the rubber industry throughout the world during the year 1930 consumed about 300,000,000 lb. of cotton spun and woven into various types of fabric, which corresponds to 2.5

per cent of the total world crop. Of this cotton approximately two-thirds is used in the construction of pneumatic tires.

Twenty-five years ago tires constructed from woven fabrics were in common use. Cord tires of a superior quality but higher cost began to appear and slowly became an important factor in the industry. With improvements in the methods of manufacturing both the tires and the cord it became possible to produce a cord tire better and cheaper than the fabric tire. The manufacture of the fabric tire has therefore ceased.

Until within the last ten years it was thought throughout the industry that the tensile strength and elongation, which are the more important criteria of the service which a fabric will give, were largely determined by the length of the cotton fiber and it was customary to use in the better grades of goods long-staple fibers, which are much more expensive than those having a short staple. In cords intended for use in pneumatic tires Egyptian and Sea Island cottons were thought to be indispensable. The average length of the cotton fiber from different localities is about as follows:

Sea Island	$1\frac{3}{4}$ in.
Pima	$1\frac{5}{8}$ in.
Egyptian Sakellarides	$1\frac{5}{16}$ in.
Delta Peeler	$1\frac{3}{16}$ in.
Egyptian Uppers	$1\frac{1}{8}$ in.
Texas	1 in.
Upland	$1\frac{5}{16}$ in.

During the past ten years American planters have virtually standardized on a short-staple fiber having an average length of 1 1/16 in., and to a limited extent on so-called Peeler cotton having a length between 1 3/16 in. and 1 1/4 in. During the same period the automobile manufacturer has developed automobiles heavier in weight, with higher powered engines, making it possible to develop higher speeds, which necessitates more powerful brakes, all of which means that the rubber manufacturer has been forced to develop a more sturdy tire, the backbone of which is cotton cord. The cotton manufacturer has met the situation by more careful attention to all the details of manufacture, and by developing new types of construction. With short staple fiber, which was regarded as unsatisfactory ten years ago, it is now possible to secure cord of a superior quality.* The longer life of a pneumatic tire, which is about double what it

---

* During the past ten years the ratio of the ultimate tensile strength of the fibers assembled in cord form to the tensile strength of the individual fibers has increased from 50 to 70 per cent.

was ten years ago, is in part to improved quality of the cords.

The construction of cords now in common use by the tire manufacturers in this country is as follows: about two-thirds of the cord now used in tire manufacture is hawser cord 23's/5/3 (three cords twisted to the left, each of which consists of five plies of No. 23 yarn twisted to the right); the remaining third of the cord is divided between13's/3/3, 15's/3/3, 17's/3/3, and 23's/4/3.

Some of the physical properties of cords are as follows:

Construction	Fiber Length	Tensile Strength at Rupture	Elongation at Rupture
15's/3/3	1 1/32 to 1 1/16 in.	13 to 16 lb.	18 to 22%

The above cord is used in the manufacture of the cheaper grades of tires.

23's/5/3	1 1/16 in.	16 to 18 lb.	21 to 22%

(American short-staple cotton)
    Largely used in the manufacture of tires intended for passenger cars.

23's/5/3	1 3/16 to 1 1/4 in.	19 to 21 lb.	20 to 24%

Long-staple Peeler or Egyptian cotton, largely used in the manufacture of bus and truck tires.

RUBBER COMPOUNDING AND PRODUCT DESIGN

During the last quarter century increased knowledge of raw materials—fabrics, accelerators, age resisters, and the various ingredients utilized in designing compositions to serve specific uses—has served as a basis for the development of better and more attractive products and application of rubber to new uses.

The changes in design of pneumatic tires offer an excellent illustration of how increased knowledge about materials and processing has resulted in improvement in quality and reduction in cost of rubber goods. Development took place along three lines—improvement of the cotton fabric by the use of unwoven cords in place of square-woven fabric, the application of organic accelerators of vulcanization, and the use of carbon black in the tread composition. For many years zinc oxide had been used to secure the best tread wear, but the treads were heavy and their life was not sufficiently long to balance the improved cord construction. The first step in advance in tread compositions came in 1910 when the English Silvertown Co. found that carbon black increased the resistance to abrasion of rubber compounds and introduced it into their treads. The beneficial effects of this material were quickly appreciated and its use extended rapidly throughout the industry. With increased knowledge of the properties of carbon black and increased skill in handling it in various manufacturing processes, larger proportions were introduced into the treads of tires with increasingly beneficial results. Through these improvements in the use of raw materials, the life of tires has probably been trebled and the cost of tire service has been reduced approximately 90 per cent.

INDUSTRIAL USES FOR RUBBER LATEX

During the past 10 years latex has found an increasing commercial application in the manufacture of rubber goods and in other industries, as evidenced by the importation into the United States during the first ten months of 1931 of some 9,000,000 lb. of rubber in latex form.

Latex is imported either in the state as obtained from the tree, with the addition of a preservative such as 0.5 per cent of ammonia water, or in a concentrated form stabilized by soaps or gums. Unconcentrated latex constitutes about three-fourths of the total amount imported into this country. It has been used for some time by the United States Rubber Co. in the manufacture of cord tires by a process developed by Hopkinson. Prior to calendering, a web of cords is covered with an adhering layer of rubber by drawing it through a bath of compounded latex containing pigments, sulphur, and accelerator. The treated web is dried by passage over heated drums.

Concentrated latex is available in several forms: "Revertex," developed by Hauser, prepared at the plantation by partially evaporating in a rotary dryer latex stabilized by the addition of a small amount of soap; a current of hot air is blown through the dryer until the total solids are 75 per cent. "Uterex," as developed by Utermark, prepared at the plantation by removing from latex a portion of the water by means of a special centrifuge, increasing the rubber content of the latex to about 60 per cent. "Lotol," developed by Hopkinson, prepared by the creaming of latex to which has been added between 0.1 and 0.2 per cent of a solution of Irish moss or gum tragacanth. "Vultex," developed by Schidrowitz, a vulcanized latex containing about 50 per cent of rubber.

An increasing variety of rubber goods is now being made from latex using either a dipping process or a process of electrodeposition. In one of the dipping processes a suitable form, sometimes internally heated. is dipped into a latex mixture containing all necessary compounding ingredients. It is then withdrawn and after the evaporation of the water the operation is repeated until the desired thickness of coating is obtained. In another process the form is first dipped into a solution containing metallic salts, preferably of bivalent metals which act as coagulants for rubber. The wet form is then dipped into the compounded latex and is allowed to remain therein for a few minutes. If a still thicker deposit is required, the entire process is repeated without drying the coagulum between dips. The final layer of coagulum, still on the form, is thoroughly dried and vulcanized in open steam or hot air.

The electrodeposition process depends upon the fact that when an electric current is passed through latex the rubber and added particles of pigment, being negatively charged, move toward the anode and are discharged with the formation of a coagulum. In this process water dispersions of pigments and sulphur having a particle size of 0.5 to 2.0 mu are added to the latex and the mixture is then brought to a pH value of 9.5 and a conductivity of 0.0045 to 0.0050 mho. For electrodeposition a current at a density of 0.5 to 1.0 amp. per sq. in. is passed between a zinc anode of the form of the article to be produced and an iron plate cathode through a bath of the latex composition. The current density and time of deposition are chosen according to the thickness of the deposit desired.

The quality of articles prepared by dipping from latex is much superior to that of articles made by the dipping process from rubber cement, the universal procedure of some ten years ago for the manufacture of thin articles of irregular shape. The physical, electrical, and aging properties are superior and the resistance to sterilization by steam is remarkable. A large proportion of household and surgeons' gloves, electricians' gloves, and toy balloons are now produced in this country from latex by the dipping process.

Perhaps the greatest advantage resulting from these processes is the possibility of building up at small expense rubber deposits on a great variety of articles having odd and irregular shapes without the expense and hazard involved in the use of flammable solvents or the high labor cost of hand-covering operations. From compounded latex an adhering deposit of rubber, either soft or hard, can be formed on irregular shaped articles such as plating racks, forming racks, washing trays, fan blades to resist corrosive fumes and abrasive dusts, spinnerette tubes for the rayon industry, perforated metal and screens for wet screening, and a great variety of other industrial equipment.

Separator sheets of hard rubber for use in storage batteries are now being produced in Europe from latex by the Beckman process.

In Great Britain the Dunlop company is manufacturing from latex cellular rubber for use in upholstery, and in this country carpets and fabrics in which the pile is adhered to the backing by means of a latex cement are being manufactured for use in automobiles. Latex is also being used on a large scale in the manufacture of asbestos brake linings for automobiles, as a cementing material in the shoe industry, and as a can sealing material.

MECHANICAL EQUIPMENT

Following the example set by the automobile industry, the rubber industry has adopted mechanical handling of materials and straight-line production as far as possible, also to an increasing extent the use of controlling instruments and recording devices to obtain a greater degree of accuracy and uniformity of semi-manufactured and finished products. Considerable improvement has been made in the type of machinery used in plasticizing, mixing, calendering, and vulcanizing rubber.

As a preliminary to the incorporation of compounding ingredients into rubber it has long been the custom to plasticize the rubber by "working" it on large mills consisting of two cored, internally water-cooled rolls of chilled iron rotating at different peripheral speeds. A slight oxidation of the rubber takes place on the surface, which is being constantly renewed. This process is called mastication. The oxidation causes the rubber to become soft and tacky and suitable to absorb the compounding ingredients more rapidly and thoroughly. For many years typical rolls have been 84 in. long and 24 in. in diameter, and the surface speed ratio of the two rolls between 1 :1.15 and 1 :1.50. The charge of rubber for such a mill is about 220 lb., and the average power required is between 100 and 150 hp.

During the past six years a new type of machine for the mastication of crude rubber, the Gordon plasticator, has been developed by W. A. Gordon, of the Farrel-Birmingham Co. This machine, in the "two-stage" form, consists of two tapered, threaded screws, having a receding pitch, about 20 in. in diameter and about 5 ft. long, operating in water-jacketed cylinders placed horizontally over one another, the upper screw discharging into the lower one. The crude rubber is fed through a hopper into the top cylinder and during its passage between the screw and the cylinder walls, and finally through a plasticizing cone, it is subjected to vigorous working. As a result of the high temperature developed, between 300 and 400 deg. F., a slight oxidation of the rubber takes place, with a consequent increase in plasticity. The rubber is discharged from the lower cylinder in the form of a tube about 7 in. in diameter with a wall thickness of about 1 in. When a greater degree of plasticity is desired the rubber is given a second pass through the plasticator. The capacity of the machine for a single pass is about 7,000 lb. per hour, or seven times that of the conventional 84 in. roll mill; the power required is about 500 hp. By the use of this machine there is a saving in power of about one-third, in floor space about a half, and in labor of about two-thirds. In a new type of Gordon plasticator, a 20 in. straight line machine, there is but one screw with variable pitch surrounded by a jacket. This machine is so massive that a whole bale of rubber weighing about 220 lb. can be forced into the hopper by means of an air-operated plunger.

The incorporation of pigments into rubber is usually effected on mills similar to those used for mastication. During the mixing operation dusts of the various pigments, particularly carbon black, float off into the air, some of the accelerators give off vapors which are objectionable, and there is danger of injury to the workman by being caught between the rolls. Moreover, considerable skill is required to produce batches of material uniformly mixed and uniformly plasticized. To overcome these disadvantages and with the expectation of reducing the cost of mixing, F. H. Banbury, of the Farrel-Birmingham Co., some 12 years ago developed the Banbury mixer, which is gradually replacing roll mills. In this type of mill, blades rotating inside a closed chamber take the place of exposed rolls. In some respects these mixers resemble dough mixers or the Werner and Pfleiderer mixers in common use for handling plastics. In the mixing of a great variety of batches these mills are a complete success, but from batches of certain other types highly sensitive to heat it is essential to omit either the sulphur or accelerator, or both, during mixing, the incorporation of these ingredients taking place subsequently on roll mills. Two of the most important advantages of the Banbury mixer are that the variability of human control is almost completely eliminated, and that each unit has a high capacity, one Banbury mixer of size No. 11 being equivalent to about four 84 in. roll mills in volume of output. By their use the mixing cost is reduced about one-third.

Calenders of today are not much different in essentials from those in use 25 years ago. The principal changes in design have been the increased length and diameter of the rolls, a more precise driving train, and various devices which make it possible to operate at a higher rate of speed and form a sheet having a more uniform gage.

In the interests of uniformity of product and economy of operation, the control of unvulcanized material as to plasticity, gage, and weight, and of the temperatures and speeds of mills and calenders must be carefully observed. The plasticity of the rubber after mastication or mixing may be checked by means of plastometers, such as those developed by Karrer, Marzetti, and Williams. In the calendering operation it is essential that the operator know the temperature of the surface of the calender roll so that he may be able to control it properly, either by means of steam or of cooling water which is passed through the roll. The temperature is indicated by means of a thermocouple in constant contact with the surface of the roll. Variations in thickness or weight of the calendered sheet of rubber or of a frictioned and coated fabric may be indicated continuously at the calender by various instruments. One of these, known as the Verigraph, manufactured by the Atlantic Precision Gauge Co., operates by changes in electrostatic capacity of part of an electrical circuit; another instrument, the Schuster gage, known as a magnetic gage, operates by changes in the reactance in a portion of an electrical circuit. These instruments indicate and record with great accuracy variations from a predetermined standard either in weight or thickness.

A marked change is taking place in the type of heater used in the vulcanization of automobile tires and inner tubes. Until recently, practically all tires have been cured in molds piled 24 to 30 deep on a vertical hydraulic ram located inside a steam chamber. Passenger tires (4 to 6 plies) are cured during 50 to 100 minutes, and heavy duty truck tires (10 to 16 plies) during 2 to 5 hours at temperatures between 260 deg. and 300 deg. F.

By means of vulcanizers developed during the past few years, tires are cured individually in steam heated, cored molds; one half of the mold is stationary, while the other half swings on a hinge. The operation has been made practically automatic. After the tire has been placed in the mold a button or lever is pushed, the mold closes and locks automatically, and steam or hot water at a temperature around 300 deg. F. is circulated in the curing bag inside the tire. The curing operations are controlled by means of an electric timer which operated various valves. At the end of the cure the water is blown out of the bag, the mold opens, and the tire is lifted away from the mold automatically. As the cost of vulcanizing tires in individual vulcanizers is somewhat less than in heaters provided with a hydraulic ram, individual vulcanizers are gradually coming into increased use.

With the development of the modern automobile tire having a large cross section and a small inside diameter, it became necessary that the inner tube conform ·closely to the inside contour of the tire. To accomplish this it was necessary to cure the tube in a circular mold. At the present time, in this country at least, practically all the· inner tubes manufactured are cured in individual vulcanizers similar to those described above. The temperatures of cure used are between 280 deg. and 310 deg. F.; the time of cure is between 5 and 20 minutes.

In recent years continuity of operation has received considerable attention in the rubber industry, especially in the process of vulcanization. The Western Electric Co. at its Point Breeze Works in Baltimore is insulating and vulcanizing rubber-covered wire in a machine operating continuously, using a patented process developed by their own engineers. The wire as received on reels is passed through an insulating head of special design, used in conjunction with a tubing machine supplied with compound through an automatic feeder, also of Western Electric design. The rubber-covered wire passes from the insulating head die directly into a steam chamber 100 ft. long into which is introduced saturated steam at 200 lb. per sq. in. pressure. The insulated vulcanized wire leaves the steam chamber through a seal arrangement which allows the wire to pass out without appreciable loss of steam. In the case of No. 17 wire with a wall thickness of nominal 1/32 in., vulcanization is accomplished in 16 sec. Much higher speeds are used on smaller wires with thinner walls of insulation. High speed cures are made possible by the use of suitable accelerators in the compound.

In certain branches of rubber manufacture it is the practice either to impregnate fabric with a benzol or gasoline solution of rubber or to spread upon the surface of the fabric a thick, doughy solution of rubber to which has been added various compounding ingredients. In the manufacture of such goods the cost of the solvents becomes a matter of vital importance. Accordingly, solvent recovery has been adopted to an increasing extent during the past ten years, especially in Great Britain where large quantities of fabric are surfaced with rubber as a waterproofing material. The solvent is recovered by absorption on activated charcoal or activated carbon. The horizontal spreading machines used for spreading the dough or for impregnating with cement are covered with hoods equipped with glass windows for observation purposes and so constructed as not to interfere seriously with the spreading operation. By means of a fan, air is drawn through the hood at such a rate that the concentration of solvent is about 15 grams per cu. meter of air, well below the combustible proportion of 50 grams per cu. meter of air. It is claimed that by careful operation about 85 per cent of the solvent purchased is available for recovery at the spreading machine and of this, 95 per cent is removed by means of activated carbon.

The recovery of solvent on a large scale is carried out by the Firestone Tire and Rubber Co. at their various plants. The fabric, after warming and partially drying on a series of steam-heated drums, passes through a bath of rubber cement containing approximately 1 lb. of compounded rubber per gallon of gasoline. The impregnated fabric passes from the dipping bath into a chamber maintained at a temperature of 240 deg. F. by means of steam radiators. This chamber is kept filled with inert gas (method of W. K. Lewis), the cement bath itself acting as the front seal of the chamber, functioning like a water seal. At the far end of the apparatus, where the fabric leaves the chamber, two felt-lipped seals prevent the escape of the inert gas.

The gas circulated through this chamber is prepared by the combustion of petroleum coke. This type of fuel is used because of its freedom from sulphur, extremely low ash content, and freedom from clinkering. Prior to introduction into the drying chamber, the flue gas is cooled and washed with water. It contains approximately 18 per cent of carbon dioxide and 1 to 2 per cent of oxygen. In this chamber the solvent evaporates and the resulting mixture, consisting of approximately one-half solvent vapor and one-half flue gas, by volume, is then cooled in a condenser to remove part of the solvent; and finally for the last separation is compressed to 85 lb. pressure per sq. in. in two-stage compressors. The condensate separates into a solvent layer and a water layer. The latter is drawn off and the solvent reused. The flue gas from the recovery system is recirculated. By this process, as developed by Runals and Jones of the Firestone company, an average of 94 per cent of the solvent delivered in cement form is recovered. At the Akron plant there are four complete units with a total maximum capacity of approximately 25,000 gal. of solvent per day. The length of fabric in loop form in process in the evaporation chamber is 75 yd. The processed fabric contains 8 per cent of rubber compound.

New Engineering Uses for Vulcanized Rubber

Although it has long been known that properly vulcanized rubber offers great resistance to corrosion, abrasion, and shock, its use in engineering has not been extensive until recently. This was due to the fact that there were no known methods for making rubber adhere strongly to such engineering materials as iron, steel, or brass. Successful adhesion of rubber to these materials has become possible only during recent years. By the application to the clean and usually roughened surface of the metal, of electrodeposited brass or of thermoprene (an isomeric form of rubber [1]), or of Darex (rubber latex in which haemoglobin has been dissolved), it is now possible to vulcanize rubber integrally with many common metals. The resulting bond between the rubber and the metal is so strong that it is impossible to separate them, either by shear or by direct pull, the rubber tearing in itself without separating at the metal surface.

Among the engineering uses for rubber firmly adhered to a rigid material the following are good examples. Because of its resistance to corrosive effects of commercial hydrochloric acid, 50 per cent sulphuric acid, phosphoric acid, ferric chloride solutions, nickel-plating solutions, zinc chloride solutions, and others, vulcanized rubber is now extensively used for the lining of tank cars up to 8,000 gal. capacity for railway transportation.[2] Some of these linings, after eight years of continuous service, seem to be in as good condition as when originally applied. For use in the chemical industry there are now available tanks, pipes and fittings of various sizes, and steel drums and barrels lined with rubber compounded to resist the corrosive action of a great variety of chemicals. As it is now possible to vulcanize either soft or hard rubber at a temperature around the boiling point of water, equipment of large size and irregular shape can be lined with rubber after it has been placed in a permanent position in the factory. An extreme example is a tank 80 ft. long, 15 ft. wide and 8 ft. deep used in the pickling of steel.

It is common knowledge that because of its great resistance to abrasion the modern tire tread will resist wear on concrete or macadam roads better than the hardest steel. Taking advantage of this property, rubber coatings or linings are now being used extensively in machinery such as screens, sand and gravel chutes, centrifugal pumps, fans and blowers, and mills designed for grinding or

---

[1] Vulcalock process invented by W. C. Geer.

[2] Two hundred and fifty such cars are now in use in the U. S. A.

mixing abrasive materials such as sand, gravel or concrete. An interesting example of this use is a lining [3] for ball and pebble mills for grinding Portland cement, slurry or ceramic materials. Additional advantages of such a lining over the usual silex or steel linings are in the elimination of noise, the destructive effects of vibration, decreased weight, and longer wear. However, rubber linings for ball mills have their limitations; they can be used only in the grinding of materials which are wet and which are free from oils, fats, and organic solvents for rubber, and the grinding must be carried out at a temperature not exceeding 150 deg. F.

Vulcanized rubber when wet with water has a surprisingly low frictional resistance against metal. This fact was ingeniously applied by C. F. Sherwood, a mining engineer, in utilizing rubber successfully as a bearing material for shafts operating with water lubrication, regardless of whether the water is perfectly clear or heavily loaded with clay or gritty material such as sand. Out of his discovery has come the modern "cutless bearing." The most highly developed use for this bearing is for propeller shafts in the marine industry. The shaft revolves in a soft rubber lining the surface of which is grooved longitudinally to permit the formation of a water film between the rubber and the rotating shaft; the lining is adhered on its outer circumference to a shell of brass or bronze, or cast iron or steel, depending on whether the vessel is being operated in salt or fresh water. These bearings are built in sizes varying in dimensions from 1 in. in diameter and 6 in. in length to 15 in. in diameter and 6 ft. in length, the former being intended for use in motor boats and the latter in ocean-going steamers. The revolution of the propellor may vary between 11,000 r.p.m. for bearings of small diameter (used in "Miss England II," a racing motor boat) to around 150 r.p.m. for large diameter bearings. These bearings have been rapidly displacing bearings of lignum vitae blocks, which have long been in common use. It is found that the cutless bearing will outwear the old type of bearing at least six times. Other examples of the use of cutless bearings are in deep well pumps and in water turbines. Bearings for vertical turbine shafts have been used up to $31\frac{1}{2}$ in. in diameter. Successful operation of rubber bearings requires a positive circulation of water at a temperature not exceeding 180 deg. F. and the absence of all oily lubricants.

Because of its great resistance to shock and its high resilience,

[3] Patented by J. J. Denny, of the Nipissing Mining Co., of Canada, and developed by The B. F. Goodrich Co.

rubber is finding increased new uses in the automotive industry. It is now customary on practically all American and most European automobiles to support the motor on mountings consisting of a layer of rubber from ¼ to 1 in. thick integrally attached to metal plates. The rubber is mounted under compression or shear. Further recent new uses for rubber in the body of the car are hose for hydraulic brakes, channel rubber for windshield and windows, windlace tubing, fender-weld tubing, and as a bearing in the shackles. In the modern closed car the amount of compounded rubber used for all purposes, exclusive of tires and tubes, is between 20 and 40 lb.

SUMMARY OF PAST DEVELOPMENTS

During the past 25 years the noteworthy advances in the rubber industry have included the following developments: the replacement of the so-called wild rubbers lacking uniformity in quality with rubber produced in a systematic manner under regulated conditions on plantations; the production of fabrics by improved methods of manufacture from cotton, grown exclusively in the United States, which will meet the extreme requirements of the modern automobile tire; the improvement in tread wear of tires by the introduction of finely divided pigments, such as carbon black; the marked improvement in the physical properties of rubber goods made possible by the use of organic accelerators of vulcanization; the improvement in the resistance to perishing of rubber goods by the use of anti-oxidants; fabrication from latex by methods new to the industry of articles with improved physical properties; general mechanization of production operations with improvement in quality and reduction in costs; and increased use of rubber in engineering developments.

CHAPTER XIV

PAINTS, VARNISHES AND LACQUERS SHOW MANY ADVANCES

By Edward C. Holton,

Chief Chemist, The Sherwin-Williams Co., Cleveland, Ohio

A T A MEETING of the American Society for Testing Materials at Atlantic City in June, 1907, Prof. E. E. Ladd of the Agricultural Experimental Station at Fargo, N. D. (and later a United States Senator), delivered an address on paint legislation in which he championed the North Dakota Pure Paint Law, which had been enacted some two years earlier, and pleaded for similar laws for the nation. This North Dakota law stated that "Paints composed wholly of pure linseed oil, pure carbonate of lead, oxide of zinc, turpentine, Japan drier and pure colors need not be labeled, while all others must be labeled so as to show their true composition."

For many years prior to this time the more important paint manufacturers had maintained chemical laboratories and were constantly studying and standardizing their raw materials and products as well as investigating and developing new materials and new processes. Many exposure tests were under observation and careful records kept. The public, however, knew little or nothing of this and each manufacturer carefully guarded for his own use the greater part of the information thus acquired.

Organized Research.—When the North Dakota law first went into effect many of the smaller paint manufacturers were much disturbed and an attempt was made to have the law declared unconstitutional, but on February 24, 1906, Judge Amidon, of the U. S. District Court, declared it constitutional and valid. This was a challenge to all paint manufacturers either to comply with the law or cease doing business in North Dakota and later in such other states as might follow the example of North Dakota. Many of the paint manufacturers banded together to meet this emergency by forming the Bureau of Promotion and Development of the Paint Manufacturers Association of the United States. On October 21, 1907, R. S. Perry, Director, wrote to Norris B. Gregg, Chairman, as follows:

Dear Sir:

In accordance with your request I give you herewith a report of the scientific work of the Bureau during the past year leading up to the organization of the Scientific Section and an outline of the scope of the work for this section for the future. Originally no scientific work was contemplated in connection therewith. During the past year of 1907 the necessity for scientific aid to the Bureau became apparent and the necessity for this work more and more pressing. The legislative crises brought to the Bureau the *emergency* and the *necessity* of protecting the interest of each member of the Association regarding the materials used in paint manufacture.

This Scientific Section during the last quarter of a century has acted as a clearing house in giving information and advice to the members of the Association, has investigated new materials and processes as they have appeared, has carried on original research and abstracted the published research of others which is of interest to this industry. It has published 54 bulletins, 427 circulars and numerous special circulars and books dealing with the problems of the paint, varnish and lacquer industries.

Through its work on "Preservative Coatings," the American Society for Testing Materials has contributed much to the industry. Many papers have been read at its annual meetings and its committees have conducted laboratory and field tests and have coöperated in the rating of durability tests conducted by others in various parts of the United States. Many specifications for materials and for methods of testing have been adopted as tentative or standard and are in general use by contractors and engineers in charge of both public and private construction.

In the membership of the American Institute of Chemical Engineers are more than 75 who have been actively engaged in forwarding the development of this industry. The Paint, Varnish and Lacquer Division of the American Chemical Society has become very active and much fundamental research is being carried on by its members and reported at its sessions. In the meetings of the Federation of Paint and Varnish Production Clubs, new methods and materials are discussed and the members set up definite problems, commercial, mechanical and chemical, to be studied and reported upon at subsequent sessions.

In the Bureau of Standards at Washington, through the Committee on Paint in the Federal Specifications Board and in other Federal Departments much work has been carried on directed toward improvements in protective coatings and in their specifications. In many of the universities and engineering schools, fundamental studies are being made of the chemical and physical properties of protective coatings and the materials entering into their composition. Chemists, chemical engineers and physicists today are employed in large numbers by the manufacturers of pigments, paint, varnish, lacquer and the raw materials used therein.

Today some of the larger corporations have more scientists on their payrolls than were to be found on the faculties of many of the colleges a few years ago. Those manufacturers who do not maintain their own research laboratories often maintain fellowships in universities so that fundamental research in their particular field may be carried on under most competent supervision. Never before in the history of the world has so much attention been paid to protective and decorative coatings as during the last quarter of a century, nor is this activity limited to the United States. In Germany, England, Holland, France and other countries there is similar activity. As a result of all this, it is only natural that there should be many improvements in the industry.

Paints and Pigments. During the last 25 years very little change has taken place in those paints which are marketed as a dry powder to be mixed with water at the time of application. These usually have casein or glue or some product derived from starch as the binding material. They have decorative value when used inside but are not suited for outside use in this climate.

Paint, in the language of the engineer, is "a mixture of pigment with vehicle, intended to be spread in thin coats for decoration or protection or both." Oil paints are those in which the vehicle consists of drying oils and may be of a pasty consistency, which must be further reduced with vehicle before application, or they may be of a liquid consistency ready for use. Varnish paints and enamels are those in which the vehicle is of the nature of varnish. When lacquer is used as a vehicle for pigment the product is known as pigmented lacquer or simply lacquer.

Many of the pigments in common use today are practically the same as those formerly used. There are a few notable exceptions. Great improvements have been made in lithopone and in zinc sulphide. These now possess greater hiding power, brilliant whiteness and stability to light. For normal inside painting they yield paints which are unsurpassed and when used in some of the vehicles made from the newer synthetic resins, they produce paints which offer promise of outside durability. Up to the present time, however, conservative painters are unwilling to rate them as suitable pigments for use in the conventional type of outside paints.

Titanium white has been known for more than a century but it is only in recent years that it has become an article of commerce through the untiring energy of chemical engineers. This beautiful white pigment, whether in its pure form, as titanium dioxide, or in its combination with the sulphates of barium and calcium (known by the trade names, Titanox B and Titanox C) has become very popular. Owing to its great hiding power and brilliant whiteness its only rivals for use in inside painting are the zinc sulphide pigments. When used in the conventional type of outside paint, titanium white has a tendency to chalk excessively which can be controlled only by the liberal use of other pigments such as carbonate of lead or zinc oxide in combination with it.

Titanium white pigments are the only opaque white pigments which may be considered as completely non-toxic. They may be eaten without serious after-effects and therefore are eminently fitted for use on children's toys and the stanchions in stables and other equipment which may be licked by animals. Titanium pigments are not discolored by hydrogen sulphide and therefore should be used in places wherever white lead paints rapidly darken.

Another white pigment which the chemical engineers have given us is antimony trioxide. This has recently become commercially available but its use is still quite limited.

Among the colored pigments some of the older types have been improved and some new ones have been developed. Oxides of iron, both yellow and red, have been greatly improved. This is also true of carbon black. Lake pigments, made from the brilliant but rather fugitive triphenylmethane dyes, have been greatly improved by the use of phosphotungstic acid and other stabilizing substances. The use of beta-oxynaphtholic acid in lake pigments has given us more nearly light-fast reds and maroons. The Heliofast reds, the Hansa yellows and some of the vat dyes are aiding in extending the line of usable pigments. Ultramarine and prussian blue are still our standard blue pigments, the former unstable in acid and the latter unstable in alkali. There is great need for a blue with the good properties of these but without their weaknesses.

Drying Oils. During the last 25 years chemists and engineers in all lands have been seeking new sources of oil and have found many kinds of seeds which yield oils formerly unknown to commerce. Some of these, along with those obtained from some of the denizens of the sea, are suitable for use in paint, yet linseed oil remains the principal drying oil used in this country.

In its raw state it slowly dries to a solid film, but the drying can be greatly accelerated by the use of catalytic amounts of lead, manganese, cobalt, nickel and some other substances dissolved or suspended in it.

Linseed oil is used in enormous quantities in paints, varnishes and lithographic inks. It also enters into the composition of some of the complex glyceryl phthalate resins. It can be easily refined by treatment with acids and filtration through fuller's earth and bleaching carbon, yielding an oil suitable for use in white paints or it can be given a treatment with alkali, and filtration as above, yielding an excellent varnish oil. It is universally the standard paint and varnish oil to which all others are compared. In certain respects other oils may surpass it, but for all around good properties no other single oil equals it.

Tung oil, the oil obtained from the nuts of the tung trees of China, has become of great importance to our industry during the last 25 years. The greater part of this oil exported from China is used in the United States of America.

Owing to the unsettled conditions in the Orient and the uncertainty of obtaining adequate supplies, it has been thought desirable to cultivate the tung trees in this country. At the present time there are plantings in Florida, Mississippi, Georgia and Louisiana aggregating about 30,000 acres and new plantings are being made at the rate of about 3,000 acres per year.

The early plantings have come into bearing and one commercial plant in Florida expressed 130,000 lb. of oil in 1932. It has been estimated that plantings when 8 years old will yield, under favorable conditions, about three-fourths of a ton of oil per acre. The oil produced from American-grown nuts is proving superior to the average grades imported from China.

Tung oil cannot be universally substituted for linseed oil in the manufacture of paints. In fact, in its raw state it is wholly unfitted for such use, but when processed it becomes an excellent adjuvant to linseed oil. In the manufacture of varnish it has become well nigh indispensable. It also finds use in the manufacture of complex synthetic resins.

Perilla oil is another oil which comes from the Orient, being obtained from the seeds of *Perilla Ocymoides,* a plant which grows somewhat like flax. Very little success has been attained in attempting to grow this plant in the United States. Perilla oil is quite similar to linseed oil in most of its properties and with very little processing can be substituted for it. By some it is considered superior to linseed oil for varnish making. It also finds use in the production of complex synthetic resins.

Soy-bean oil also came from the Orient, although now produced in this country to a limited extent. Manchuria still grows more soy beans than all the other countries in the world. Soy-bean oil is a weak drying or semi-drying oil. Many attempts have been made to produce from it a paint oil which can be used as a perfect substitute for linseed oil. Up to the present time, however, all attempts have failed, and it can be used in paints to only a rather limited extent. It would be a boon to agriculture and the paint industry also if this oil could be economically processed to yield a satisfactory substitute for linseed oil. Soy beans yield good crops in this country and at the same time increase the nitrogen in the soil. The cake obtained by expressing the oil from the beans is a valuable food.

Some marine oils, such as herring or manhaden, find a limited use in outside paints. They usually produce objectionable odors in drying and their films are somewhat soft yet very water repellant.

The estimated consumption of these five drying oils in the United States during 1930 is approximately as follows:

Linseed oil	351 million lb.
Tung oil	87 million lb.
Soy-bean oil	26 million lb.
Manhaden oil	16 million lb.
Perilla oil	9 million lb.

Improved Equipment. Chemical engineers have greatly improved the equipment used in varnish and lacquer making. In addition to kettles, tanks, stills and other equipment made of steel, copper and aluminum, they are now also made of nickel, monel metal and of glass-lined steel. Filter presses and centrifugal clarifiers are more efficient than formerly and varnish plants have been constructed in which the objectionable fumes arising from oil boiling and gum melting are largely condensed and kept from polluting the atmosphere.

Advances in Varnish Making. During the last 25 years there have been some radical changes in varnish making. In the early part of this period varnish makers under the direction of chemists and chemical engineers, developed great skill in the manipulation of tung oil and rosin-glycerol-ester and for the first time in the history of the art succeeded in establishing rosin, colophony, in the form of its ester, as a respected member of the varnish makers family of accredited resins. Petroleum distillate, varnish makers' naphtha, in its improved form, also has become recognized as a legitimate and well nigh indispensable ingredient of varnish and in many instances has entirely displaced spirits of turpentine. Since the War other drastic changes have been taking place and many new forms of synthetic resins are appearing on the market and are displacing natural resins to a considerable extent. These resins are very complex and cannot be described in a few words even in those instances where the chemical composition is thought to be known.

Resins of the general type of the phenol-formaldehyde condensation products, yet modified so as to be compatible with and soluble in varnish oil mixtures, have come into quite general use and are of real value to the industry. This is also true of the glyceryl phthalate types of resin, modified by various fatty acids and glycerides. Paracoumarone resin, made from coal-tar oils, has also established itself. Resins synthesized from urea, from cracked petroleum, from acetylene, from benzol, from the products of fermentation and from other organic sources are all demanding attention and look very promising.

In addition to the petroleum solvents, which chemical engineers have so improved that they are considered as superior to spirits of turpentine in many instances, other solvents used in varnish and lacquer have been improved and new kinds produced. Solvents from coal tar have been improved. Alcohols and esters which were rare or even unknown a few years ago are now obtainable in large quantities and at reasonable prices. Chemical engineers are producing a wide variety of these by synthesis from calcium carbide, from the products of cracking petroleum and from the products of controlled fermentation.

Development of Lacquers. Spirit varnishes, or lacquers, have long been known to industry and the use of nitrocellulose in lacquers is not new. A few years ago, however, there was such a sudden and tremendous increase in the use of nitrocellulose in lacquers that the past was almost forgotten and many thought that lacquer was an entirely new development and that the name should be restricted to those spirit varnishes in which the non-volatile material consisted largely of nitrocellulose.

There were several causes leading to this rapid development. The old-time spirit varnishes, or lacquers, formed by dissolving resins in alcohols and other volatile solvents gave quick drying, lustrous films which usually became brittle soon after becoming thoroughly dry. Solutions of nitrocellulose yielded films which were very thin, had little or no lustre but were quite tough. Combinations of these solutions of resin and nitrocellulose yielded films possessing both toughness and lustre and laid the foundation for the modern lacquer industry. The nitrocellulose used in these early lacquers was usually of the high viscosity type, it was rather costly and required the use of high-priced solvents. Despite these drawbacks lacquers containing nitrocellulose and resins were used quite generally but not in large quantities.

At the close of the World War there were very large stocks of nitrocellulose in the form of smokeless powder and the price was extremely low. By utilizing methods for the conversion of this smokeless powder into lacquer material of low viscosity and at a price below that of ordinary varnish resins the industry was provided with the raw material for a cheap and useful lacquer.

At the same time the demand for automobiles was so great that the factories were overcrowded and trying in every way to speed up production. Pigmented nitrocellulose resin lacquer solved the problem. Easy to spray and quick to dry, this type of finish soon superseded all the older types of auto finishes. This created an unprecedented demand for solvents, which chemical engineers quickly supplied. Lacquers are being constantly improved. With the advent of new solvents, volatile and non-volatile, and the development of many new synthetic resins the lacquer of today is different from that of a very short time ago and the lacquer of the near future will probably be still more improved.

Paint Mixing and Grinding. In order to convert pigment and vehicle into good paint, it is necessary to make use of a mixing or grinding machine so that the pigment particles may be brought into intimate contact with the vehicle and thoroughly dispersed in it. The old buhrstone mill which has been in constant use since the early days of the industry has been slowly yielding to other methods of milling during recent years. Today many types of mills are in use. The modified buhrstone, water cooled and ball bearing, the steel mill of similar type, the edge runner mill or putty chaser, the roller mill with single roll or multiple rolls, the ball mill, the pebble mill, and the so-called colloid mills are all in use.

Some years ago it was customary to mix the pigments with the vehicles and then put the mixture through the mill without regard to the nature of the pigments. Even though the texture of the pigment might be soft or hard, the particles might be fine or coarse, all had the same treatment. In recent years much study has been given to the milling problem and it has been found that those pigments with particles of very small size, as a natural result of their method of production, do not need to be ground. It is only necessary to break up the aggregates and disperse the particles and this can be done better and more economically by mixing to a pasty consistency with suitable vehicles in some type of a kneading machine, subsequently diluting the mix to proper painting consistency by the addition of suitable thinners.

Excellent results are often obtained by mixing the pigment and vehicle to a liquid consistency and passing the mix through a high-speed colloid mill. Today much attention is paid to the particle size of pigments, and when practicable it is considered better and more economical to reduce the particle size before the pigment reaches the paint factory and therefore much less actual grinding is done in the paint mill now than formerly.

Ball mills and pebble mills find their greatest use in making lacquer and varnish or enamel paints which contain much volatile solvent. Since these mills are closed the loss of volatile solvents is reduced to a minimum. On open mills the loss is considerable.

Dryers. Those paints in which the vehicle consists solely of raw drying oils dry very slowly and are rarely used. Some pigments, such as white lead, oxides of iron containing manganese, etc., accelerate the drying of the oil, while lake pigments and others often retard it. The drying of an oil paint may be accelerated by the addition of dryers or it may also be accelerated by raising the temperature of the room in which the drying takes place. Paint dryers are usually compositions containing lead, manganese, cobalt, nickel, iron, or several of these metals in chemical combination with resins or fatty acids or other organic acids dissolved in linseed oil and spirits of turpentine or other paint vehicle. Occasionally dryers are used which are not in solution but are merely suspensions of the oxides or salts of these metals in linseed oil or other paint vehicle.

Oil paints are used principally for outside painting. For inside painting the general custom is to use paints in which the vehicle consists, at least in part, of varnish. These paints often contain much volatile solvent and therefore the drying is due to both evaporation and oxidation. During the last 25 years great improvements have been made in these paints and today any desired effect from extreme flat to high gloss may be obtained by their use.

Paint Application. Brief mention may be made of the methods of applying paint. The old-fashioned manual methods of using brushes of various styles and sizes are still in universal use for general painting both inside and outside of buildings whether on new construction or old. Spray painting is not altogether new but great improvements have been made in the apparatus and today it is very largely used in shop painting where the articles to be painted are placed in spray booths or under ventilating hoods, from which the injurious vapors and spray dust are rapidly removed by suitable ventilating systems.

There is a well-founded prejudice among painters against the use of the spray gun except in shops which are properly equipped for its use. Spray painting on the outside of large structures is frequently engaged in but in all such cases the operator should have his mouth and nostrils protected from spray dust. In shop work, paint is often applied by dipping.

Parts of farm implements, machinery, sheets of metal, metal stampings, tools, and toys are dipped and the dipping tanks are of necessity often large and contain much paint. The paints and varnishes used for dipping are very skillfully prepared. They must have the right consistency, proper rate of flow, cover well, set up in the desired time and dry flat or with lustre as specified. They may be made for drying in the open or the drying time may be greatly hastened by drying in ovens. They must not sag nor curtain, nor wrinkle, unless a wrinkle is desired, and the final film must be hard and elastic. The paint in the tanks must remain in usable condition for long periods of time, new paint being added little by little to replace that which has been used.

Small articles are often painted by rolling in tumbling barrels. Sheets of metal may be painted in roller coating machines. Even in those shops where the greater part of the paint is applied by the more mechanical methods, brushes are still used for touching up, for striping and for lettering.

Great advance has been made in the art of preparing paints to meet the many requirements of industry which become more exacting every year. In order to insure uniformity in these various paints it is necessary to keep a large force of chemists, physicists and technicians constantly employed in testing the raw materials to be used and the final products obtained.

Methods of Testing. During the last quarter of a century many new forms of apparatus and some new methods of testing have been devised. It is well known that sunlight has a destructive action on paint, varnish and lacquer film. For this reason in the testing of protective coatings to determine their durability and probable life it is preferred to expose the test panels in those places where there are many hours of bright sunshine. In the cities of the North, where much of the paint is made, there is often much smoke in the atmosphere; also there are many days of foggy and cloudy weather.

In addition to the exposure tests which the manufacturers are always conducting in the neighborhood of their plants, many are now sending test panels to Florida for exposure in the bright sunshine there. A comparison of the results obtained under local and under Florida conditions gives the manufacturer a much better idea of the probable life of the paint, under normal conditions, than can be obtained by accelerated tests under ultra-violet and sunshine lamps in "weather machines." Various types of the latter have been developed for the purpose of making accelerated tests, but it is difficult to correlate the results obtained with the different machines and those obtained by outside exposures.

It has been found that a white-lead linseed oil paint film exposed to sunlight may have its life considerably prolonged if slightly tinted yellow as in Colonial Yellow. It has also been found that some of the newer synthetic resins yield varnish films which have greater durability when exposed to sunlight than is shown by some of the older types of varnish films.

These facts lead us to the hope that in the future we may have more light stable protective coatings. In the meantime we are faced with a new source of trouble. The use of sunlight, health lamps is rapidly increasing. It is even proposed to introduce these into the general scheme of illumination so that in the home, and office and in the factory we may have the benefit of the health-giving rays of light. These health-giving rays, as now used, will change the colors in our wall papers and tapestries and paints, and they will cause the paint and varnish films to rapidly deteriorate. Perhaps in the future the industry may be able to produce finishes which will be sufficiently resistant to these rays. In the meantime it is hoped that this scheme of illumination may not be installed in our art museums and libraries.

CHAPTER XV

MODERN PLASTICS—A NEW-OLD INDUSTRY

By Archie J. Weith and A. V. H. Mory
Bakelite Corp., Bloomfield, N. J.

THE PLASTIC ART is as old as the potter and his clay, but in recent years certain materials, largely organic and synthetic, which are made plastic by heating or by the aid of a solvent, and which may be molded or pressed directly and rather expeditiously into more or less finished forms, or fabricated by machining from solidified stock materials, have been referred to as "Modern Plastics."[1] They have come into being, or into greatly increased use as plastics, during the period covered by the life of the American Institute of Chemical Engineers.

At the time the Institute was being organized the manufacture of the pyroxylin plastics was an old established industry. But though "Celluloid" had long been a household word and an important plastic material, an increasing need for technical improvement of its manufacturing processes was beginning to be felt. The development of cellulose acetate plastics received a great impetus at about this time through Miles' discovery that by a process of "ripening" the primary acetate could be stabilized and made soluble in an inexpensive solvent. Casein plastics had been on the market abroad under the trade name, Galalith, less than a decade. A time-honored member of the plastics group, shellac, had previously found use in the new electrical industry as molded insulation and was now finding still larger use as the important ingredient of phonograph records. Bituminous plastics, originated abroad, were just being introduced here by Hemming who coined the term "cold-molding" to describe one method of fabricating them.

At about the same time phenol-formaldehyde condensation products were being studied by Baekeland who was first seeking a substitute for shellac, then selling for a dollar or more a pound. When,

---

[1] Rubber, an organic plastic long known and of great industrial importance, presents somewhat different fabrication problems and possesses characteristics all its own. Ordinarily, as in this volume, it is accorded separate consideration.

in 1909, he announced and patented, under the trade mark, Bakelite, a synthetic resin of a new order of industrial usefulness, research in the whole field of synthetic plastics was greatly stimulated. Since then patents have flowed increasingly from all industrial countries. Thus one by one, in addition to the phenolic plastics, have come the aminoplastics, prepared from thiourea-formaldehyde or urea-formaldehyde resin, of which Beetle was the first commercial representative; the alkyd plastics prepared from polybasic acids and polyhydric alcohols, and commercially designated Glyptal plastics; vinyl plastics, prepared from polymerized vinyl esters and marketed as Vinylite; and styrol plastics, prepared from polymerized styrol (aromatic derivative of vinyl), and marketed as Victron—to name a few of the newer plastic materials that have acquired, or give promise of acquiring, industrial importance.

Fabrication of the modern plastics is effected by (1) molding or pressing while in the plastic state induced, in most cases, by heating: or by (2) machining from solidified stock materials which have been formed while in the plastic, or, in some cases, the liquid state. Naturally, procedure varies with the different characteristics of the materials employed. Thus certain of these materials when kept at the temperature of plastic flow remain plastic for a considerable period, or even indefinitely, while others, though first made plastic by heat, quickly set under the heat employed in molding (or pressing) to a hardened mass. The former, the so-called thermoplastic materials, must be solidified by cooling before discharging from the mold. Included are the pyroxylin, cellulose acetate, shellac, vinyl, styrol, and certain bituminous plastics. The latter, the heat-hardening materials, since they solidify at the temperature of molding, may, without distortion, be discharged from the mold while hot. Of this heat-hardening type are the phenolic plastics, and the aminoplastics. The alkyd plastics are on the border line; certain of them harden under heat, but too slowly for ordinary, commercial molding. So also, in a way, are the casein plastics, which after being extruded into rods, and pressed into sheets or other forms, are hardened with formaldehyde to a tough, horn-like mass, which when still slightly moist softens with heat but is no longer free-flowing. The cold-molding bituminous plastics provide the proverbial exception to the rule. They owe their plasticity to the presence of a small amount of a volatile solvent, are stamped into form while cold, and are finished in a high-temperature oven. The final product, however, remains rigid under heat.

Pyroxylin Plastics. Pyroxylin, a low-nitrated cellulose, was successfully plasticized in 1869 by John W. Hyatt assisted by his brother, Isaiah S. Hyatt. Earlier experimenters had employed liquid solvents which were wholly or in part volatile and which on being driven off gave flexible, but non-plastic or poorly plastic final products. Hyatt employed a solid solvent, camphor, in connection with a small amount of alcohol, which was afterward expelled by slow drying, or "curing." The camphor remained to provide a thermoplastic mass. Hyatt was thorough in his work and established an industry that went on with no revolutionary change until the beginning of the period covered by this survey.

John Hyatt is said to have been a man of unusual physical and mental vigor, a man of directness and originality. He was more interested in invention than in industrial exploitation, and at an early date turned over the production of Celluloid to his associates that he might busy himself with his other inventions, probably the best known of which is the Hyatt roller bearing. His brother early engaged abroad in manufacture of their product, Celluloid.

John H. Stevens, associated with the Hyatts from the beginning, carried on as leading technologist. He was known in his day as the dean of the industry. It was Stevens who introduced the wheel for making continuous film, and also the use of amyl acetate as a solvent in the preparation of Celluloid coatings. As these lines are being written, news comes of Stevens' death in his eightieth year, still a consultant to the industry. Later came William G. Lindsey, who contributed much to the art as director of research for the Celluloid Corp.

Writing in the first number of *Plastics* magazine, E. G. Loomis, mechanical engineer, tells how he and Jasper E. Crane, works chemist and later manager of the old Arlington Co. (now duPont Viscoloid Co.) worked together in introducing mechanical handling of materials. They mechanized nitration, acid extraction, and "drowning." They developed alcohol dehydration, a great improvement over the old system of centrifuging, and absorbing residual water with blotting paper. They introduced mechanically driven bladed mixers with provision for solvent recovery, and built a large press for filtering the plastic mass, in the latter case following and improving on German practice.

Later developments of importance were the duPont dipper system, devised during the late War, a marked improvement over the mechanical nitration, acid extraction, and drowning systems mentioned above. There have been many other contributions made by the technicians of the four largest companies now making pyroxylin plastics in this country: Celluloid Corp., duPont Viscoloid Co., Fiberloid Corp., and the Nixon Nitration Works. Apparently, the most important of these developments was that of greatly increasing the stability of the pyroxylin employed. This was brought about by an acid boiling or hydrolysis purification process by which are removed all but insignificant traces of acid and of sulphuric esters, the presence of which contributes greatly to the instability of the nitrated product.[2] Closely identified with this important development were J. F. Walsh and Amerigo F. Caprio of the Celluloid Corp. and V. C. Edwards of the duPont Viscoloid Co.

Pyroxylin plastics are characterized by extreme toughness at ordinary temperatures and a workable plasticity under moderate heat. Any color or shade from "water white" to opaque black may be produced. They have long been employed in the production of toilet articles and novelties. Fabrication is by machining or by hot-pressing, or molding, from sheet, rod, or tube stock. The number of different applications of Celluloid, Pyralin, Viscoloid, Fiberloid, Xylonite—to mention important trade names in the field—is said to have reached 25,000.

Pyroxylin plastics have found their most important industrial application as the material of photographic film and as the middle layer of shatter-proof glass. They tend slowly to discolor with exposure to sunlight, and when the film is used for motion picture projection, or for large-scale X-ray photography, the flammability which characterizes even the modern, relatively stable product becomes a distinct hazard. Search for a more light-stable and less flammable ester of cellulose than the nitrate, led to the development of the acetate.[3]

Cellulose Acetate Plastics. The development of cellulose acetate plastics encountered certain inherent difficulties. As early as 1894 Cross and Bevan patented a process for making the acetate, but the process was slow and gave a product that was soluble in only expensive solvents, mainly chloroform. Also the resulting product was one that rapidly became brittle. What started cellulose acetate plastics on the way to industrial success was the discovery, in 1906, by G. W.

---

[2] J. W. Hyatt, speaking of his first celluloid billiard balls on the occasion of his Perkin medal award, said: "We had a letter from a billard saloon owner in Colorado mentioning this fact" (*i.e.*, that the balls when brought into violent contact would sometimes produce a mild explosion like that of a percussion cap) "and saying he did not care so much about it, but that instantly every man in the room pulled a gun."

[3] From data prepared by Amerigo F. Caprio of the Celluloid Corp., and from other sources.

Miles, an American, that the primary acetate, the so-called triacetate, could be transformed by a simple process of "ripening" into a secondary product of increased stability and of ready solubility in an inexpensive, non-toxic solvent, notably acetone. It remained for the brothers, Camille and Henri Dreyfus, to give the process industrial significance by working out optimum conditions for the employment of the acetylating agents, acetic anhydride, acetic acid, and sulphuric acid. This work, begun in Switzerland in 1911, was given practical application during the War, both here and abroad, in the production of "dope" for airplane wings. The Dreyfus brothers' earlier efforts were in the field of synthetic fiber, but to them appears also to belong most of the credit for the commercial production of cellulose acetate plastics in the form of sheets, films, and molding powders. Cellulose acetate plastics provide non-flammability and greater stability to sunlight, but at the expense of the extreme toughness that characterizes the pyroxylin products. Like the pyroxylin plastics their possibilities by way of color effects are unlimited.

An interesting development is that of a film of the acetate reinforced with wire cloth and commercially known as Vimlite. Millions of feet of this product are said annually to find their way into poultry houses, green houses, and hospitals because of its transparency to ultraviolet light. Cellulose acetate plastics are coming into use in the production of film for X-ray and light photography, and for motion picture projection. Also being more stable to light than the pyroxylin products, they are finding increasing use in the production of shatterproof glass. The Eastman Kodak Co. has been a pioneer in the production of cellulose acetate film. The duPont-Pathe Film Manufacturing Co. and the Agfa Ansco Corp. also have made important contributions.

Casein Plastics. E. E. Childs of Brooklyn, New York, took out a German patent in 1885 covering a process for making plastic masses from milk curd, but apparently did not develop his process commercially. A decade or more later Adolph Spilleler in Germany produced a horn-like product which led to commercial production by an allied German-French company styled the Internationale Galalith Gesellschaft Hoff & Co. Their trade name, Galalith, has stuck to the product with well-nigh generic significance. The principal producer of casein plastics in this country is the American Plastic Corp.

Casein plastic, which is essentially milk curd hardened with formaldehyde, has never achieved large industrial importance. Its defects are a low degree of plasticity and a relatively high water absorption. It is not unlike horn in that it is very tough, burns with difficulty, and softens slightly on heating, but only enough to form the simplest shapes by bending, punching, or pressing. It may be produced in light colors, however, and does not darken with age. It is easily machined or ground into any form desired, and takes an excellent polish. It has been largely employed as a material for buttons and for other uses in which toughness and decorative effects are most important. Although the material itself has not been greatly improved since the beginning, there has been much progress in the method of manufacture. The most important innovation appears to have been the dry process which employs rennet casein, instead of acid casein as in the earlier, wet process. The dry process is said to be shorter and cheaper and to give a tougher product. Improvement in equipment for handling and reduction of costs compares favorably with that in other industries.

Alkyd Plastics. "Alkyd" is a term coined to cover, generically, the products obtained by esterfying polyhydric alcohols and polybasic acids. Such products were first described in 1901 by Watson Smith.[4] Alkyd resins were first developed industrially by the research laboratories of the General Electric Co. and given the trade name, Glyptal.

"Commonly, glycerol and phthalic anhydride are the raw materials employed, but the glycerol is frequently replaced wholly or in part by one or more of the glycols, and the phthalic anhydride by linseed or tung oil or their respective acids, and especially by succinic or adipic acids when flexibility is required."

"These resins are either (1) non-heat-convertible, (2) heat-convertible, or (3) oxygen-convertible, depending upon their composition. The glycol resins are of the non-heat-convertible type, the glycerol of the heat-convertible type, while those combined with drying oils or drying oil acids 'set' also with oxygen."

"The new plastic forms can be extruded, calendered, molded, or shaved down by the standard celluloid sheeting machine. They are finding use in coverings for printing rolls, oil and gasoline resistant hose, gaskets, floor coverings, and for cable insulation."[5]

The largest present use of alkyd resins is in the field of protective coatings.

In the laboratories of the Bakelite Corp. alkyd resin products have been developed as plastic masses to be machined into pencil barrels, and other forms of utility and decoration. More recently there have been developed alkyd dental resins which when hot-molded possess great strength and toughness along with permanent color-

4 *J. Soc. Chem. Ind., 20*, 1075 (1901).

5 Communicated by J. G. E. Wright of the General Electric Research Laboratories.

ings closely approximating those of the oral tissues. A new development is "Permacrome," prepared by superimposing a hardened alkyd plastic onto laminated products. Also the last few years have seen the development of rapid, free-cutting grinding wheels in which alkyd resins of the heat-convertible, i. e., the heat-hardening type, because of their toughness and resiliency, serve effectively as bonding agents. Economical operation is obtained by a rapid rate of cutting with low power consumption.

Vinyl Plastics. The univalent radical, $CH_2 : CH$, of which ethylene is the hydride, is called "vinyl." The double linkage of the vinyl radical ($CH_2:CH$) favors the polymerization of its esters with the formation of resins. These resinous polymers have long been known, but it has remained for the research staff of the Carbide & Carbon Chemicals Corp., under the guidance of George O. Curme, Jr., and J. G. Davidson, to develop certain of them during the past five years into products of commercial value. The practical problems were those of choosing the compounds and the methods and degrees of polymerization that would produce products of greatest value.

The vinyl resins are clear or translucent, and suffer no change in the light so that pure whites which remain colorless and permanent pastel shades may be easily obtained. They are without odor or taste, and are insoluble in alcohols, ethers, or gasoline fractions, but are soluble in ketones, esters and certain chlorhydrocarbons such as ethylene dichloride. Phenol and glacial acetic acid also exert solvent action. They are very inert in their behavior toward chemical agents. A low coefficient of heat-expansion makes possible the molding of large objects without subsequent distortion. They are low in water absorption, and are said to be unattacked by strong alkalis or by strong mineral acids, not excluding chromic acid.

At about 125 deg. C. vinyl resins may be extruded in the form of rods, tubes, or sheets, and stamped into various forms, such as combs or toothbrush handles, or in the case of the tubes, blown in molds to form hollow objects, such as toys, light fixtures, or containers. Being non-flammable, they are expected to enter fields now closed to pyroxylin plastics. They have good electrical properties, including good arc-resistance.

Vinyl resins may be dyed or pigmented and may be molded either pure or with any of the common fillers up to 85 per cent of the weight of the finished object. These materials, like the resins themselves, are truly thermoplastic. Before discharge from the mold, the surface of the molded object must be cooled to 70 deg. C. The resins themselves are inherently tough and require no plasticizing agent. This toughness, along with faithfulness in molding, has brought about the use of vinyl resin in "long playing" sound records, in which the sound grooves are placed closer together than heretofore. It has also made possible a thinner record. The vinyl plastics are new but their properties suggest a broad field of future application.[6]

Styrol Plastics. A vinyl derivative, phenyl ethylene ($C_6H_5 . CH: CH_2$) is called styrol. We are told by Scheiber and Sändig that "the phenyl group adjoining the ethylene linkage increases the

_____
[6] Submitted by J. G. Davidson of Carbide & Carbon Chemicals Corp.

tendency to polymerize to an exceptional degree." The tendency of styrol to polymerize has long been known, but the control of this tendency with the production of polymers of commercial value has been the work, during the past several years, of Willis R. Gibbons, M. G. Shepard, and O. H. Smith of the General Laboratories of the United States Rubber Co. Before their work no method was known by which styrol could be produced at a reasonable cost or by which it could be polymerized so as to give with certainty a resin having valuable physical properties.

The first problem was to make styrol cheaply. Preliminary work pointed to ethyl benzene as the most promising "intermediate," although at the time it was available only in small quantities and was expensive. The problem therefore became first that of producing ethyl benzene cheaply. This was accomplished. For the cheap production of styrol from ethyl benzene various materials were found, sulphur and sulphur compounds in particular, which influenced the dehydrating process favorably, and by the use of these materials, accompanied by rigid temperature control, a method was finally developed which appears to be satisfactory from a practitcal point of view.

Formerly polymerized styrol, long known as "meta styrol," was obtained as a gum, as a strong, tough resin, or as a brittle resin, depending on the molecular weight attained, and this had never been controlled. It was discovered at the General Laboratories that the quality of meta styrol could be controlled satisfactorily by controlling the concentration of styrol in solution and the temperature of polymerization. Further refinements in the method of polymerization were initiated subsequently and it is now possible to produce styrol of uniformly high quality.

Commercial meta styrol has excellent dielectric properties, is exceptionally waterproof and highly resistant to acids, inorganic bases, alcohols and mineral oils. It is soluble in benzene, ethyl acetate, carbon tetrachloride and similar solvents. It is a true thermoplastic and can be molded and remolded indefinitely without changing its physical properties. Due to the fact that the resin itself is colorless it can be colored to any shade. It can be made more flexible by the addition of plasticizers.

Meta styrol is of particular interest in the radio field due to its resistance to high frequency voltage, which increases with increase in frequency, and to its excellent dielectric properties generally. It is particularly adapted for certain other commercial applications due to its unusual resistance to water and chemical reagents. Its acceptance in the plastic field generally appears to be largely dependent upon price.[7]

Shellac. Lac is the secretion of a scale insect. Shellac is lac in "shell" or flake form. Being the most common form, shellac has come to be the common name of the material. As a plastic, shellac is superior to resins of purely vegetable origin. It comes only from India where the world's annual requirement is gathered and prepared by the natives.

Shellac's thermoplastic properties were early recognized and employed to some extent. Large-scale use of shellac as a plastic began in the late nineties when Berliner adopted it as the material best suited for the production of his

[7] Communicated by G. P. F. Smith of the Naugatuck Chemical Co., subsidiary of the United States Rubber Co.

disc phonograph records. About the same time another Edison invention, the incandescent electric lamp and the generating and distributing systems for light and power that sprang from it, were turning for their insulation from porcelain to something less brittle. Hard rubber first served, but with a rise in price, shellac as well as bituminous compositions began to be used in a large way. As insulation, shellac compositions were molded; also coil forms prepared from paper rolls coated with shellac varnish were employed.

Phonograph records were prepared by T. H. MacDonald in 1908 by sandwiching a much cheaper material between two shellac-coated sheets of paper. But for years shellac blended with fine mineral or other filler has been the principal material employed.

The toughness and strength of shellac early led to its use as a bonding agent in grinding wheel manufacture, in lamp basing, and in preparing laminated mica products, but the heat-hardening plastics have replaced shellac in the two first-named and in many other uses calling for high heat-resistance.

We speak of shellac as a thermoplastic material, and so it is for all practical purposes, but its fusion point rises substantially with rising temperature and prolonged heating. Aylsworth and Edison, in 1915, and Daniels and Snell, in 1924, raised the fusion point by chemical treatment.

The most important recent fact in the shellac industry is that the Shellac Importer's Association has established a Shellac Research Bureau. This is under the direction of John C. Olsen, with W. H. Gardner as research fellow. The latter informs us that he has discovered a "variety of new compounds and resins from shellac that show promise of combining many of the properties of synthetic resins and those of shellac." He reminds us, however, that the work is in its infancy and adds that "what may be its development will be the story for the Golden Anniversary issue." [8]

Bituminous Plastics. Under bituminous plastics we should include (following Abraham, in his "Asphalts and Allied Substances") plastic materials prepared from "native bitumens, pyrobitumens, pyrogenous distillates (pyrogenous waxes and tars) and pyrogenous residues (pyrogenous pitches and asphalts)"—in other words, most of the materials we know, both native and pyrogenous, which in their unrefined state are black and thermoplastic.

The plastic use of native bitumen, or asphalt, is very old. Abraham tells us there exists a heraldic device dating back to 2850 B.C., which is cast in an artificial composition of clay and asphalt. Pyrogenous bituminous products, on the other hand, date from the latter part of the seventeenth century and were not made on a large scale until a hundred years later.

Of the utilization of bituminous substances in plastic compositions there is little record in patent literature. Unlike the synthetic resin plastics, each fabricator has always made his own molding materials and has preferred secrecy as his protection. With the probable exception of road building, which would appear to be without the purview of this brief survey, hot-plastic bituminous compositions find their greatest single use in the production of storage battery boxes. Formerly wooden boxes lined with a molded rubber cell were used. Then came a box all of hard rubber. This was later replaced by a much cheaper and equally serviceable box molded from a bituminous mixture

---

[8] From data submitted by W. H. Gardner, Shellac Research Bureau of the Shellac Importers' Association, and from other sources.

the exact comparison of which is best known to the makers. In general such mixtures appear to consist of a bituminous base of suitable flow when hot and of suitable rigidity when cold filled with a siliceous mineral, such as diatomaceous earth, and asbestos or vegetable fiber to give added strength.

Of chief historical interest, though of decreasing industrial importance, are the cold-molded bituminous plastics. These were first made in Germany, under the trade name "Gummon," and were introduced here in 1908 by Emile Hemming. In the cold-molded art asbestos is wet with a solution of the bituminous bonding agent and the solvent, which is volatile, is allowed to evaporate until the mass has attained the consistency desired for cold molding. The pressed forms are baked to drive off the residual solvent and further to harden the bonding agent.

Cold-molded bituminous plastics slightly anti-dated the heat-hardening phenolic plastics, and provided heat-resistant wiring insulation at a low cost. Their main virtues were the cheapness of their materials and production methods; their main weaknesses were inferior strength and appearance. With the lowering in price of the phenolic molding materials, cold molding has been applied to other plastic materials, including the phenolic heat-hardening resins. More recently "specially treated" drying oils have been introduced as binders. But with the shortening of the molding cycle of the hot-molding phenolic plastics, the cost advantage of the cold-molding process was lessened to the point that hot molding heat-hardening materials, mainly phenolic, are supplying the bulk of the insulating parts in use today. The cold-molding process is still employed, however, supplying molded products satisfactory for some uses.[9]

Phenolic Plastics. The year, and almost the month that the A. I. Ch. E. pre-organization "Committee of Six" was sounding out sentiment relative to the advisability of forming a society of chemical engineers, Dr. L. H. Baekeland was applying for his "fifth-mol" and "heat-and-pressure" patents. It was about 35 years earlier that Baeyer had called attention to the resin-forming tendencies of phenol and formaldehyde. The introduction of cheap formaldehyde, about 1891, stimulated commercial interest in the reaction. It was then that Kleeberg discovered the heat-hardening "perversity" of certain of the reaction products. Subsequent experimenters carefully sought to avoid this type of product in favor of fusible, soluble products. None of these "workable" resins, however, displayed properties of industrial interest. Smith in 1899, and Luft in 1902, employing solvents and relatively low hardening temperatures were able to prepare non-porous masses, but thick plates required a period of weeks or months to harden. Story in 1905 dispensed with the use of a solvent, but likewise employed low temperatures and slow hardening.

Baekeland began in 1905 reviewing the work and repeating the experiments of his predecessors. Like Hyatt, he brought to his task much physical and mental vigor. His work was thorough and exhaustive. Unlike Hyatt, he had the advantage of a thorough grounding

---

[9] Aid in preparing the statement on bituminous plastics came from several sources, including L. E. Barringer, of the General Electric Co.; W. F. Lent, of Cutler-Hammer; and E. O. Rhodes, of American Tar Products Co.

in chemistry and the related sciences. His goal was suggested by the failures of his predecessors. As in his work with photographic emulsions, he built his success on what others had sought to avoid. And so it was Kleeberg's porous, unmanageable, worthless mass that challenged his attention. His "fifth-mol" patent gave his answer to the problem of reaction control, while his "heat-and-pressure" patent tells how he turned Smith's, Luft's, and Story's weeks or months into minutes, or at the most, hours.

The main principles established by Baekeland for the practical production of heat-hardening phenolic resins, called by him "resinoids," may be summed up as follows:

1. Bases used as condensing agents direct the chemical action, in a continuous series of reactions, toward the formation of polymerizable and finally infusible and insoluble end products. (One-step process.)

2. A base (ammonia, for instance, which in the presence of the formaldehyde used in the process is equivalent to hexamethylenetetramine and acts as a mild base), permits carrying out the chemical reaction in three stages, which can be controlled: namely, (1) stage "A" which gives a liquid or a brittle resinous solid, still soluble and fusible, but which on further heating is progressively transformed into harder stages; (2) an intermediate stage, "B," in which the resinoid is partially polymerized, and, although infusible, is softened considerably by heat, swells in solvents, and when cold is solid and brittle; (3) a final stage, "C," in which by concurrent use of sufficient heat and pressure during the process of hardening, there is rapidly obtained the resinoid of maximum strength and hardness.

3. Acids used as condensing agents direct the formation of permanently fusible resins of the "shellac substitute" type, called by Baekeland "Novolaks." These fusible phenolic resins may be converted into heat-hardening resins, or resinoids, by addition of methylene-containing substances. (Two-step process.)

4. Judicious incorporation of fibrous substances provides increased resistance to shock in the final, heat-hardened product.

It was at the February, 1909, meeting of the New York Section of the American Chemical Society that Baekeland announced his achievement. That it was noteworthy was everywhere recognized. In fact, it is still accounted one of the outstanding developments of synthetic chemistry. J. W. Aylesworth, who was associated with Thomas Edison, immediately turned his attention to the new product as a promising material for phonograph records. At Kansas University, L. V. Redman, A. J. Weith and F. P. Brock working on a Karpen fellowship to develop a superior furniture varnish, turned their attention to a phenol-methylene reaction, and later to its possibilities in the plastic field. In 1922, after patent litigation favorable to Baekeland, the General Bakelite Co., established in 1910 by Baekeland, the Condensite Co. founded by Aylesworth, and the Redmanol Chemical Products Co. founded by Redman, were merged under the name, Bakelite Corporation.

The amber-like color of the pure resin, its high refractive index and hardness, opened an early use for decorative purposes. Rough-casting the liquid resin, curing, sanding, and polishing was the usual manufacturing procedure. Because of the simplicity of the process, the ease of obtaining pleasing colors and cloudy effects, the casting method has retained its popularity and is in commercial use today.

The first to make use of Baekeland's new molding plastic for electrical purposes was Edward Weston, who employed it in molding small bushings for his electric meters. But the electrical industry as a whole had long been in need of an insulating material having the properties of the new product, most important of which were its strength, its rigidity at temperatures well above normal, its imperviousness to water and to oils, and the accuracy and rapidity with which it could be molded.

For electrical insulation and for structural uses as well, laminated materials have found extensive use. In these, paper coated with a solution of the heat-hardening resin, or fabric similarly prepared, is hardened under pressure in multi-layer thicknesses between steam-heated platens to prepare sheets, or on steam-heated steel mandrel to prepare tubing. From these as stock materials suitable forms are machined or punched. Also simple forms such as trays and gear blanks, are hot-molded from the varnish-treated paper or fabric.

The production and the fabrication of phenolic plastics, in contrast with the plastic materials that have been under discussion, have represented two separate industries. The first to engage in the commercial molding of Bakelite was R. W. Seabury of the Boonton Rubber Co. The first licensees for commercial production of laminated products under the Baekeland patents were the Continental Fiber Co., the Westinghouse Electric and Manufacturing Co., and the General Electric Co.

Development of the industry since Baekeland's original work has represented steady improvement of product and extension of application. In ease and rapidity of molding the industry has made important progress. The early materials stained the hardened steel molds in which they were fashioned. Also the mold formerly had to be cooled before discharge and the molding cycle was ordinarily from 5 to 20 minutes. Today's materials leave the mold bright, are discharged hot, and employ a molding cycle of only a minute or two. With the reduction in fabrication costs incident to such improvements, with cheaper raw materials, and with an active competitive market that came with expiration of basic patents, the field of application has steadily advanced until the uses of the phenolic resins embrace the structural, the mechanical, and the chemical as well as the electrical industries.

The development of materials adapted to special uses has accounted for most of the research effort of these later years. In fact, the industry has become one of "custom made" products in which special requirement is met by special properties in the material. In other words the demands of the trade have exacted special materials for special uses, instead of one standard type of material for all uses. Thus materials have been developed that are flexible; materials that have marked superiority in impact strength, in electrical properties, and in water, alkali, acid, and solvent resistance. One such special material for a special use is a phenolic denture resin which leaves little to be desired in the way of a permanently light color, along with strength, rigidity and low water absorption.

Among the industries signally served is the automotive industry with its silent timing gears and the accurately dimensioned, interchangeable, molded insulating parts of its ignition system which must remain undistorted under the heat of the nearby engine. Also the industry is indebted to the phenolic resin-bonded snagging wheels which, by their higher working rates, greatly lessen labor and power costs in operation.

An important, rapidly growing field of application is that of "air-drying" protective coatings based on the employment of newly developed oil-soluble phenolic resins. But, as with the cotton lacquers, the alkyd coatings, and the phenolic coatings of the baking type, their discussion belongs to another chapter.

Later entrants into the phenolic plastic field include among others Stokes & Smith (Durite), General Plastics Co. (Durez); International Tar & Combustion Co. (Indur); Resinox Corp. (Resinox); Makalot Corp. (Makalot); Haveg Corp. (Haveg).

Aminoplastics. "Aminoplastic" is an adaptation of the term "aminoplast," "coined by Manfred and Obrist to describe the products obtained by reaction of urea or thiourea with formaldehyde." [10] "Urea and thiourea react readily with formaldehyde, and the type of product obtained is determined by the proportion of the reactants, by the temperature and by the hydrogen ion concentration."

"The names of Carl Goldschmidt, Hans John, Fritz Pollak, Kurt Ripper and E. C. Rossiter are associated with the development of the urea plastics in Europe. The objectives of their work were dictated largely by previous expe-

---

[10] Kolloidzeitschrift, *42*, 175 (1927).

rience with phenolic plastics, namely toward adhesives, cast materials, laminating varnish, coating compositions, and molding powders. All of these names except that of Rossiter are German or former Austrian."

"The activities in Europe were directed to cast or glass-like products for which the urea resins are especially adapted, due to their high refractive index and transparency to ultra violet light, as well as to the production of molding powders. Rossiter, associated with British Cyanides, was the first to produce commercial molding powders of the thiourea-urea-formaldehyde type. His production was begun in 1926 and the products were marketed under the trade name 'Beetle.'"

"The urea-formaldehyde condensation products marketed on the Continent were sold under the trade name 'Pollopas, the name being derived from that of the Austrian inventor, Fritz Pollak. World rights to Pollak's processes were acquired by the English syndicate known as Pollopas, Limited, which later licensed the I. G. in Germany and Kuhlmann in France. Both companies now produce urea plastics and market them under the trade name 'Pollopas.'"

"In the United States, Synthetic Plastics Corp., Inc., a subsidiary of American Cyanamid Co., made arrangements with British Cyanides for the acquisition of the Beetle processes and with Pollopas, Limited, for the processes of Pollak. Manufacture of urea molding powders in the United States was started in 1929, the American product also being known as Beetle. Both urea-thiourea and all-urea powders are now being made. In 1931 another manufacturer, the Toledo Synthetic Products Co., placed on the market a urea molding powder developed at the Mellon Institute, the product being known as 'Plaskon.' In 1932 manufacture of a urea molding powder known as 'Unyte' was begun by the Unyte Corp., associated with the American I. G. and with the Ellis-Foster Co., of Montclair, N. J."

"Aqueous solutions of the urea-formaldehyde condensation products may be employed as adhesives. On evaporation a glass-like resin is produced which is capable of being hardened by heat. Mixed with suitable fillers a molding powder is obtained."

"The methods employed by the various manufacturers have not been disclosed, although there is an extensive patent literature. The clear resins (that is, the resins containing no filler), have found some application for the production of decorative objects, but this use has been limited, particularly in America, by their tendency to crack when stored under conditions of low atmospheric humidity. This tendency toward cracking is largely overcome by the addition of fillers, and the largest application of the urea resins is as a constituent of molding powders along the lines originally developed for phenolic plastics. Most of the fillers used with phenolic plastics are available, but in view of the fact that light color is the outstanding feature of the urea plastics, preference is usually given to the best grades of cellulose for this purpose."

"The unfilled urea resin is perfectly clear, transparent and colorless. It is completely fast to light. Its specific gravity is about one-half that of glass. Its hardness on Mohr's scale is just under three. Molding powders made from the resin have as their base color the color of the filler used, since the resin itself has no color. The color of the "natural" powders made by most producers is a pale ivory. This pale base color permits the production of an infinite variety of pastel shades which, together with the high refractive index of the resin, results in molded products of great and permanent beauty. The esthetic appeal is the outstanding characteristic of the urea plastics."

"Although the aminoplastics have found some application in fields formerly served by the phenolic plastics, their principal present and future possibilities appear to lie in fields not heretofore reached by the older plastics. For the production of drinking glasses, table ware, cosmetic containers and the like, the urea plastics have the advantage over ceramic and glass of lightness and relative unbreakability. Their color possibilities and freedom from odor commend them for uses to which the phenolic plastics are not applicable."

"Molding technique is similar to that employed with the phenolic plastics. Molding temperatures are usually lower and curing times correspondingly longer. Production of light colors necessitates special attention to cleanliness."

"Water resistance has been improved with the development of the art and is now nearly, although not quite, equal to that of average phenolic material. Molded objects are not appreciably acted upon by dilute acids or alkalis or by mineral or vegetable oils." [11]

ENGINEERING ASPECTS OF THE PLASTIC ART

For detailed discussion of the engineering problems peculiar to each of the plastics industries neither experience nor information is available. Some of the problems involved in the production of pyroxylin plastics have been disclosed in the literature and were mentioned in our discussion of these plastics. The truly synthetic plastics are rather too new for their processes to have been reviewed in the literature, if we except the patent literature which, so far as actual practice in production is concerned, is any man's grab bag of information and misinformation alike.

Common to all, of course, are problems connected with heat flow which in the case of thermoplastic materials would appear to be rela-- tively simple. Of the two heat-hardening plastics, the phenolic plastics being a couple of decades the older, naturally paved the way. They, in turn, found some equipment already developed by other chemical manufacturers awaiting adoption and adaptation to their special needs. It may be worthy of mention, however, that while a strongly exothermic reaction was not new in the chemical industry, the control of a strongly exothermic reaction whose product tended rapidly to pass into a hard, insoluble, infusible mass was something of a new problem. Control was, of course, obtained through provision for rapid cooling as well as proper heating.

In the operations of dehydrating, blending, rolling, grinding, sifting, conveying, the problem has been largely that of adapting standard equipment to special use.

Molding Practice. While the phenolic plastics found industry, particularly the electrical industry, awaiting a dielectric of their special characteristics they found the fabricator of insulation had much to learn about the handling of a heat-hardening plastic. The shellac molder employed a flash mold with his plastic in sheet form which was kept soft on a steam plate ready for use. As a concession to custom the first phenolic molding materials were made in sheet form. Obviously, there is a limit in time and temperature to the preheating of a heat-hardening plastic. There followed molding-powders and the closed type of mold with a deep chase to hold the bulkier charge.

---

[11] The matter on aminoplastics was communicated by the late G. H. Buchanan of the American Cyanamid Co.

The next step was the use of preformed material, making possible a shallower mold, or a return, if need be, to the flash mold. Early molds, as well as preforming machines, were of the hand type. A big step was that to the automatic preforming machine and the semi-automatic press with a fixed multicavity mold arranged for automatic discharge. Later came the tilting head press which gave better view of the mold interior.

In the efficient molding of heat-hardening materials, as contrasted with those that are thermoplastic, there is, of course, the complicating factor of heat-hardening. In early molding practice, the molder, following the procedure employed with thermoplastic materials, *cooled* the mold before discharge of the molded piece. It was soon recognized that a material that hardened in the heat of molding could be discharged hot. This saved much time but called for a rather fine balancing of conditions. Early molding cycles were from five to twenty minutes; today one to three minutes are sufficient for similar results. Efficient molding practice involves advancing the hardening process in the material to a degree which leaves as small an interval of time as possible between the closing of the mold and the proper hardening of the material of the molded object. This means a nice adjustment of the factors: rate of heat flow; rate of plastic flow; rate of hardening, each influenced by the degree of pre-hardening of the material.

A recent development in the molding of heat-hardening plastics is injection molding, first employed with thermoplastic materials, notably cellulose acetate. In this process the plastic material is fused in a separate container and while hot is injected through one or more small ducts into the unheated mold. In the case of thermoplastic materials this avoids the necessity of alternate heating and cooling of the mold. In the case of heat-hardening plastics injection molding has produced deep, thin-walled forms not easily obtained in standard molding practice.

The fabrication of laminated materials was initially a hand operation of dipping, draining, and drying individual sheets. A continuous process of coating and drying was early introduced. The paper was fed from a roll into long drying ovens making possible better control of the amount of varnish added to the sheet; also better control of speed and temperature which are important in the proper advancing or conditioning of the resin. In modern practice provision is made for first driving off and recovering the major part of the solvent, and then "conditioning" the coated (or impregnated) sheets.

The first presses were hand-loaded and had one or two openings. Polished copper plates that required frequent buffing were employed between the steam-heated platens and the material. Modern large-scale practice employs mechanically loaded hydraulic presses, having as high as a dozen openings. The polished copper plates are now chromium-plated, or are of stainless steel, with or without chromium plating. Laminated sheets formerly limited to those 3 ft. square, are now made 10 ft. long, and 4 ft. wide.

In early practice desired forms were machined from sheet stock. Later many forms were produced by punching. Early punching stock was of low resin content and had to be heated before punching. Today "cold-punching" stocks are available which though high in resin content may be punched or sheared without heating.

Comparisons

Detailed discussion of the relative values for specific uses which characterize the modern plastic materials would call for more space than is available, and for disinterested opinion, if in fact such could be found. It will not be attempted here. A little non-controversial information on the subject will be volunteered, however, as of general interest.

As previously stated, one important difference in these materials is in their behavior under heat. This is of importance in two ways. It not only influences the technique in molding but it determines availability for specific uses, notably such as demand non-deformation under load at ordinary temperatures, and at temperatures well above normal. The two are generally related. Thus "cold-flow" under pressure characterizes thermoplastic materials, generally, not excluding hard rubber, whereas absence of cold-flow and relatively high rigidity at temperatures above normal characterize the heat-hardening type of plastics, and the "cold-molded," after-baked materials. On the other hand, there are many uses in which this property is of little or no importance as compared with that of a light and stable color. With light color as the criterion of major importance the bituminous plastics drop out immediately, as do also the shellac plastics, while the phenolic plastics, though now made in relatively light and stable colors, are not the equal in this respect, of some of the thermoplastic materials, or of the aminoplastics.

Resistance to deformation along with pronounced strength and chemical inertness have long given the phenolic plastics preferment in uses that may be styled industrial. Here, the matter of a light color is of secondary importance. The aminoplastics, on the other hand, are rapidly entering a field in which with adequate toughness and inertness, color is the determining factor. They are finding increasing use in the production of table ware and decorative structural materials. Much the same may be said of the light colored thermoplastics, each according as its other characteristics fit the use intended.

A multitude of uses have developed for pyroxylin plastics in spite of their handicap of flammability, their ease of deformation under heat, and their tendency to cold-flow. The cellulose acetate products having overcome the infirmity of flammability are coming rapidly to the front in spite of their lower resistance to shock and their equal deficiency in the other respects named. The vinyl plastics claim to superiority is based on their extreme inertness, toughness, and good molding qualities as evidenced by their utilization in sound record production. The styrol plastics stand out, in their extreme resistance to water absorption and exceptional "low loss" with high frequency currents. Casein products make their bid for favor through their toughness, fine color effects and ease of fabrication in spite of their high water absorption and poor molding qualities. Shellac, because of its toughness and fine molding qualities, still enjoys a large tonnage demand; this, in spite of its dark color, its easy deformation under heat, and its cold-flow. Cold-molded bituminous products held their own for some years because of their high heat-resistance, and their low price, though possessing low strength, poor surface and dark color. For a time phenolic resins were added to improve their strength and appearance, and, as stated, we now have improved cold-molded products employing specially treated drying oils as bonding agents. Hot-molded bituminous plastics enjoy a very large tonnage in a use in which strength, low water absorption, resistance to acids, notably sulphuric acid, and a low cost are the determining factors. We are little concerned about the color of our storage battery jars.

The matter of fabrication technique also is involved. Generally speaking, the method of machining from cast forms is expensive when many like forms are to be produced. On the other hand, molding involves large mold costs, which must be absorbed by large production. When the element of exact duplication also enters, molding has the advantage over machining in both cost and accuracy. When, as is often the case, metallic inserts are required, labor saving is generally still further increased. Again, to the extent that wastage may occur in molding, as in the case of "flash" molding, advantage plainly lies with the thermoplastic materials since they may be softened and remolded at will.

But advantages and disadvantages in technique must all be expressible in terms of cost and character of finished product, and these in terms of the character of use intended. Advantage will be found now with one, now with another material. Otherwise, they would not all be with us, successfully competing for opportunity to serve in these highly competitive, changing times. Some will advance while others recede, only to have conditions further change as research brings about important improvements, or entirely new products of superior properties.[12]

WHAT OF THE FUTURE?

The trend of the times is toward increasing utilization of modern plastic materials. They have come in answer to the needs of modern methods of manufacture in which the rapid production of many, like forms, employing materials suited to exacting conditions of use, is the growing requirement. It would appear that we are only just entering this "plastic age."

The extent to which modern plastics already serve other industries is perhaps not generally realized. Thus far they have advanced on merit in the face of high costs. The automobile, as an important instance, was built on rubber, which thereby has become so important that it has a chapter in this volume all to itself. The same automobile owes the trouble-free operation of its ignition system to phenolic plastics. Its timing train is made noiseless in its operation with the aid of phenolic resin as bonding agent. It is free from the dangers of splintering glass, thanks to cellulose plastics. Bituminous plastics play their humble, efficient part in its storage of electric energy. Interior body parts of utility and ornament are provided by both phenolic plastics and aminoplastics.

In what direction future progress will be made, we can only surmise from present needs and trends. Lower cost is the important present need. Cheaper raw materials, cheaper production methods will come. We may expect research to provide these along with new products and improvement of the old. Continuous methods may be looked for in production as well as in fabrication. With reduced cost will come increased use. The trend is toward structural uses, which means tons instead of pounds.

---

[12] A case in point may be provided by benzyl cellulose, an ether of cellulose, for which much is being claimed by way of stability and other characteristics.

Price alone keeps our modern plastics from being employed in ways now less well served by materials evolved by nature for other uses. The grain of wood better serves a tree than a table top, a chair, or a clock case. Yet we carry over the weakness of the natural material in our design of plastic materials which do not possess this weakness. A big step forward will be made when we stop thinking of modern plastic materials as substitutes for something time-honored but different, and base design on a true concept of the inherent characteristics of the newer materials. Research will bring new plastics into the field and new types of the old, but a widespread extension of the use of the materials now available will come with growth in knowledge of their characteristics and application possibilities.

CHAPTER XVI

SOME PHASES OF PROGRESS IN VEGETABLE OIL PRODUCTION

By DAVID WESSON

Technical Advisor, Southern Cotton Oil Co., Montclair, N. J.

ACCORDING to Report to Congress No. 41, by the United States Tariff Commission, on certain vegetable oils, the total production of oils from domestic materials in 1930 was 2,124,850 thousands of pounds listed as follows:

Material	Thousands of Pounds of Oil	Percentage of Total
Cottonseed	1,616,084	75
Corn	120,747	5.7
Peanut	26,495	1.3
Soya bean	14,387	.66
Edible olive oil	2,184	.1
Linseed	345,463	17.8

In addition the following production was obtained from imported materials representing about 25 per cent of the total vegetable oil production: Coconut, 375,063,000 lb.; linseed, 223,547,000 lb.; castor, 43,241,000 lb., and sesame, 25,605,000 lb. Taking the combined totals it will be noted that 52 per cent of all the vegetable oils produced in this country, came from the cottonseed, which we might say, is the national oil-bearing material in the United States.

A student of the history of this industry will find almost as many places where the first cottonseed oil press was started as there are cities in Greece which are said to be the birthplace of Homer. The first mill, according to some claims, was erected at Charleston, S. C., in 1826. Another was claimed to have been erected at Raleigh, N. C. at about the same time. It was well established, however, that Dr. Benjamin Waring, of Columbia, S. C., built a mill there in 1826, which turned out an oil suitable for paints and for burning in lamps. About 1832 another mill was erected in Savannah, Ga., and one was established at Natchez, Miss., around 1854. Several mills were started in New Orleans in 1850, at which time refineries were also established. It was not until after the Civil War, however, that the industry attained comparatively large size.

The methods in use at the beginning were crude as compared with those of today. The oil mills took the seed as they came from the gin, chopped them up in hullers, separated the meats from the hulls by screens, and cooked the meats in steam jacketed kettles. After this they were pressed in box presses with camels' hair mats instead of in the plate presses of the present day. These old presses allowed from 8 to 12 per cent or even more of oil to remain in the cake. The separation of the hulls from the meats was crude, a great deal of the meats being left in the hulls, which were burned under the boilers to furnish steam for operating the mill. A ton of hulls was worth about a half ton of coal in those days. The ashes from the hulls were sold for fertilizer on the basis of their potash and phosphoric-acid contents.

It was about 1885 that the oil millers became aware that they were burning up a great deal of cotton which adhered to the hulls. Accordingly special gins, known as linters, were introduced in the mills, to save this short staple cotton adhering to the seed, as it left the ordinary cotton gins. The first linters saved from 20 to 25 lb. of lint per ton of seed, which was considered very satisfactory. At present, the production is about 100 lb. per ton.

About this time, a hungry cow called attention to the fact that the hulls which were being burned under the boilers, containing as they did 3 to 5 per cent of meats, were valuable as fodder. Chemical analysis showed that the hulls had about the same nutritive value as low-grade hay, and ever since that time, they have been a source of income to the oil mills.

EARLY REFINING METHODS

The crude oil, as it left the mills, was claret colored, and not suitable for edible purposes. It is believed that Jules Aldige, who owned one of the first mills in New Orleans, brought from France the process of treating the oil with caustic soda. His refinery consisted of a number of cylindrical tanks provided with vertical shafts, on which were large paddles. These were worked by means of suitable gearing to agitate the oil. The caustic soda was mixed in old sugar caldrons placed on the floor above the tanks and the strength tested by rubbing the oil between the thumb and finger. It was then run into the oil where it was mixed by the agitating gears. When, in the judgment of the refiner, sufficient alkali had been added, the machinery was stopped and the soap stock allowed to settle to the flat bottom of the kettle. Needless to say, it was practically impossible to make a clean separation of the oil from the soap stock and the latter always carried off a large excess of entrained oil.

The Union Oil Co. shortly after this time, put up rectangular kettles with semi-cylindrical bottoms. Horizontal shafts with paddles, working like steam boat wheels were used for mixing, and the oil was settled in a manner similar to that used in the Aldige refinery.

The refinery losses were out of all proportion to the amount of impurities necessary to be removed from the oil. It was not until 1887 that more rational methods of refining the crude oil were adopted. Laboratory samples were tested to determine the acidity and the amount of caustic soda needed to remove it, and also cup refinings were made to determine the amount of alkali needed to dissolve out the coloring matter and other impurities in the oil.

Improvements were made in the shape of the refining kettles, and in the methods of heating and drawing off the oil and soap stock. Tanks with accurate gages for measuring the amount of caustic soda used in the refining were set up. With the exception of certain refinements for the determination of the proper amount of alkali to be used and its proper strength, the basis of refining of crude cottonseed oil has remained unchanged for the last fifty years.

Strange as it may seem, the direct growth of the cottonseed oil industry in this country can be directly traced to the American hog. Coincident with the growth of the middle western states, enormous quantities of pork and lard were produced. The lard was sold all over this country and abroad. Next to butter it became the principal edible fat of the world. As the population increased, American lard became more and more in demand, and working on the theory that "blessed is the man that makes two barrels of lard where there was but one before," American manufacturers, starting in Chicago, looked about for a means of increasing their output, regardless of the hog production in this country. It was found that edible tallow, mixed judiciously with lard, could be used to the advantage of the manufacturer. Too much edible tallow made the lard too hard, and in order to secure the right consistency of the lard, a soft oil was needed to combine with it. Cottonseed oil was found to answer this purpose, and pure refined family lard became a Chicago product. The chief objections to the use of cottonseed oil, which was much cheaper than lard, were its flavor and yellow color. It was found that by heating the oil and mixing it with a small quantity of fuller's earth, most of this color would be absorbed by the earth, which could then be removed, either by settling the oil in tanks and squeezing out the earth by means of presses, or, better yet, by pumping the oil with the suspended earth, through filter presses. This filtered oil was of practically the same color as melted lard, and could be used to the extent of about 30 per cent in the mixture.

About 1885, the oleomargarine industry was started in Chicago, with the result that large quantities of pressed edible tallow, known to the trade as oleosterine, were made available for mixing with lard. Oleosterine, having a melting point around 52 deg. C. needed a soft fat to bring it to lard consistency, and cottonseed oil was found an ideal material from both the physical and commercial standpoints. The use of oleosterine greatly stimulated the use of cottonseed oil in lard, with the result that Congress held an investigation, resulting in all such mixtures being branded "compound lard." This gave legal status to material which previously had been nothing but an adulteration and the result was the greatly increased use of cottonseed oil. Unfortunately, cottonseed oil which had only been treated with caustic soda and then bleached with fuller's earth, had a somewhat disagreeable flavor, and did not produce as good lard as that obtained from the hog. About 1893 it was discovered that if cottonseed oil were heated to a high temperature and steam were blown through it for several hours, the bad flavor of the lard could be removed. When the oil, so treated, had been mixed with oleosterine, a very superior product was obtained, so it became quite unnecessary to add any lard to the mixture, which continued to be sold, however, as "compound lard."

This, of course, greatly increased the demand for cottonseed oil, which the mills kept turning out in larger quantities each year. The deodorizing process was carried on in strongly made cylindrical tanks, with conical or dome shaped tops. These tanks were fitted with large steam coils, and suitable exits at the top for the steam which was carried into the atmosphere. The steam was applied to the oil by means of closed coils which raised its temperature up to about 160 or 170 deg. C., then live steam was blown through the oil from perforated pipes. After deodorizing, the oil was cooled as quickly as possible, by passing through suitable cooling coils in some cases, and in others, by circulating cold water through the steam pipes which had been used for heating the oil. This process of deodorizing was known as the Eckstein process, having been named after the man who had brought it from Europe.

HYDROGENATION APPEARS

In 1900 it was discovered that if the oil were deodorized under reduced pressure and kept in a vacuum until cool, a far superior product could be produced. This process, with several variations, has now become standard in America and Europe. About 1905 or 1906, manufacturers of lard compound found it necessary to obtain if possible a cheaper method of hardening their products, than by the use of oleosterine, the price of which was controlled by the meat packers. Norman, in Germany, found a practical means of applying the newly discovered hydrogenation method of Sabatier to the hardening of oils in such a manner that the oleic and linoleic acids therein could be converted into stearic acid, thus producing hard fats. The process, with sundry variations, became prevalent in America, and vegetable shortenings came into use as lard compounds. It was not only possible, but practical to heat up cottonseed oil to which some finely divided nickel had been added, and after blowing hydrogen through the heated oils with the nickel catalyst for a suitable length of time to filter off the catalyst and obtain a fat having a consistency similar to that of hog lard. These products, being purely vegetable, and free from the animal odor and less prone to oxidation, have attained great popularity for shortening purposes both in the household and in the factory.

The highly refined cottonseed oil, free from odor and flavor, has become the basis of another large industry. It has been found particularly adaptable to the manufacture of mayonnaise salad dressing, in which it is the chief ingredient, amounting to 75 or 80 per cent. In order to produce an oil suitable for this purpose, it is necessary to remove the palmatin, one of the normal constituents of cottonseed oil, because its presence in the mayonnaise will cause a breaking up of the emulsion. Large quantities of cottonseed oil are annually converted into what is known as winter or salad oil. This is done by cooling the oil in suitable apparatus, so as to cause the solid glycerides, commonly called cottonseed sterine, to separate out. They are then removed, generally by passing the chilled oil through filter presses. If the sterine remained in the oil and the mayonnaise were exposed to low temperatures, when the mayonnaise was again brought up to the temperature of the room, the sterine would melt, forming oil particles which would run together and break up the emulsion. To avoid this difficulty, manufacturers of mayonnaise often use corn oil during the winter season.

Corn and Other Oils

Corn oil is made by cooking and pressing the corn germs which are separated from the corn in the manufacture of starch and glucose. It is turned out in considerable quantities, as indicated in the figures previously cited, and is used mainly as a salad oil, although under certain market conditions, it is used frequently for making lard compound. Corn oil is extracted largely by means of the Anderson expellers, instead of by the ordinary plate presses.

On account of the large demand by confectioners, peanut oil is produced in this country mainly from broken or culled peanuts, which are obtained in the operation of shelling, either for the confectioners or the shelled peanut trade. The peanuts are handled by the same process as cottonseed, or in Anderson expellers, as the case may be, and the oil refined in the same manner as cottonseed oil. As noted above, the production in this country is quite small.

During recent years, the production of soya beans has become a rapidly increasing source of vegetable oils. The beans, after hulling and cleaning, are passed through rolls, heated to the proper temperature, and the oil taken out by Anderson expellers, which seem to be particularly adapted to the handling of this material.

The linseed oil industry is one of considerable importance, on account of the large demand for the use of linseed oil in paints and varnishes. Linseed oil manufacturers obtain a large portion of their raw material from abroad, the linseed crop in this country not being sufficient to supply their demand. The pressing methods are practically the same as those used for cottonseed.

Castor oil is obtained mostly by pressing, although some plants have extraction apparatus which is used largely for recovering the residual oil from the cake.

The demands of the oleomargine and soap industries have led to the development of a large coconut oil industry on the Pacific coast. The oil is pressed from imported copra by means of standard plate presses, and also by Anderson expellers. The crude oil is refined by washing with caustic soda and filtering in a similar manner as cottonseed. It is then deodorized by steam under vacuum. Refined coconut oil is chilled and pressed so as to obtain coconut oil sterine which finds its use in the biscuit and confectionery industries. A hardened coconut oil is also produced by hydrogenation by the same methods as those used in the cottonseed oil industry.

SOLVENT EXTRACTION

Solvent extraction of oils, though used extensively abroad, has never made any great progress in this country. Various attempts have been made from time to time, to extract cottonseed, by means of volatile solvents but these experiments have failed as a rule, because of improper apparatus for doing the work. One plant in North Carolina was arranged for recovering the volatile solvent from the oil by distillation under atmospheric pressure in a pot still. Needless to say, the solvent was never thoroughly removed, and the oil was naturally heated to such a temperature that it was impossible to refine it. Another process was tried on a large scale near Chicago, where an extraction apparatus had been used successfully on linseed oil but failed for the reason that the cottonseed meats were separated from the hulls at some point in the south, and then sent by freight to the northern plant. By the time they reached the extractors, considerable decomposition had taken place, so the oil produced ran very high in fatty acids, and was difficult to refine. In other words, solvent extraction, to be successful on cottonseed oil, which runs high in moisture, must be so arranged that the kernels or meats can be treated as soon as they are separated from the hulls, before enzymic action has set in with the consequent injury to the oil.

Experiments made by the writer, in a commercial extraction plant, which worked very well on some materials, did not prove a good commercial proposition on cottonseed, for the reason that when the oil was taken out by solvent, it was very difficult to separate it from the residual meal. The filtering surfaces became clogged by gummy materials which had been loosened from the kernels by the solvent so that an operation which should have taken not over three or four hours at the outside, was necessarily prolonged for a period of ten or twelve hours.

The use of volatile solvents for extracting oil from oil-bearing materials is theoretically the ideal method of removing the oil from cottonseed, providing the proper apparatus can be developed for the purpose. The protein contained in cottonseed has very high biological value, and can be worked into a food product, if produced cheaply in large quantities. To do this, it is necessary to have an apparatus which will allow the solvent to be removed from the meal under vacuum, in order to keep the temperature low enough to prevent any injury to the protein which should not be cooked in the machine. Examination of various equipments on the market has failed to locate one meeting conditions of practical use. Some which have been used for the extraction of garbage grease and thereby meet the requirements of large scale production, are not properly arranged for handling a food product like cottonseed. Many of the extraction plants used in Europe are operated on a comparatively small batch system, which does not lend itself readily to handling the enormous quantities which have to be put through a cottonseed oil mill.

Some plants are operated in Germany, however, which handle an enormous tonnage of soya beans by a continuous process, require very little labor, and turn out excellent products in the shape of both oil and meal. It is believed that it is only a matter of time, before similar processes will be developed in this country and that they will insure the future success of our vegetable oil industry.

EDITOR'S NOTE: For a more complete account the reader is referred to Dr. Wesson's paper on the "History and Development of the Cottonseed Oil Industry in America," which was read at the Savannah meeting on December 4, 1914, and was published in the Transactions of the American Institute of Chemical Engineers, Vol. 12, Part 2.

CHAPTER XVII

LIME INDUSTRY TURNS TO CHEMICAL ENGINEERING

By W. D. Mount

Consulting Chemical and Mechanical Engineer, Lynchburg, Va.

I T SEEMS to be generally accepted by writers on the subject that the use of lime mortar, in some form or other, is as old as the art of building or of civilization itself. Evidences of its use are found not only in the older countries of Europe, Asia and Africa, but in the ruins of Mexico [1] and Peru. The pyramids of Egypt contain plaster work executed at least 4,000 years ago, which, where not disturbed by man, still appears to be perfect. From the writings of Vitruvious we learn that the art of using lime mortars and lime in architectural work was well known long before the beginning of the Christian era.

In Isaiah 33:12 we read: "And the people shall be as the burnings of lime"; and again in Amos 2:1: "Thus said the Lord; for three transgressions of Moab, and for four, I will not turn away the punishment thereof; because he burned the bones of the king of Edom into lime."

Suffice it to say lime is one of the earliest of chemical reagents to be used by man, and its production—lime burning—is probably the most ancient of our chemical industries. It is certain that it was used for building purposes at a time long ante-dating the Christian era, and also at an early date for strengthening, or causticizing wood ashes, and for depilatating hides before tanning.

The generally accepted meaning of lime, per se, is the chemical compound known as oxide of calcium; its most common sources are carbonate of calcium, and the combination of calcium and magnesium carbonates in the so-called dolomitic rocks. Preparation of lime, in theory at least, is a very simple process; the earliest methods probably involved nothing more than covering pieces of limestone, or sea shells, with a heap of wood, which, when burned, left a mixed pile of partially burned raw material and lime; the latter, after cooling, was separated from the unburned portion. A step in advance over this

---

[1] Lasalle.

crude method was effected when permanent walls were built to form a circular shaft, or kiln, into which fresh stone could be charged for each cycle. This simple type of kiln still exists in remote districts where labor is cheap and wood is plentiful.

The next forward step in the art was undoubtedly the use of coal as a fuel. The intense heat developed with coal, its chemical composition, and its ash required a different type of kiln in the development of the art into what, with some degree of truth, might be recognized as the beginning of an industry. In the early use of coal it was charged directly into the kilns along with the limestone; there exist, at this time, large kilns, which the writer has seen in operation, both in Belgium and in England, that may be designated as "mixed-feed" and which, in spite of any lack of chemical and physical control, give quite satisfactory lime to fuel ratios. Certain kilns of this type are still found in this· country, although not as large as those observed in Belgium and England.

To correct the troubles incident to the use of coal, when charged directly with the limestone, a method of external firing was developed, in which the fuel was burned in furnaces built in the walls of the kiln; in later developments so-called "Dutch Ovens" were built on the outside of the kiln proper to prevent direct contact between the fuel and the stone or the lime produced. The products of combustion passed directly into the kiln which acted as a chimney, from which fact the name of "flame kilns" was derived, in contradistinction to the "mixed-feed" type where the solid fuel was charged with the stone at the top of the kiln.

In regard to quality of product the flame kilns undoubtedly marked a step in advance, but in regard to fuel consumption their adoption was decidedly a retrogressive step. Average lime to fuel ratio was not more than three-fifths of that possible in the operation of a mixed-feed kiln.

Fuel Efficiencies. Fuel efficiencies have never seemed to be of great concern to the average lime producer. In this connection the writer has had a number of amusing experiences; one of the most interesting being that of the superintendent in a small lime plant in the Valley of Virginia where an excellent grade of stone was burned in very antiquated wood-fired kilns. When asked about his lime to fuel ratio, he made the naive statement that they were "not concerned about fuel efficiencies" in as much as their "fuel cost nothing," being obtained from their own wood lot. The expense involved in cutting and hauling, to say nothing of the possible value of the wood itself, on the stump, apparently had not occurred to either owner or opera-tor. When asked the further question as to how they ascertained whether operating at a profit or loss from month to month the reply was, "we don't try, we know how much money we have at the begin-ning of the year and if at the end of the year we have more, we have made something; if we have less, we have lost."

Perhaps this fatalistic conception of lime-plant operation is as good an explanation as any that may be adduced of the fact that in 1915 there were 906 lime plants in operation in the United States, while in 1924 there were only 439. In the same period, however, total production was increased 450,000 tons, which indicates a tendency, at least, toward fewer and larger if not better plants.

Another personal recollection may be pardoned at this time, that of the operator who had employed a well recognized authority [2] on lime burning to make certain plant improvements with a view to bringing about at least a semblance of chemical control, and who in his disappointment over "expected results, not realized," expressed the wish that some day he would "have time to write a book on how to 'de-science' a lime plant." Unfortunately for the advance of the art which such a contribution would undoubtedly have made the would-be author sold his interest in the lime industry and passed to other fields of usefulness, where it's to be hoped "science ceased to trouble."

That fuel efficiencies, in the early days of the lime industry, did not greatly concern the lime producer may be attributed to several reasons, one of which was, that the kilns were generally wood-fired, wood being plentiful and relatively cheap; as a matter of fact, wood-firing is not a condition of the remote past, as there are still lime kilns utilizing wood as a fuel, either in whole or in part.

The first installation of continuous gas-fired kilns made by the writer nearly 25 years ago was at a plant not a great distance from New York City, where kilns of the old type were in use, some fired with wood, and some with both coal and wood. The owner, how-ever, did not figure his wood fuel as costing nothing, although "cut on his own land."

Advent of coal as a fuel was not caused by a desire for a better fuel, in respect to quality of product; it was rather a condition caused by growing scarcity of wood and mounting cost. The fact is generally admitted, backed by many years of practical experience, that wood,

---

[2] R. K. Meade.

both technically, and in respect to quality of product, is the most desirable fuel. The chemist and chemical engineer, however, may very properly question this ancient dogma and ask why wood is generally considered the best fuel. Is it because its chemical composition and physical character confer upon it any singular property as a combustible? Or is it merely because it has been found to be "foolproof.[3] The use of coal brought problems differing from those in burning wood; although these problems were recognized to some extent, there was but scant realization of the fact that their successful solution might involve radical changes in design of kiln plant and equipment.

Too many lime producers have attempted to adapt new methods to old equipment, or vice versa, and because the results have not been satisfactory, the new methods, new equipment, and scientific control rather than the old methods and the antiquated equipment have been condemned. It would not be true to state that the industry generally has been lacking those who, like John the Baptist, have preached the day of better things and pointed out essential improvements both in design and operation; but the preaching has not always been fruitful, and the sound of the preacher's voice has been lost in the great wilderness of skepticism and indifference.

While not altogether true now, lime burners in the recent past seemed intolerant toward new ideas and scientific methods. Much of this feeling was doubtless due to the fact that the manufacture of lime, per se, from a practical point of view, and regardless of quality of product, offered nothing more complicated than applying heat to limestone.

Some years ago the writer in an address before the Virginia Section of the A. S. M. E. made the following statement: "It may be taken as a truism that a thing 'anybody can do' is seldom well done.[4] A case in point is the salt industry. Today the manufacture of salt is a highly efficient process; 30 years ago it was a very wasteful one. Still salt has been used since the first days of the human race. As the manufacture of salt is a problem of evaporation anyone could do it, and it was done for centuries in simple open pots at a fuel expenditure of probably one pound of coal for every three or four pounds of water evaporated. Today the salt industry is carried on in specially designed multiple-effect evaporators under vacuum, where one pound of fuel evaporates from 20 to 30 lb. of water. An-

---

[3] Address by A. D. Little, National Lime Association, 1921.
[4] Industrial Wastes and Inefficiency, by W. D. Mount, Richmond, Va., 1923.

other illustration is the lime industry, in which there has been no radical improvement in methods of manufacture for generations, and this, too, in spite of the fact that the manufacture of lime is a basic industry, the product of which enters, as a raw material, into about 120 listed industries."

In a paper entitled "Science and Engineering in Lime Burning," [5] Victor J. Azbe makes the following statement: "Lime is a most interesting substance, but this fact, due to a great 'superficial familiarity' with lime on the part of most of us, is not appreciated and is in consequence abused. Limestone lends itself readily—too readily—to conversion into lime, therefore the most crude methods can and are used in burning, or in lime manufacture: Limestone, to most, is a common rock and hardly worthy of careful study. What actual reactions take place during the burning periods are known to extremely few; what methods to use to regulate these reactions are known to even a lesser number." The lack of knowledge, cited by Azbe, is not the worst feature. The condition of the industry for two generations past, in regard to technological advance, clearly indicates a general indifference, on the part of the average lime producer, toward improvements in kiln design and adoption of scientific methods. Unquestionably this attitude has retarded the advance of the industry to a far greater extent than mere lack of knowledge.

The history of our country, in respect to its productive industries, prior to the beginning of the 20th century, has been that of a nation busily engaged in converting enormous natural resources into marketable raw materials. Although our great stores of natural products have become necessary to the world's industrial progress, only in a few cases have the raw materials been converted into finished and marketable products at home.

Great technical skill was not required in cutting down our forests, developing our mines, or raising enormous crops on virgin soil; the products of these operations were, however, largely primary raw materials and were sold as such. Although we made the beginning of many great industries, and manufactured for our own use finished products, which, in many cases, equaled the best that could be procured anywhere in the world, the fact remains that our exports were mainly raw materials.

Arthur D. Little writing of this period states that "we as a nation acquired the habit of being vastly satisfied with what we had accomplished. We marveled at our enterprise in scraping iron ore from

---

[5] Read at American Chemical Society Meeting, Richmond, Va., 1927.

the earth's surface by steam shovels, in stripping great areas of primeval forest, in burning natural gas, and allowing petroleum to spout from the ground. Even Germany acknowledged that she could not compete with us in raising cotton. We controlled the copper market of the world, because we have the copper. If you want cheap sulphur, you must come to us, we pump it from the ground. We developed great centers of power distribution because our rivers run so fast down hill. To these vast resources we brought, indeed, a native energy, an unusual capacity for organization, and a genius for mechanical affairs. What we do, we do on a great scale, but we often do it very badly. It is quite time for us to pause, in our self-congratulation, long enough to inquire whether the things we are doing cannot be better done, whether, in fact, other nations have not developed and put to use better methods, which, given equal opportunity, would put our own performance to the blush." [6]

The advent of the World War did not mark the beginning of chemical industry in this country, although undoubtedly that explosion did jar the nation into a sensibility of what chemical industry means to the welfare of the average citizen, and to bring to the realization of our industrialists the value of byproducts.

The lime industry has not lacked writers or skilled engineers, capable of pointing the way to the attainment of better methods and better production. One of the earliest and, in my opinion, the best treatises on the subject of limestones and lime is that of Orton and Peppel, published in 1906 as Bulletins 4 and 5 of the Geological Survey of Ohio. Although written 26 years ago, and confined to the lime industry in but one state, these bulletins, from the standpoint of the scope and manner of treatment of the subject, original data published, and the discussion of the technical and practical sides of the problems of kiln operation, are in my estimation, equal, if not superior to anything yet published. Many specific topics, both physical and chemical, having a direct bearing on the scientific manufacture of lime have been treated by other writers at greater length and in greater detail, but none have covered the field in a better manner than have Orton and Peppel.

They clearly point out that "Every step and every factor in the operation of lime burning has a definite significance, and the production of high-grade lime with high-grade economy is as truly a technical process, demanding skill and knowledge, as any other chem-

---

[6] Address by A. D. Little, 1921.

ical manufacture, and there is need of trained chemists and engineers in this industry to put it upon a distinctly scientific plane." [7]

A later work than that of Orton and Peppel is the excellent book entitled "Lime and Magnesia," by N. V. S. Knibbs, B. Sc. and Chief Chemist of the Denny Chemical Engineering Co., Ltd., and the Callow Rock Lime Co., Ltd., published in 1924 by Messrs. J. W. Arrowsmith, Ltd., II. Quay St., Bristol, England.

Mr. Knibbs says of lime burning that it may be appropriately termed the Cinderella of the chemical industries; it has been neglected by technical writers and investigators, and manufacturers have been content to use antiquated and inefficient methods of manufacture without any serious attempt at their improvement, and this, too, in face of the fact that no other inorganic compound has played so important a part in human affairs for so long a period.

Azbe has recently contributed a series of articles of outstanding merit covering the entire field of limestone and lime products. In these articles he discusses in detail scientific methods of operation and problems of kiln design necessary to the rehabilitation of commercial lime-burning into a true chemical industry; each step in the process is found to have vital bearing on the quality of the product and on the cost of production, and should, therefore be under complete and constant chemical control.

James McNamara, one of the oldest and wisest of commercial lime-burners, a man who has spent his entire life in the business, is right in his dictum that "burning good lime begins back in the quarry"; in support of this statement Mr. McNamara told me that he spent three-fourths of his time in his quarry. In so far as time so spent makes for clean stone, of uniform quality and size, Mr. McNamara is on firm ground; for it may be assumed without argument that uniformity in quality of output pre-supposes a similar condition in regard to input, and that a high-grade product cannot be predicated on variable raw material.[8]

Thus far this paper has been only leading up to the assertion that the production of lime is a chemical process, as truly susceptible of chemical control as any other chemical industry. Without such control, and the recognition of the factors essential to that end maximum efficiency, economy in operation, and high quality of product can-

---

[7] Orton and Peppel.
[8] Bulletin No. 7, "The Efficient Production of Chemical Lime," by W. D. Mount, Lynchburg, Va.

not be attained; nor can lime-burning take its rightful place among the other chemical industries.

Kinds of Lime.[9]—According to its use lime may be classified under three general headings: agricultural lime, building lime and chemical lime. In recent years the industrial use of lime has increased to such an extent that the lime industry now finds its most important outlet in chemical and allied fields. In this connection the accompanying chart, covering the period of eleven years from 1919 to 1930 is of definite interest, and its careful inspection is recommended to all directly or indirectly connected with the production and use of lime and lime products.

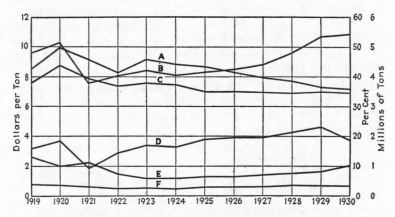

Chemical and Agricultural Lime Production and Sales

A. Average price per ton of Chemical Lime sold.
B. Percentage of total lime production sold for chemical uses.
C. Average price per ton for Agricultural Lime.
D. Chemical Lime sold in millions of tons.
E. Percentage of total lime production sold for agricultural uses.
F. Agricultural Lime sold in millions of tons.

With the increased demand for lime in the chemical industries has come a demand for a product of invariably high standardized quality, in regard to both physical and chemical properties. That this fact is recognized by one concern engaged in the manufacture of lime is clearly evidenced by the published bulletins of the Allwood Lime Co., Manitowoc, Wisconsin. "The true value of lime, used in the manufacture of commercial products, depends entirely upon its chem-

9 Bulletin No. 7, "The Efficient Production of Chemical Lime," by W. D. Mount, Lynchburg, Va.

ical ingredients. Experts know that lime varies considerably in quality, hence all the various grades on the market cannot be suitable for all purposes, and unless the kind required is specified by the customer, he may be given a grade entirely unsuited for his particular use." [10]

Those who attended the meeting of the National Lime Association in June, 1922 and heard the address by Miss Mary E. Squire, president and general manager of the Allwood Lime Co., cannot forget the sound common sense, the clear recognition of the value of scientific methods, the striking illustrations taken from her own experiences, and her pungent and forcible comments on the possibilities to the industry of scientific control. Miss Squire's paper was nothing less than "a gem," and I doubt if the records of the National Lime Association can match it with any article of equal merit. It is to be regretted that space will not permit the incorporation of Miss Squire's entire essay; while this is impossible I feel that any discussion of the lime industry within the scope of the present article would be incomplete without including some excerpts from Miss Squire's address. No better argument for chemical control and no better proof of its value could be adduced.[11]

"But, gentlemen, what I have learned about my own stone was a case of necessity. I soon found that I could not compete with any Wisconsin competitor in anything except quality, because you all know that the amount of lime each one of us produces in twenty-four hours regulates and controls the cost for us. I have a little 50-ton a day capacity plant; not worth talking about. But I found I had a quality of lime similar to that which for 200 years we had to import from Germany and pay them, laid down on the dock in Hoboken, from $80.00 to $200.00 a ton. And immediately I started to find out which particular stone was that in my plant. And I made 240 tests. And it took me the better part of four years before I finally caught the rascal and identified him every time and could teach the common Italian who he was and give him an artificial name."

"When I found out that I had him. I made him. But I didn't make him in the form in which the consumer, if you please, wanted him. That was an additional investigation, and I made twenty additional tests at a cost to our company of $3,500 cash to find out what machinery was needed."

"I went to New York with my lime. And the largest and oldest firms in the metal polishing business said to me, 'Why, Miss Squire, we can't experiment with your Vienna lime. Do you know that $50 worth of that lime goes into $250 worth of other products, and if it doesn't go in, we have to throw the whole mix into the sewer. We can't stand such experimentation.'

"I said, 'Well, if we gave a bond to guarantee that the $50 worth will go in, not once, but every time, will you try it?'

"Well, it isn't likely. We can't afford it."

"In December, 1915, every pound of German imported lime was used up in this country. Then they began to ask for me. I sent samples. One very clever gentleman in Newark with his partner came all the way West and found me and

10 Bulletin No. 3, Allwood Lime Co., Manitowoc, Wis.

11 Address before National Lime Association at New York, June, 1922.

said, 'We have come to make a contract with you.' He beat me down to the lowest possible price. When I got his contract he said, 'Now, I am going to tell you something, Miss Squire. We had some of the German lime left and we made 32 tests of the Allwood, and we found that 31 tests of the Allwood were better than the German, and on the other it fell down. Now I didn't tell you this until I got your contract.' "

"Gentlemen, suffice it to say that the Allwood Lime Co. has supplied the entire United States, Canada and England with steel ball finishing lime. The last two-thousandths of an inch is cut or burnt or eaten off all steel balls with this particular lime. It has to eat even every particle as you can readily understand, to insure sphericity. What would our ball-bearing cannons be without it? I don't know. I didn't stop to think. How could we have finished our surgical instruments? For every surface and polish on all metals is produced by lime cake. And yet the United States only needs 1,500 tons a year of lime."

"One funny little incident. I had been corresponding with some people in England, and not ten miles from Manchester, where I was sending our lime, I could have gone over and made the stuff from the deposit located there. I felt like saying. 'Why don't you get your geological chemist busy? Now, the one thing that has induced me to tell you this little bit of a personal experience is this: My company and myself and four other women associates would have lost the savings of a lifetime by going in the lime business to make building lime. We saved our business and we have a profitable small concern; and because I happen to have chemical and geological knowledge which I applied to this, I merely ended the trail. I hope above all things if I never come here again, that this association will realize that the very foundation stones of our business are the chemists, the men who can tell you that this is the thing and that isn't."

"I have belonged to this association only the first year, because I didn't need a set of expert salesmen to go out and sell my product. As soon as you can make the best material for any specific use, the man comes to your door for it; but it must honestly be the best; it can't be a bag of wind that a glib salesman can put across with smooth talking and low practices."

I have quoted Miss Squire at length for two reasons. First, she has pointed the way to better things by means of scientific methods; second, she has demonstrated in practice that scientific methods are sound and a firm basis for good business. What other commercial lime burner could make a statement as frank as the following, or would consider it good business so to do? How many possess sufficient knowledge of the chemical and physical characteristics of their products to make such a statement?

"Allwood Lime is not recommended for the following purposes:
The purification of water, not because of its lack of purity, but because of its known chemical action in the presence of liquid chemical combinations.
The manufacture of aqueous ammonia or bichromate of potash.
The manufacture of acetic acid and bleaching powder.
As a chemical reagent for laboratory purposes.
For scouring cotton in the textile industry.
The manufacture of sand brick.
The manufacture of bone ash.
For use as a sugar refiner.
No user of lime can afford to pay the market price for a raw material that gives him only 50 per cent of a desired result, especially when he can secure 100 per cent of efficiency at the same price. Think it over and specify ALLWOOD LIME for the purposes for which we recommend it." [12]

[12] Bulletin No. 3, Allwood Lime Company.

Markets for Lime Developed by Science. "It is one thing to make good lime, but quite a different thing to find a market for it. The creation of the broad market which exists in normal times is due in large measure to scientific research. . . . Still more obviously must "chemical research" be depended upon for the better control of the quality and characteristics of the product and the elimination of those anomalies which are now the cause of irritation and complaint. Nearly 60 per cent of the country's production of lime is utilized for chemical purposes, and it is therefore especially important to consider carefully the actual availability for such purposes of the lime that is produced and offered to the trade."[13]

Future of the Lime Industry. The development of lime-burning into a true chemical industry must proceed along radically different paths than those traveled in the past; and these paths will not be found by catering to the whims of the journeyman plasterer, or the man "with the hoe" presiding over the "mortar bed." There must be due recognition of the fact that lime can function in other ways than serving as a binder for bricks or stones or as finish for walls, ancient and honorable as these uses may be.

Lime as an Alkali. "Lime has long been the cheapest industrial alkali and one would naturally think that it would have been utilized to its fullest extent in the chemical industry. However, this seems not the case in this era of rapidly shifting chemical processes. Apparently, in the early stages of the commercial development of new processes, it is often necessary to use higher priced alkalis, which through later improvements in technical details may then be replaced by a cheaper alkali, such as lime." [14]

"The question as to what alkali should be used for a specific purpose depends not only on the relative cost of the various alkalis but also on the problems involved in the particular chemical process and the particular product which is to be made. In certain cases these latter factors may be of primary importance and therefore the determining ones, rather than the price itself. For certain processes, lime is very often desired, not because it is the cheapest alkali available, but because of its property of forming insoluble precipitates with certain acids, particularly sulphuric. This property is frequently utilized in order to remove as insoluble calcium sulphate the sulphate radical resulting from the use of sulphuric acid in the process."

The Byproduct. Again there is the problem of the byproduct. "The world at large and business in general has no sympathy for the fellow, be he manufacturer or what not, who continues to adhere to time-worn methods to produce his products. Science is responsible for wonderful advances in perfecting means for the manufacture of almost every commodity, and woe to him who fails to get aboard the train of progress.

"Among the industries that have not profited to any appreciable degree by the innovations and discoveries in science, and have not grasped the advantages science has made possible for it, is the lime industry.

"With the aid of science the industry should long ago have been able to come through a period such as it is experiencing now. Even now science has made it possible for a lime producer to make much more money than his plant will ever make by depending upon the sale of lime alone." [15]

"There is much food for thought in Mr. Deringer's statement that 'even now science has made it possible for a lime producer to make much more money

[13] A. D. Little's address delivered at the third annual convention of the National Lime Association, New York, June 16, 1921.

[14] Editorial January, 1931, issue *Chemical & Metallurgical Engineering.*

[15] A. S. Deringer, Rocky Ridge, Ohio, July 6, 1929, issue *Rock Products.*

than his plant will ever make by depending upon the sale of lime alone.' [16]

The development and sale of byproducts wherein the kiln exist gases are utilized is a virgin field for the operator with vision, and is a logical step following the bringing of all kiln operations under systematic chemical and technical control. Many products for which there is a growing demand, and in the manufacture of which lime is a basic raw material, can be more cheaply made in connection with the lime plant operation than elsewhere." [17]

Miss Squire believes that the future of the lime business will depend on the development of new products and new uses for lime. She is backing her belief by installing a modern research laboratory in Manitowoc, Wisconsin. Some of the uses to which her products are put are for cleaning the fine parts of watches and for a variety of medical purposes, one being a special lime for water for use in children's hospitals. Her highest priced lime is marketed under the name of "Horologic" lime, and is, as the name implies, used in watch manufacturing. The amount used of this special brand is small and the methods of production are so exacting that it is not likely that many lime producers would care to enter the field. Her main object, however, is to develop enough specialties to keep the plant in operation and give steady employment to her staff and operating crew.

Agriculture. The use of lime in our great basic industry, the production of food crops, cotton and tobacco, and the regeneration of our worn-out soils (exhausted, not eroded) is largely a virgin field for the development of ultimate markets for lime, in comparison to which its use in the purely chemical industries will take second rank. Preliminary to this, however, the farmer must be educated about the value of lime and how to apply it; the lime-burner must also be educated in scientific control and methods of low-cost production, to make lime available to the farmer at a price comparable with the commercial fertilizers now used, which are largely stimulants, for one time and for one crop only. Intelligent use of lime on the farm will mark the dawn of a new birth for agriculture, and will be of far greater benefit than all the nostrums of the vote-seeking politicians in Congress. Lime, however, is not a fertilizer; neither is ground limestone. Use of either as such will result in failure. The true function of lime in agriculture is as an alkali, to correct soil acidity.

Among the prophets of better days for the farmer, resulting from the methodical use of burned lime, was Prof. W. F. Massey, formerly agricultural editor of the Richmond *Times Dispatch,* and associate

---

[16] Bulletin No. 7, "The Efficient Production of Chemical Lime," by W. D. Mount, Lynchburg, Va.

[17] Article by W. D. Mount in *Refrigerating Engineer,* May, 1932.

editor of the *Progressive Farmer,* the *Southern Planter,* and *Market Growers Journal.* In addition to being an experienced, practical farmer and an agricultural and horticultural expert and counsellor, Prof. Massey was a college man who applied his knowledge to a practical as well as a scientific cultivation of the soil and a study of its needs. It has been said of Prof. Massey "the value of his advice to farmers can be counted in millions, and they will some day build a monument to him." Any account, therefore, of lime and the lime industry, even as fragmentary as the present attempt, would be unfair without due recognition to Prof. Massey, not as a lime-burner or producer, but as a lime user, and, as such, I quote, as fully as space will admit, from his story of the true function of lime in agriculture.[18]

"*My Own Theory.* Then they soon found that the red clover, which had been so valuable in their farming, no longer flourished, and again the question was, 'What is the matter with the land?' In those days we knew that, somehow or other, clover and other legume crops did help the land, and investigators discovered that where clover grew the soil did in some way contain more nitrogen than elsewhere. The puzzle was, how did the clover get the nitrogen, and all sorts of theories were broached in regard to this fact. Finally it was discovered that all those plants belonging to the natural order of leguminosae had on their little roots, knots or nodules, and the scientists began to study these. They found that these nodules were the homes of certain microscopic plants, which at first they called bacteroids, as they seemed to differ in form from any known bacteria. But finally it was determined that they were really a form of bacteria. Further experiment showed that where these bacteria were absent the clover and other legumes got no surplus nitrogen, and the legitimate conclusion was that it was due to these bacteria that the plants were able to fix the free nitrogen gas of the air in a combination to make organic nitrogen in the soil. Just how this is done no one has as yet found out. One writer says that the bacteria simply absorb the nitrogen and leave it in the plants. But nitrogen is a gas in the air and the absorption of the gas could not account for the combination in which it is found. My own theory about this is—and one theory is as good as another until proved wrong—that these minute bacteria are of the nature of ferments. The yeast plant we know is a saccharine ferment, and these little forms are nitric ferments, oxidizing the free nitrogen gas and making nitric acid. As soon as there is nitric acid in the soil it seeks a base either of lime or potash or some other element and a nitrate is formed, and green-leaved plants always take their nitrogen as a nitrate and in no other form. That the combination is made in the soil and not in the plant is shown by the fact that other plants, growing with the legumes, benefit by the association. Corn, with cow peas sown among it, will make more corn than corn without the peas, and hence it would seem that the combination is made in the soil and the legumes get the nitrogen, and whatever plant is associated with them gets some of it also." . . . "But, as I have said, the farmers began to find that they could no longer get the luxuriant growth of clover they formerly made. . . . I asked them why they did not adopt a shorter rotation and grow more clover. 'We cannot grow clover any more,' was the reply, and they simply seemed to accept the fact without trying to find out why clover no longer throve. But now, when there is a renewed interest in lime and we have found out that it was soil acidity that mainly caused the difficulty in growing clover, it is hard to convince

---

18 "A Farmer's Experience With Lime," by Prof. W. F. Massey.

the farmers in the old heavily liming sections that lime is what they now need."

"Unburned Lime Not Available. About thirty-five years ago I took charge of a large estate in Northern Maryland, in a beautiful limestone valley. There was a field which was said to be 'clover sick.' Now all over that field there were protruding rocks of the white, coarsely crystalline limestone, peculiar to that part of the country. This limestone decomposes rapidly, and the surface of these protruding rocks was coarse white crystals that could be kicked off by the heel, and they washed off from every mass of rock. And yet the soil where those limestone crystals were continually washed down was found to be very acid. Lime was burned and spread on this land, and at once the clover-sick field made a wonderful growth of red clover.

"Burned Lime Doubly Valuable. That ground limestone will finally to some extent sweeten an acid soil may be true, but what the farmer needs is a speedy effect, and for this there is nothing equal to slaked burned lime. But there is a great work to be done in the educating of the farmers to a proper realization of what lime will do for them, and what cannot be expected from liming alone. In the old lime craze they demonstrated the truth of the old proverb that 'lime enriches the father and impoverishes the son.' Lime is an efficient aid to the farmer who farms in a systematic rotation, and maintains and increases the humus in his soil through the growth and using of the legumes."
. . . "It is not the mere growing, but the use that is made of the legume crops which helps the land." . . . "Liming land never made poor land rich and never will, but lime and legumes properly used make a team that will help the farmer to maintain and increase the fertility of his soil." . . . "So far as my experience goes I had rather have one ton of burned lime of good quality than two tons of the ground rock. Good lump lime I found to slake nearly two to one, and 1,000 lb. of this slaked lime will have a better immediate effect than a ton of ground rock. . . . An application of 1,000 lb. of slaked lime an acre every five or six years will not be an unsurmountable expense to any farmer who farms right in a good rotation with legumes, and the results in his sale crops will soon show him that the use of lime is profitable, even if it costs him $10 a ton delivered. He can get humus-making material into his soil without the lime, that will only increase its acidity, but he will soon find that he will lose in his corn, cotton, and other crops every year more than lime would cost."

Taking a total of 200,000,000 acres planted to the six principal food crops alone, corn, wheat, oats, rye, barley and potatoes, and using the amount of lime Prof. Massey suggests once in five years, the potential annual consumption of lime in agriculture would reach the staggering total of 20,000,000 tons, without taking into account non-food crops such as cotton and tobacco.

What then of the future of lime industry? It would seem clearly indicated, and from the various writers quoted, its form of development should be clearly outlined. Due recognition must be given to the fact that the conversion of limestone to lime is a chemical operation, that its large-scale production constitutes an industry comparable to other chemical industries. Rule-of-thumb methods and crude and unscientific design and operation which ignore the fundamentals of chemical control are outworn and outmoded in a nation greatly given to vaunting its superior technological skill. Well may we pause to ask "Can it be done better?"

CHAPTER XVIII

GLASS MANUFACTURE CHANGES FROM AN ART TO A SCIENCE

By J. C. HOSTETTER and A. E. MARSHALL

Respectively Director of Research and Development and Consulting Engineer
Corning Glass Works, Corning, N. Y.

FOR THREE CENTURIES after its founding in America by Captain John Smith, at Jamestown in 1608, the glass industry, as indeed it had been for many centuries before, was essentially rule-of-thumb and manual in process. Throughout this period improvements in chemical technology were reflected in purer batch materials; increasing knowledge of fuel technology gave the industry more efficient application of fuel in the melting processes. Some relations had been established between the chemical composition of glasses and their optical and physical properties, but, generally considered, the glass industry about 1900 was an art, the practices of which, founded on centuries of experience, were to provide a fertile field to be successfully tilled by the scientist and engineer. As a result, the glass industry, formerly an art with closely-guarded, secret formulae and empirical processes, today uses all of the tools of modern science in its control and development laboratories. Recent laboratory studies have shown that some of the ancient glass compositions have a sound scientific basis—thus attesting the acumen and skill of the pioneers in the industry. Similar studies have led to the development of new glasses with properties demanded by the operation of the newly developed automatic glass-forming machines, on the one hand, to characteristics imposed by new and widely diversified uses on the other.

Today glass is a universal material with a variety of uses which, in the United States, yields annually an aggregate volume of some 3,000,000 tons of product valued at $300,000,000.[1] With very few exceptions commercial glasses are silicates, containing, generally, about 70 per cent silica, which, as "glass sand" is used in the United States to the extent of about 2,000,000 tons annually. To flux this

---

[1] These and the following data are from the fifteenth census of the U. S. (1929).

silica, over 600,000 tons of soda ash, 45,000 tons of salt cake, and 350,000 tons of lime and limestone are consumed. In addition, there is a heavy consumption of lead oxide, pearl ash, saltpeter, niter, borax and boric acid, arsenic, feldspar, and fluorspar. For colored glass a large variety of metallic oxides, carbonates, and other salts are required; while in finishing operations large tonnages of such diverse products as abrasives and hydrofluoric acid are consumed. Nor are the materials consumed in this industry restricted to inorganic chemicals. Safety glass, of the laminated type, requires a large tonnage of plastic. Other materials required are fuels and refractories, and a respectable quantity of metal, for molds and furnace and machine parts.

While glass making may not today be classified as an exact science there has been a real advance in the transition from art to science in the last quarter century. Paralleling the progress of the glass technologist, the mechanical engineer has successfully introduced his machines into every branch of the industry, thus replacing the highly skilled glass blower more or less generally in many lines. The processes introduced by the mechanical engineer have been most spectacular and revolutionary. However, the detailed story of his achievements, important as they are, cannot be told here. Our primary task is to record accomplishments in glass technology in America. In doing this we plan to discuss developments in the important commercial glasses and then in processes and operations. The order of discussion sequentially follows the major processes in glass making: I. Composition. II. Batch materials and mixing. III. Melting. IV. "Gathering." V. Forming. VI. Annealing. VII. Finishing and VIII. Engineering Applications.

I—COMPOSITION

For this purpose we will classify and discuss commercial glasses as: (1) vitreous silica, (2) alkali silicates, (3) lime glasses, (4) lead glasses, (5) borosilicates, and (6) special glasses.

(1.) *Vitreous Silica.* Vitreous silica is frequently, although erroneously, designated as "quartz glass." Such a glass, made by fusing pure silica without fluxes, represents the end member of the silicate glasses. Its low expansion and high softening point give it extremely high thermal resistance, thus permitting uses beyond the temperature range of other glasses. This glass is also remarkably transparent to ultra-violet radiation. In recent years Professor Elihu

Thompson [2] and his colleagues at West Lynn have so perfected the method of producing this glass, originally developed in this country by Day and Shepherd [3] that it is now possible to secure excellent quality in fairly large sizes. The process consists essentially of electrically melting in vacuum, with subsequent application of air pressure to the molten material to condense bubbles of vapor. Slugs of silica glass so produced are then reheated and worked into final form.

Another method of producing pure silica glass recently developed at West Lynn consists in feeding carefully purified and sized particles of quartz through a special burner which preheats the particles and causes them to melt down into a beautifully clear solid mass. This method [4] has been used in the production of vitreous silica mirror blanks for reflecting telescopes.

Silica, our primary material, is a most unique material as viewed by the physical chemist. Its properties have been the subject of many research investigations both here and abroad. Sosman [5] in his encyclopedic monograph on the properties of silica, lists seven crystalline modifications in addition to the vitreous form. The stability relations between the crystalline modifications and the relations between them and the vitreous form are now fairly well established. A knowledge of these relations is of value to the glass technologist not only because silica is extensively used as a raw material in glass, but also because his furnaces are built of silica and silicate refractories. Equilibrium relations and rates of reactions between silicates are the scientific foundation on which glass technology is building. The work on such systems, especially that done at the Geophysical laboratory, is of the utmost importance to scientific glass making.

(2) *Alkali Silicates.* With several minor exceptions sodium silicates represent the only two-component glasses of present commercial importance. Such glasses are readily soluble and, hence, are not suited for uses ordinarily associated with glass. However, when dissolved in water, the resulting solutions find wide application in many industries. The commercial importance of soluble silicates can well be realized by a perusal of Vail's monograph [6] on this subject.

---

[2] Berry, *Chem. Met. Eng., 30,* 715-17 (1924).

[3] *Science, N. S. 23,* 670-2 (1906).

[4] *Glass Industry, 12,* 125-7 (1931).

[5] "The Properties of Silica," R. B. Sosman, A. C. S. Monograph, No. 37, N. Y. (1927).

[6] "Soluble Silicates in Industry," J. G. Vail, A. C. S. Monograph, No. 46, N. Y. (1928).

The sodium silicates are of importance to the glass technologist since a knowledge of the equilibrium relations in the binary system, Na_2SiO_2 SiO_2, gives us a basis on which to establish similar relations in more complicated glasses. Morey & Bowen [7] have thoroughly investigated this system which has a silica range from about 50 to 100 per cent, thus corresponding to that of commercial glasses. An interesting fact brought out by this study is that the $Na_2O . 2SiO_2$ —quartz eutectic is 793 deg.*; a melting point lowering of over 900 deg. caused by the addition of about 26 per cent Na_2O. This fact is of far-reaching importance to the glass technologist. There is another low-melting eutectic in this system; that of $Na_2O . SiO_2 — Na_2O$. $2SiO_2$ at 846 deg. corresponding to 62.1 per cent SiO_2. It is not without significance that ancient glasses often possess silica contents that would bring their melting characteristics within this zone.

(3) *Lime Glasses.* Lime glass (soda-lime-silica glass) represents by far the largest tonnage of glass melted today, embracing, as it does, "containers" of all kinds, "flat" glass (window, plate, wired, and figured), tumblers, and tableware. While lime glass has been melted commercially for many years—even centuries—it has been only within the last 10 years that the phase-rule relations have been determined in the binary system soda-silica (already referred to) and in the ternary system soda-lime-silica. These systems have been studied by Morey and his colleagues, Bowen and Kracek, at the Geophysical laboratory. Morey has also determined the effects of small quantities of magnesia,[8] alumina [9] and boric acid [10] in commercially important fields of the soda-lime-silica system, thus definitely establishing the effects of these oxides.

Our knowledge of lime glass has been extended greatly by a study of the ternary system sodium metasilicate and calcium metasilicate—silica.[11] This investigation is of such fundamental importance that it deserves far more attention than we can give it in a review of this kind. The lowest melting mixture in the system is the ternary eutectic $Na_2O . 2SiO_2 — Na_2O . 3CaO . 6SiO_2$ — quartz at 725 deg. having a composition of 21.3 per cent Na_2O. 5.2 per cent CaO. and 73.5 per cent SiO_2. A glass of this composition, while most difficult to crystallize (devitrify) and hence quite suitable for reworking, is, on account

[7] *J. Phys. Chem., 28,* 1167-1179 (1924).

* Temperatures reported in this chapter are in Centigrade unless otherwise indicated.

8, 9 and 10 Morey, G. W., *J. Am. Ceram. Soc., 13,* 714-7 (1930) ; *13,* 718-24 (1930), and *15,* 457-475 (1932).

[11] Morey & Bowen, *J. Soc. Glass Tech., 9,* 226-264 (1925). Morey, *J. Am. Ceram. Soc., 13,* 683-713 (1930).

of the high soda content, not sufficiently resistant to "weathering" to be commercially acceptable. Glasses in this composition zone are rendered more insoluble by decreasing soda and increasing lime. This change, while reducing the tendency to "weather," decreases stability towards devitrification; correction for this in turn is usually attained by addition of other oxides, such as alumina, magnesia, or boric acid. Lime glasses modified in this manner are no longer 3-component glasses, but actually all commercial lime glasses, whether by accident or design, are poly-component systems. The electric bulb glass of today is a lime glass, containing magnesia and alumina, a composition of remarkable stability against devitrification. Its development has permitted the continuous operation of high speed bulb producing machines.[12]

The relation between composition and viscosity in the soda-lime-silica system has been investigated in this country by Washburn & Shelton.[13] Other studies of viscosity have been carried out abroad and, more recently, viscosity-temperature curves have been determined by Lillie [14] over the range from annealing to melting. Change in viscosity with temperature is one of the most important relations in glass technology, playing a major part in all operations used in producing glass. Obviously, it is a controlling factor in melting and "fining"; it determines the working quality of the glass and, finally, the annealing conditions. It is interesting to note that the viscosity of a typical lime glass at melting temperature is approximately 10^2 poises and at the "annealing point" 2.5×10^{13} poises.

(4) *Lead Glasses.* An interesting series of glasses is obtained by using lead oxide with alkali and silica, yielding the so-called Flints.[15] These glasses are extremely important in optical work on account of their high index of refraction and high dispersion. By increasing the lead content up to above 80 per cent, a range in refractive index from 1.55 to 2.0 can be obtained, corresponding to a change in density of 2.5 to 6.4. The systematizing of these data was of the greatest help in the production of optical glass during the war.[16]

---

[12] *Glass Ind., 7,* 159-165 (1931).

[13] *Bull. No. 140, Eng. Exp. Station,* Univ. Ill. (1924).

[14] *J. Rheol, 3,* 121-6 (1932). *J. Am. Ceram. Soc., 15,* 418-424 (1932).

[15] A term, however, often commercially applied to lime glass of "good color"—i.e., *colorless.*

[16] For an account of the war-time developments in optical glass production by the Geophysical Laboratory, Carnegie Institution of Washington, see the "Manufacture of Optical Glass and of Optical Systems," by F. E. Wright, Washington (1921).

The brilliancy of good "cut" glass is due to the use of lead-bearing glass, with its characteristic optical properties. Other glasses of this series are used in large quantities in the construction of mounts for electric lamps and radiotrons because of superior re-working qualities and high electrical resistance.

(5) *Borosilicates.* The use of boric oxide in optical glass dates back about 100 years to the experiments of Michael Faraday. Borosilicate crowns are extremely important in optical work, possessing low index of refraction and low dispersion. The borosilicates that we have in mind, however, are of an entirely different kind—having low expansion combined with superior resistance to heat shock, excellent chemical stability and high electrical resistance. The wide and ever increasing number of uses to which these glasses are put has revolutionized the ideas of the layman and engineer regarding the properties of glass. That this development is an outstanding accomplishment has been recognized by the Franklin Institute in honoring the inventors, Sullivan and Taylor,[17] with the Potts medal, and by the chemical fraternity in bestowing upon Dr. Sullivan the Perkin medal for his work on resistant glasses.[18]

The unique characteristics of these glasses have led to such diversified applications as baking dishes, laboratory ware, pipe lines, high tension insulators, and wash tubs.

(6) *Special Glasses* (a) *Colored Glass.* In earliest times colored glass was used exclusively for decorative purposes—to look at, so to speak, rather than through. In fact, transparency in glass dates only from about 600 B. C. and very little was produced until some centuries later. Today colored transparent glasses are important, not merely for decoration, but for definite commercial and scientific purposes.

Glasses may be colored by adding the appropriate coloring agent to the batch, but such agents act differently as the batch type is changed. To illustrate: nickel oxide dissolved in a sodium-lead glass yields a brown color, while in a similar potash glass it produces a heliotrope. This difference in coloring effect is greatly enhanced when heat resisting glasses are considered, as, for instance, in the development of railway signal glasses. This is a rather interesting story. First, a psychologist determined, after considerable study and experimentation, that certain colors, made up from dyed gelatin, were most

---

17 *J. Ind. & Eng. Ch.*, 7, 1064 (1915).

18 E. C. Sullivan, "The Many-Sidedness of Glass," *Ind. & Eng. Ch.*, 21, 177 (1929).

readily differentiated by the eye. The next problem was to duplicate as nearly as possible these colors in glass, preferably heat-resisting. Considering the change in coloring power of metallic oxides when dissolved in different batches, the difficulty can be appreciated, but the problem was eventually solved. The present series of signal colors has proven to be very satisfactory.

Many hundreds of colored glasses are produced today but some have unique spectral transmissions. The range covers glasses absorbing the visible but transmitting ultra-violet, as one extreme, to "opaque" but infra-red transmitting, on the other. Then there are glasses with fairly high transmission in the visible that absorb the ultra-violet, or, in other cases, the infra-red.[19] With the other extreme represented by glass of such high transmission to ultra-violet radiation that it approaches that of fused silica.

It has been previously mentioned that glasses are colored by certain metallic oxides in solution. While this is generally the case, there are other colors produced by precipitation of colloidal particles within an originally colorless glass, by appropriate heat treatment. A classic example of this type of color is gold ruby which contains colloidal gold in suspension.

(b) *Translucent Glasses.* Translucent glasses owe their peculiar optical effects to the presence of minute particles. "Opal" glasses are clear when molten but "devitrify" readily and hence become opalescent as the glass is worked into form. The size of the precipitated particles depends on the composition of the glass and the heat treatment during forming. These glasses are of great commercial importance as diffusing media in illumination, as containers, and as construction material.

(c) *Safety Glasses.* Under this heading we shall mention laminated glass, which is built up of alternate layers of glass sheet and a transparent plastic. As used in windshields two layers of polished plate are usually bonded with a relatively thin layer of pyroxylin. In bullet-proof glass of this type more layers of heavy plate and plastic are used. When this type of glass is broken, the pieces are held in place by the plastic.

Another, more recent, type of safety glass is the glass called "Sekurit," in France and "Armour plate" in England which is "casehardened." The high mechanical strength of glass so treated permits its use under conditions that would break ordinary untreated glass,

---

[19] H. P. Gage, *Trans. Soc. Mot. Pict. Eng., 12,* 1063-7 (1928).

and when such glass is broken the sheet disintegrates into small pieces that are not dangerous.

II—BATCH MATERIALS AND MIXING

The rôle played by the chemical engineer in producing the chemicals used as raw materials in the glass industry will be considered in other chapters and needs no further comment here.

Handling of raw materials, cullet and coal, in the modern glass works is by conveying machinery of recognized types. Large storage bins discharge into traveling mixers and the mixed batch is carried to the furnaces by elevator and conveyor. Usually the tank furnaces are fed continuously by automatic feeders, which may be of the gravity, "pusher," or screw-feed type.

III—MELTING

Developments in melting may be discussed with reference to the two important processes now in use, (1) pot furnace and (2) tank furnace. Space will not permit an account of the extensive work done on furnace design with respect to regenerators, recuperators, burners, ports, arches, flues and, in fact, on all of the factors entering into improved efficiency of combustion. Although fuel consumption per ton of glass has been reduced, a wonderful opportunity to improve efficiency in the process of melting glass still exists. Electric melting has been actively investigated and small furnaces have been operated with some success; however, the cost of power will have to be materially reduced before electric melting can be economically justified for ordinary glasses. Melting. by any process can be improved with better refractories. Our resumé will be confined primarily to developments in this field.

(1) *Pot furnaces* have, to a large extent, been superseded by the so-called tank furnace but there are certain conditions under which pot furnaces are used advantageously. With small production of special glasses, or where it is essential to protect the melting batch from the products of combustion, pot furnaces are practically indispensable. The most important developments in pot-furnace melting have been in the quality of the pot itself. Obviously, it is a rather difficult problem to produce a silicate pot, or crucible, in which to melt silicates, without contaminating the product or melting the container. The chemical composition of the crucible walls is of importance but equally so is the physical condition—pore space, size and character of "grog" and bond. Developments to improve melting

pots have been along several lines. In the pot method for melting plate glass, Kerr produced the so-called "sand pot"; he developed a pot that dissolved slowly, but evenly, by introducing powdered sand into his clays. Glass melted in such pots contained much less "stones" than that made in the pots previously used. However, the "sand pot" had disadvantages for other types of glass, and, in order to obtain pots for special optical glasses, such as the heavy flints and dense barium crowns, Bleininger,[20] at the Bureau of Standards, developed a dense, porcelain-type of pot which was produced by casting in plaster rather than built up slowly by the century-old manual process.

(2) In the tank type of furnace the crucibles of the pot furnace are replaced by a large, relatively shallow, box or tank. Batch materials are fed into one end of the tank and "fined" glass is worked out of the other. Such furnaces are continuous in their operation, as contrasted to batch melting in pots, and hence permit uninterrupted production. The refractory blocks, forming the walls of the tank, gradually wear away under the action of the hot glass, and it is obvious that the life of a tank and the quality of the glass are dependent upon the quality of these blocks. In an effort to improve them, tank block refractories have been studied in several ways.

(a) Compositions have been investigated with particular emphasis on the alumina-silica ratio. These investigations were helped tremendously, and greatly stimulated, by the phase rule studies on the alumina-silica system [21] at the Geophysical Laboratory. But it must be confessed that the actual results obtained in practice with a given composition were frequently masked by effects attributable to physical structure.

(b) Such results led to investigations of methods of formation in an effort to produce a denser block. Various methods were used to obtain this end, with the usual clay materials, but only one will be mentioned here, namely, the continuous pugging and extruding of blocks through a die. This process, which was indeed quite an advance in the art, also employed a vacuumizing treatment during the pugging operation in a somewhat successful effort to reduce pore space. However, the structure of the resulting block was essentially that of preceding blocks—"grog" bonded by more or less vitrified clays.

---

[20] *J. Am. Ceram. Soc., 1,* 15-24 (1918).

[21] Shepherd, Rankin & Wright, *Am. J. Sci.* (4), *28,* 293-333 (1909).
Bowen & Grieg, *J. Am. Ceram. Soc., 7,* 238-254 (1924).

(c) More recently a dry press process for producing blocks has been developed, followed by a high-temperature firing; this process yields a dense block of satisfactory performance.

(d) That still better blocks could be produced by departing radically from tradition led to the most important contribution to glass house refractories in centuries. This new process, developed by Fulcher,[22] is simply that the raw materials, correctly proportioned, are melted electrically and then cast to size and shape in a mold, much as metals are cast. Such castings, followed by appropriate annealing, yield a remarkably resistant block of nearly zero porosity, and, furthermore, the time of production has been reduced from months to a few days. "Electrocast" refractories, as they are called, have found great favor in the glass industry. Their use has increased tank life and improved glass quality.

IV—"GATHERING GLASS FROM THE FURNACE

Space will not permit more than a mere mention of the many developments in transferring molten glass from the furnace for subsequent forming. The methods used for pot glass—"gathering," "ladling," "pouring,"—have to be modified for effectively feeding continuous automatic forming machines. The epoch-making invention of the vacuum gather on the first automatic bottle machine, by Michael Owens in 1899, marked a new era in glass production methods.[23] Since then there have been invented such notable processes as the Colburn continuous drawing of sheet glass;[24] the Brooke flowing device feed for presses and blowing machines; and the "gob" feeding device of Peiler, which delivers a charge of glass of predetermined size and shape. Extensive applications of these methods to the forming of all kinds of glass have naturally followed. The vacuum gather has been adapted to bulb and tumbler production; continuous flow is used for plate glass blanks, figured sheet, tubing, and bulbs; the "gob" feeder has applications to all types of ware made by pressing, blowing, or a combination of press and blow. Each of these developments has been a significant advance in the art. Their description in detail, while most fascinating chapters in the history of glass technology, cannot be presented here.

---

[22] *Glass Industry*, 7, 257-261 (1926).

[23] This development has been interestingly described by Walbridge, "American Bottles, Old and New," Toledo (1920).

[24] See "Flat Glass," A. E. Fowle, Toledo (1924).

V—FORMING

The history of the development of machinery for the semi and fully automatic forming of glass is somewhat apart from the theme of this resumé. However, those who have witnessed the modern high-speed glass-forming machines in operation can well realize the nature of the problems involved. The outstanding condition to be considered in glass-machine design is, essentially, that the completed article must be produced in a few seconds, the period during which the glass changes in viscosity from a syrup consistency to a solid. The problems in heat flow, stability of metals, clearances of bearings, etc., can well be pictured and the success of such machines is an outstanding tribute to the designing engineers. The metallurgist has also helped by contributing heat resisting alloys and special treatments for molds and machine parts.

VI—ANNEALING

No better illustration as to the state of the art of annealing glass can be cited than the impression, generally prevalent some years ago, that days, and even weeks, at elevated temperature, was required to relieve the strains developed in glass during shaping. Under the stimulation of War-time production of optical glass, the theory of annealing was developed and this operation placed on a scientific basis. The work of Adams and Williamson [25] on the release of strain in glass, the correlation of stress and birefringence, and the development of annealing schedules, is a classic. The applications to the immediate problems of obtaining optical glass for instruments of war—important as it was—has been more than overshadowed by the general adoption of their results by the glass industry. By mathematical analysis and laboratory experiment it was found that the release of strain is a function of time and temperature, the time doubling for a decrease of some 9 deg. C. This relation has removed empiricism from a most important operation of the glass industry. Not content to stop with this accomplishment these investigators established some quantitative relations between stress and birefringence, factors of great importance in designing glass to meet certain mechanical conditions or thermal stresses.

With such quantitative data available the engineer has produced continuous annealing equipment with automatic temperature regulation and controlled circulation of air that has saved fuel, improved

---

[25] *J. Frank. Inst., 190,* 590-631; 835-870 (1920).

annealing, and as a consequence produced a more uniform product with less loss in process. Electrically heated and controlled annealing "lehrs" have been developed and are in successful operation.

VII—FINISHING

Operations performed on glass after it leaves the annealing oven are termed "finishing." Such operations consist of grinding, polishing cuttnig, sandblasting, enameling, grading, gaging and similar operations. Of particular interest to the chemist is the use of hydrofluoric acid for polishing finely ground surfaces. Similarly, other solutions of hydrofluoric acid act as etching media, as, for instance, in the inside frosting of bulbs. In this interesting process the first action of the fluoride mixture (etching) is to render the bulbs exceedingly brittle. Under the microscope the etch pattern is sharp and crystalline in appearance. In a subsequent treatment, with washing between, the etched bulbs are subjected to the action of a dilute hydrofluoric acid mixture, which rounds out the pattern with restoration of strength.[26]

Other developments in finishing operations have been: continuous grinding and polishing equipment for plate glass; flame-cutting for bulbs, chemical ware and tumblers; needle-etching for decorating. More recently abrasive wheels have been developed for rapidly cutting glass. Their use will undoubtedly be extended.

VIII—ENGINEERING APPLICATIONS

While all the various types of glass find some industrial use, and are therefore engineering materials, the chemical engineer—dealing as he does with hot corrosive liquids and gases—has found extensive applications for the special borosilicate types referred to on preceding pages.

Prior to the development of these special types, industrial uses of glass were closely related to its unique property of permanent transparency. The chemical industry inherited glass as a laboratory material from the alchemists but, with the exception of 25-gal. flasks used before the advent of platinum pans for sulphuric acid concentration, plant-scale glass equipment was unknown.

The glasses then available had useful corrosion resisting qualities but they possessed only moderate resistance to temperature changes, and unless the article was made with heavy walls (which increased

---

[26] *J. Am. Ceram. Soc., 10,* 402-410 (1927).

the risk of thermal breakage) there was the added disadvantage of mechanical weakness.

When the chemical engineer of 25 years ago had to translate laboratory technicque from its glassware stage to durable plant equipment, he was faced with a limitation of materials and the necessity for undesirable compromises between fabrication possibilities, corrosion resistance, and costs. Today we have a wealth of new construction materials which have revolutionized plant design, and there is probably no phase of chemical engineering which has undergone more profound change in recent years than equipment materials.

While industrial borosilicate glass is but one of the many new materials, it possesses a combination of properties which have led to its extensive use in chemical plants and changed its conception as an engineering material from the dictionary definition as "the hard brittle substance in windows."

Compared to ordinary glass the borosilicates have much lower coefficients of expansion, higher melting points, and greater resistance to mechanical shock and chemical attack, without, however, any loss of the useful property of transparency.

When present day industrial uses of borosilicate glasses are analyzed, it is evident that no single property has dictated the types of application. In practically all uses one property may be of importance, but some or all of the other qualities are also of direct benefit.

As examples transparency, heat resistance, and chemical stability are useful in chemical plant pipe-line construction and these factors, combined with satisfactory heat transfer rate, have resulted in the development of interesting types of tubular heat exchange equipment.

Data on comparative rates of heat transfer have been given in papers [27] presented to the Institute by Littleton and Bates of the Corning Glass Works Research Laboratory.

Under actual operating conditions values as high as 120 B.T.u. per square foot per hour per deg. F., have been obtained in high rate of circulation tubular coolers designed for liquid to liquid transfer.

Surface hardness and smoothness are the predominant factors in a group of applications best illustrated by silk bobbins and guides, and again these characteristics in combination with the high elec-

---

[27] J. T. Littleton, Jr., and H. C. Bates, *Trans. Am. Inst. Chem. Eng., 17*, 95-105 (1925). J. T. Littleton, Jr., and H. C. Bates, Schenectady Vol. Trans. *A. I. Ch. E.* (in press).

trical insulating values of special borosilicate compositions, have resulted in the development of radio, carrier current telephone and power transmission line insulators.

Processes of manufacture have been continually improved and the earlier limitations of size of unit pieces are gradually disappearing. Absorption and reactions columns 24 in. diameter by 20 ft. high and built up from ten or more sections are regular production items.

Borosilicate glasses can be fabricated into sculptured and architectural shapes by casting processes and as the transparent or translucent glass has unusual textural qualities, castings are being employed to secure a new permanent richness in architectural details. Another type of casting process now in the experimental stage holds promise of one piece containers and reaction vessels of large capacity.

The development of the borosilicate glasses has placed interesting construction materials, with some unique properties, in the hands of chemical engineers, and the engineer, as has been briefly outlined, has applied these materials to a variety of forms and uses, and in so doing has developed new and interesting types of plant equipment.

CHAPTER XIX

FRACTIONAL DISTILLATION ASSUMES MORE IMPORTANT ROLE AMONG CHEMICAL ENGINEERING OPERATIONS

By E. H. Leslie and H. B. Coats

Respectively, Vice-President and Technical Director, Leader Industries., Inc., Decatur, Ill.; and Director, The Leslie Laboratories, Ann Arbor, Mich.

APPRECIATION of the principles of rectification in Europe a century and more ago led to the development of column apparatus of various types and its use in the beverage alcohol industry. In 1893 Sorel developed a mathematical basis for the interpretation of the distillation of binary solutions, and in this same year Hausbrand published a book in which he interpreted the phenomena of distillation and presented the methods of calculation and design that have been accepted by the engineering profession as fundamental and even standard. However, the subject aroused no widespread interest in this country and, aside from a paper by W. K. Lewis in 1909, little of engineering importance, other than articles on vapor pressures of substances and solutions, was published until 1922 when a symposium on fractional distillation was held in connection with the 63d meeting of the American Chemical Society. Interest in the subject has greatly increased during the last 10 years as a result of the widening use of fractionation and, particularly, the awakening technical consciousness in the petroleum and natural gasoline industries.

Concurrent with the increasing industrial importance of distillation has been the gradual evolution and acceptance of the conception of the so-called "unit operations" of chemical engineering and the designation of distillation as one of these operations. This assumption of the position of a specimen, as it were, for study within the confines of the academic walls, has led to many useful contributions to our knowledge of various phases of the subject.

Several types of information are required by the engineer for the successful solution of any given distillation problem. First of all, fundamental data on vapor pressures, vapor-liquid equilibria under different conditions of temperature and pressure, latent heats and specific heats are needed. With these in hand the number of "theoretical plates" or "equilibrium units" required to effect a given separation can be calculated for different reflux ratios. After balancing fixed investment against operating cost, the best combination of plates and reflux can be selected, whereupon the heat quantities involved can be determined.

Real progress has been made, particularly in the last 10 years, in the accumulation of necessary fundamental data. Furthermore, the calculation of number of plates by the tedious algebraic method has been superceded by graphical methods, the simplest of which is probably that of McCabe and Thiele.

Once the number of equilibrium units has been determined, it is then necessary to know the efficiency of the plate to be used in practice. The definition of plate efficiency that has received general acceptance is that of Murphree (1925):

$$E = \frac{Y_n - Y_{n+1}}{Y_n^* - Y_{n+1}} 100$$

in which

Y_{n+1} = composition of the vapor rising to the plate
Y_n = composition of the vapor leaving the plate
Y^{n*} = composition of vapor in equilibrium with the
liquid leaving the plate

An application of the conception of plate efficiency to the graphical method of McCabe and Thiele has been given by Baker and Stockhardt (1930) whereby the number of working plates of known or chosen efficiency is determined directly.

Data on plate efficiency are too few. This subject will undoubtedly be investigated much more thoroughly in the years to come. Lewis and Wilde (1928) and Lewis and Smoley (1930) have published data on columns operating on complex solutions and found higher efficiencies that were anticipated from data on binary solutions, for example 85-95 per cent rather than 59 per cent. Shirk and Montanna (1927) found that the efficiency of a small column handling ethyl alcohol and water ranged from 30 to 90 per cent, depending on the reflux ratio and on the rate of distillation.

In general, it is now believed that small caps, with small slots, well immersed in the liquid, will give higher efficiency than large caps with large slots. Depth of immersion must not be excessive or the pressure drop through the column will increase out of proportion to the efficiency. Plates on which the liquid flows in a directed course longer than the plate diameter are more efficient than the ordinary cross-flow plate. However, the obstruction to liquid flow must not be such as to cause an appreciable difference in liquid head at different points on the plate. For any given plate, the efficiency will vary with the diffusivities of the substances composing the system distilled.

Little of a specific nature has been written on the subject of column capacity. Chillas and Weir (1930) have published a few data on entrainment. Fairly dependable data are in possession of users and suppliers of column equipment, but few of these have been published. It is recognized that the rate at which a column is run depends on the overflow from plate to plate. If this is high the column can be run at rates that cause fairly large entrainment. Plate efficiency will be affected only slightly. The limiting vapor velocity in a column is that that will blow the liquid from one plate to the next or that will cause a pressure drop so high that the overflow will not descend the downpipes. Many columns used in the organic industries, for example, alcohol columns, are run at high rates without serious sacrifice of efficiency. On the other hand, columns used in the petroleum industry under conditions of low reflux must be operated at low vapor velocity to avoid entrainment.

The above discussion has been confined to columns of the cap type. Although these are by far the most important, the packed column is not without its field of usefulness. Packed columns hold less liquid and can be used in batch distillation to give sharp separations of components present in small quantity. The small liquid holdup makes this type of column convenient for stills that handle different materials from time to time. Exceptionally corrosive material can be distilled in columns packed with glass rings. However, experience has shown that packed columns are not efficient if built in large diameter because of channeling of the fluids flowing. The conception of the H. E. T. P. (height equivalent to theoretical plate), introduced by Peters, permits calculation of the required height of a packed column once the value of the H. E. T. P. has been determined for any given packing and for the system to be distilled. The usefulness of the packed column is limited, and it is hardly to be expected that it will be greatly extended.

With this brief review of the subject of distillation and distillation equipment in the abstract, it will be of interest to consider a few of the more important applications to the problems of specific industries.

DISTILLATION OF PETROLEUM

Distillation of petroleum and petroleum products overshadows all other applications of the principles of fractionation because of the size of the plant units, the varied nature of the materials handled and results to be achieved, and the aggressive manner in which the petroleum refiners proceeded to improve their methods when the need for better technique was urgent enough to justify the large investment required. The entire development of modern distillation technique, as applied to petroleum, has taken place within the 25-year period since the American Institute of Chemical Engineers was founded, and most of it in the last 15 years of that period.

The petroleum industry has been accused of being slow to adopt distillation methods that were well known in the alcohol, tar and organic chemical industries. However, as is usual in the evolution of technological procedures, barring a fundamental and revolutionary discovery, the actual course of events was the resultant of several factors, the most important of which was the growth of the automotive industry and the consequent need for large quantities of motor fuels and lubricants. Modern cracking and distillation equipment would have had little place in a picture in which gasoline mysteriously found its way on dark nights onto the waters of Oil Creek or the Allegheny River.

In the period 1908-1920, with the exception of the war years, demand for petroleum products was easily met through application of conventional methods of distillation and the chemical engineer had little place or recognition in the business. However, from 1920 to 1933 the requirements as to quantity and quality of petroleum products resulted in an almost complete rebuilding of facilities for distillation and related procedures. The industry afforded an opportunity to large numbers of young chemical engineers, unhampered by long years of association with the time-honored and conventional methods of the business, and imbued with knowledge of processing operations and equipment based on the newly formulated interpretation of these procedures in terms of what are now recognized as the unit operations of chemical engineering. Nor was the academic invasion of the industry confined to the new graduate, for many members of the teaching staffs of leading universities, and chemical engineers from other industries, found therein abundant opportunity for professional endeavor. Today the industry is technically manned as are few others.

The pipe still distillation of petroleum was practiced widely in California from 1910 to 1920, in plants such as those designed by, or after the methods of M. J. Trumble, A. F. L. Bell, I. W. Fuqua, E. I. Dyer, and others. Although without many of the refinements of the units of today, these plants employed once-through heating of the oil, flash vaporization, steam stripping of bottoms, and limited fractionation of vapors. The problem, in general, was to remove a small percentage of gasoline and distillates from heavy crudes and to make a satisfactory residual fuel oil comprising 70-90 per cent of the crude. In most of these plants fractionation was effected by partial condensation, or this in combination with redistillation or steam stripping of condensates. However, the Pyzel "dephlegmator," as used by the Shell Co. in its Trumble plants at Coalinga (1915) and Martinez (1916), was a continuous fractionating column of the "disk and doughnut" type, with rectifier above and steam stripper below the feed point and with refluxing coil at the top of the column. Although less effective as a means of countercurrently contacting vapor and liquid than the well-designed cap columns of today, it no doubt accomplished all that was desired at the time and had the advantage of simplicity.

From 1920 to 1925 the fractionation of petroleum and petroleum cuts and products was studied by a few refiners and equipment companies as a scientific and engineering problem. Some of the earlier results of this work bore fruit in the application of fractionating columns, or "bubble-towers" as they were called in the jargon of the business, to batteries of shell stills operated continuously. A few new shell-still batteries were constructed, but the advantages of the pipe still and flash vaporization were becoming recognized at this time, and this, combined with the rationalization of the design of the pipe heater, largely by engineers associated with refinery equipment companies, resulted in the widespread adoption of the pipe-still distillation unit.

The first pipe-still units were topping or skimming plants used to remove gasoline, naphtha, kerosene and gas oil from crudes of different types, leaving a residual fuel oil or reduced crude. In these plants crude is pumped through heat exchangers that raise the temperature to 300-350 deg. F. and through the tube system of the heater where the temperature is raised to a point such that, when the oil exits into the vaporizer and is brought into contact with steam to effect a reduction of the oil-vapor partial pressure, the products to be taken as distillates are vaporized. The unvaporized bottoms pass downwardly through several bubble-cap plates, countercurrent to steam. Thereby, the equilibrium proportion of the overhead products, that inevitably remains in any bottoms material from a separation by flash vaporization, is removed as a result of the oil-vapor partial pressure reduction in the presence of steam, and the consequent vaporization of part of the bottoms by conversion of the sensible heat of the liquid to latent heat of the vapor formed. By causing this conversion to take place in a countercurrent manner, as in the flow of the liquid over three to seven bubble-cap plates, the bottoms is stripped of the most volatile components contained in it after the flash vaporization.

The vapor flashed in the vaporizer is rectified in a 15 to 20 plate column supplied with gasoline reflux in controlled quantity. Naphtha, kerosene and gas oil are drawn as liquids from selected plates of the column. Each of these products contains a small proportion of gasoline components that can be removed by reboiling or steam stripping. The conventional procedure is to flow the side stream from the main column over three to five plates in a small stripping column and to supply steam to the base of this column. Steam and volatile components are returned from the top of the stripper to the main column. In many instances the use of these strippers is unnecessary because of the small proportion of volatile components contained in the side streams.

A principal difference between the procedure just described for the separation of crude petroleums into several products, and the older operations of alcohol, tar, ammonia, and similar distillations, is related to and is occasioned by the composition of the material distilled. Petroleum is composed of numerous hydrocarbons and related homologs, each present in relatively small quantity. Likewise, petroleum products are solutions of several to many components grouped into chosen boiling ranges. The basic principles of the separations effected are, however, exactly the same as those on which the separations of systems of a few components are based.

The next step in the development of petroleum distillation technique was an extension of the above described procedure to the direct production of lubricating oil stocks, including wax distillate and residual or overhead stocks containing amorphous wax. Prior to 1925, it was learned that wax distillate could be freed of colloidalizing contaminants by fractionation, and that a distillate so made could be chilled and pressed at temperatures down to 0 deg. F., or even lower. This was a distinct advance in the art of neutral-oil production for, theretofore, wax distillate had been "cracked" for the supposed conversion of amorphous to crystalline wax, or, whatever the interpretation of the operation, for the production of "pressable" distillate. The "cracking" of wax distillate actually resulted in extensive destruction of valuable neutral oils. The elimination of this operation was a worthwhile contribution of the chemical engineer to the art of petroleum refining.

Steam refined stocks, or the raw material for making cylinder oils, had long been made as residual stocks in shell stills. The most important and valuable source of these oils was, and still is, the petroleums produced in the Appalachian oil region or the so-called "Pennsylvania grade" petroleums. From these crudes the residual product is a green stock that requires no treatment other than percolation through fullers earth, and removal of amorphous wax, to fit it for use as a "bright stock" from which motor oils and other lubricants are compounded.

On the other hand, the petroleums of the Mid-Continent, Gulf Coast, and California contain asphaltic substances in small to large amounts. The production of so-called "overhead stocks" by distillation has made it possible to concentrate the asphaltic substances in a heavy bottoms, thus avoiding the necessity for a heavy sulphuric acid treatment and, furthermore, making it possible to produce stock from crudes that, theretofore, could not be utilized because of their high asphalt content.

In order to run crudes to stock bottoms and to permit the production of overhead stocks, two types of plants have been used. The steam-atmospheric unit is a single-flash plant charging crude and producing, directly, gasoline, naphtha, kerosene, gas oil, wax distillate and residual stock. The two-stage unit charges crude and tops it to reduced crude in the atmospheric-pressure stage. The reduced crude is then flashed at higher temperature and under vacuum to produce wax distillate and stock or, possibly, a heavy gas-oil overhead in addition to these products. If running asphaltic or semi-asphaltic crude of fairly high asphalt content, the stock is also taken as an overhead product.

The choice between the steam-atmospheric unit and the two-stage plant depends on the nature of the oil to be run and its sensitivity to temperature. At present the steam atmospheric unit is most popular for running Pennsylvania crude to residual stocks, and the two-stage unit is preferred for the asphalt containing crudes. In a few instances three-stage units have proved desirable, the third stage operating under a low vacuum and flashing a heavy oil from the bottoms from the second stage.

Space does not permit more than mention of the numerous other applications of fractionation to the operations of the petroleum refinery. Pressed distillate is now fractionated to produce gas oil, nonviscous neutral oils and residual viscous neutral oils. In most instances this operation is conducted at atmospheric pressure, although vacuum units are in operation ,for the manufacture of neutrals.

Pressure distillates are rerun to make gasoline and bottoms. An interesting variation of this operation is one in which a two-stage unit is employed, the second stage operating under vacuum so that the temperature at no time exceeds 250 deg. F. The necessity for the low temperature lies in the thermal instability of compounds formed in the refining treatment applied to the pressure distillate before it is rerun.

Bright-stock solutions, from decolorizing and dewaxing operations, are rerun for removal of naphtha. Pipe-still practice in this connection has permitted denuding without serious loss or reversion of color.

Fractionation has been applied in cracking operations to effect separation of the gasoline formed and to segregate cycle stocks from residual fuel oils. The operations of topping and cracking have frequently been combined, using the waste or excess heat of the latter operation to supply the energy necessary for the former.

All in all, the application of fractionation to the operations of the petroleum refinery has increased the yields of the more valuable products, improved the quality of the products made, reduced costs of fuel, steam and labor directly, and indirectly has reduced the costs of and simplified other processing operations involved.

NATURAL GAS GASOLINE AND REFINERY VAPOR RECOVERY

One of the most interesting and important applications of the principles of distillation has been seen in the operations of the natural gasoline industry and the analogous procedures that are a part of refinery methods for the recovery and separation of the volatile hydrocarbons produced in cracking heavier oils. Although the methods involved were undoubtedly incubating in the minds of a few engineers in the period from 1915 to 1923, as is evidenced by publications and patents since issued, the commercial use of rectification in these fields has been limited to the last decade.

A stranger to the minds of many, if not most of those engaged in the natural gasoline industry, rectification no sooner was put to work than it found itself in the limelight of litigation that was pursued with such determination as to leave little to the imagination regarding its family tree and closeted skeletons. The result was a victory for the freedom of diffusional processes and, of equal importance, the education of the industry to such a degree as to have an important effect on progress in the application of the art.

Today, substantially all natural gasoline is rectified for removal of ethane, propane, and such part of the butane as is necessary to meet the particular requirements. Within the last three or four years, propane and butane have been separated and marketed as such for use as fuels or in making air-gas. Pentane is also separated to a limited extent and used as raw material for making chlorpentane and amyl alcohol.

Pressure distillates from cracking operations are now debutanized or stabilized. The volatile materials removed are, in some instances, rectified for the separation of ethylene, propylene, butylenes, and amylenes. These are raw materials of increasing importance.

Many of these operations are of unusual technical interest in that they involve distillation at high pressure, use of reflux liquids that are gases at ordinary pressure, high reflux ratio and reboiler heat input, column operation frequently under conditions of unstable equilibrium, and the necessity for properly applied automatic control in its highest state of development.

INDUSTRIAL ALCOHOL, LIGHT OIL AND SOLVENTS

Distillation methods in use in the alcohol industry have been in essentials those of European origin, as, for example, the Barbet continuous rectifier. However, improvements have been made and the trend, in general, has been to replace batch stills with continuous stills. The cost of distillation is an important item in the total cost of manufacture of industrial alcohol. Multiple-effect evaporation of the "slop" has been combined with continuous "beer-still" operation in such manner as to supply the steam for the beer still.

The most interesting development in the alcohol industry, from the standpoint of distillation technique, has been the direct production of absolute alcohol by distillation. One of the earliest attempts was based on distillation under a vacuum, for no constant-boiling mixture of alcohol and water exists if the absolute pressure on the system is less than 70 mm. The vacuum method has not been extensively used, however, because it is less satisfactory than the method based on the addition of a third substance, such as benzene.

The azeotropic method was commercially practicalized · in this country shortly after the War, and its success is attested by the fact that absolute alcohol is now available at a cost only slightly in excess of that of 95 per cent alcohol. The basis of the procedure is the alteration of the vapor-pressure relationships in such manner, by the addition of a third component, that a constant-boiling mixture of increased water content is formed, thereby permitting the separation of a portion of the alcohol free of water.

The byproduct and light oil industry has not been notable for revolutionary improvement in distillation practice. This has probably been occasioned by the fact that it was rapidly expanded, almost necessarily along conventional lines, during the war period. Since that time, prices for the products have, in general, afforded little incentive for new developments and the writing-off of previous heavy investments.

Numerous applications of column equipment have originated in the fine chemical and solvent industries as, for example, continuous esterification for the production of ethyl acetate. However, space limitation makes it impossible to review them here.

Conclusion

In the short period of 25 years, distillation practice has advanced in this country from the status of an imported and empirical art to the importance and dignity of a widely applied "unit operation" resting on a sound scientific and engineering basis. Progress has been made at an accelerating rate. However, much more is to be known about the subject and its applications than is now known. Marked improvement in apparatus and increasing ingenuity in application can confidently be expected in the years to come.

CHAPTER XX

PROGRESS IN EVAPORATION IN THE UNITED STATES IN THEORY AND PRACTICE

By W. L. Badger

Professor of Chemical Engineering, University of Michigan, Ann Arbor

I F THE TOTAL CONTRIBUTIONS of this country to the general subject of evaporation in the last 25 years were to be summed up in a single sentence, that sentence would be difficult to frame. From the standpoint of theory the period has been disappointing, as no really basic advances have been made. Practically all of the fundamental experimental work that has been done anywhere in the world has been carried on in this country. No important experimental work has been done in Europe but from the standpoint of practice the case is just reversed. Probably fifty articles giving actual operating data have been published in Europe for every one of that kind published in this country. Progress in the development of evaporator types has not resulted in important changes either here or abroad, although the development of the forced-circulation evaporator in this country is probably the most important contribution in this direction. However, no development of first importance either in basic theory or principles of design, has appeared in the past 25 years either in this country or abroad.

When one considers the advances that have been made in the theory of heat transfer, especially in the case of heat transfer to nonboiling liquids; the extensive studies that have been made on the design and performance of distillation apparatus; and the very great advances that have been made in our understanding of the flow of fluids in pipes, the progress made along the lines of evaporation seems disappointingly small. It is true that there are reasons for the difference, and it is true that there are many of the unit operations in which less progress has been made than in evaporation. In view of the number of evaporators in commercial operation; the value, not only of the equipment itself but of the products that go through it; and the gain that could be made by a relatively small increase in either economy or capacity; it is decidedly disappointing that no more progress has been made.

Evaporator Practice in 1908.—Evaporator practice in the United States at the beginning of the period under discussion is easily summarized. The most common form of body was the Wellner-Jelinek type; and, excepting in beet sugar mills, these were seldom operated with more than two or three effects. The next most popular type was the standard short-tube vertical, although there were a few basket-type verticals in operation. There were also some Lillies, a few Yaryans, and a very few Kestners.

Although for at least 30 years before the beginning of this period, it had been known that overall heat-transfer coefficients were conditioned entirely by the characteristics of the fluid films, the average engineer dealing with evaporators not only did not understand this, but seemed to be totally ignorant of the fact that there was such a thing as a heat-transfer coefficient. Evaporators were designed on the basis of so many gallons evaporated per square foot per hour, with some approximate allowance in case the overall temperature drop was much greater or much less than 100 deg. F., or if there were considerable elevations in boiling points. Very few multiple effect evaporators were designed in the proper sense of the word, and outside of the beet-sugar industry few people even pretended to calculate the performance of a multiple effect or to use any of the more complicated flowsheets involving step-wise preheating of the liquor or extraction of the vapors.

The only important book on heat transfer and evaporation was Hausbrand's "Verdampfen, Kondensieren und Kühlen" which appeared in its first edition in 1899 and was translated into English in 1902. Although the periodical literature abroad, especially the periodicals of the German beet-sugar industry, had been full of articles on every phase of evaporator theory, design and operation, practically nothing had been published in the United States.

Evaporator Practice in 1933.—In contrast with the situation in 1908, the situation in 1933 shows considerable changes. While many Wellner-Jelineks are still in operation, very few have been built for several years; and this type is becoming obsolete. When horizontal tube evaporators are used they are now built with bodies in the form of a vertical cylinder. The short-tube submerged-type vertical tube evaporator is much more common (both in the central down-take type and the basket-type than it was in 1908, but it is giving way to long-tube high-speed evaporators. The inclined tube types have appeared and have begun to disappear. The Lillie and the Yaryan are no longer of any importance. The Kestner has made no advances and has not been actively marketed in this country for some years. The one advance in this direction has been the introduction of the long-tube forced-circulation evaporator. This and the long-tube natural-circulation vertical, seem destined to become the only important forms of evaporator construction in the near future.

During the past 25 years there have been a number of publications in the United States covering experimental work on overall heat transfer coefficients in various types of evaporators on various liquids. These have come either from the laboratory of the Louisiana Sugar School or from the laboratory that was maintained as a co-operative enterprise by the Swenson Evaporator Co. and the University of Michigan. While such determinations of overall heat-transfer coefficients have been useful to a considerable extent, they have not really advanced our basic knowledge of heat transfer co-efficients in evaporators as much as might have been accomplished by more highly theoretical work. These determinations have, however, served to show how greatly the rate of heat transfer in an evaporator varies with such factors as boiling point, temperature drop, viscosity of the liquid, and details of the construction of the apparatus. At the present time not only many engineers who specify or operate evaporators, but practically all engineers concerned with the design of evaporators are familiar with the idea of heat-transfer coefficients and also of the qualitative effects of various factors on the individual film coefficients of which the overall coefficient is composed. Unfortunately, there still appears at intervals the engineer, sometimes in a responsible position, who bases his reasoning entirely on the thermal conductivity of the metal, and who is unaware of the significance of the fluid films.

Great advance has also been made in the calculations for multiple effect evaporators. The basic ideas involved are not different from those presented by Hausbrand in 1899, but the encouraging feature is that they are more widely used. Proposed evaporators are now calculated in detail. Complicated steam flowsheets are now found, and there is in general a greater familiarity with the advantage to be derived from the various modifications of the simple multiple-effect flowsheet for both liquor and vapor.

The last 25 years have seen no important changes in methods of operation. The pressure range through which evaporators may work is considerably larger than 25 years ago, mainly because it is no longer necessary to assume that exhaust steam will come from reciprocating engines at about 5 lb. back-pressure. Thermocompression, which was extensively discussed in the foreign literature in the late 70's and again in the 1900's, was revived in 1920-25, but has not been found to be of value in the United States. The high vacuums made possible in modern central station practice have little value for most evaporator installations. Calcium sulphate scale is still a curse (although important work on the mechanism of scale formation has been accomplished), and no sure cure for foaming has been found, although high velocities have a beneficial effect on both scale and foam prevention. The only radical change in operation is in the common salt industry, where the salt is removed from the evaporators by pumps instead of by bucket elevators.

In the field of auxiliaries, the general replacement of slide valve vacuum pumps by rotative dry vacuum pumps, the beginnings of the use of steam jet-nozzles for producing vacuum, the use of self-priming centrifugal pumps for thick liquor and condensate, and the tendency to handle salt (if produced in large amounts) on rotary continuous filters, are worthy of notice.

Literature on Evaporation. During the last 25 years Hausbrand's original book ran through several editions; the sixth and last appeared in 1918 and Hausbrand died in 1922. In 1931 a new Hausbrand, carrying the old name but completely rewritten by M. Hirsch. was published by Springer in Berlin. This is undoubtedly the foremost book on the subject and contains all the knowledge now available on heat transfer coefficients in evaporators. During the same period some other books on evaporation of lesser importance were published in Germany, while in this country the only two have been "Heat Transfer and Evaporation" by the writer, and "Evaporation" by Webre and Robinson, both published by the Chemical Catalog Co. in 1926.

During the earlier part of this 25-year period a number of general articles on evaporation and the general principles of evaporator design were published in various periodicals. This ground has been repeatedly covered in so many of these articles that it now seems that the time for them has definitely passed. This is especially true since there are at least two widely accepted text books of chemical engineering in which these fundamentals are covered, and it is expected that there will shortly be published a handbook of chemical engineering which will cover the same field in more detail.

To sum up the progress of the past 25 years, there has been a gradual reduction in the number of styles of evaporator bodies commonly used. Great progress has been made by both designers and operators in an understanding of the principles of heat transfer and of multiple-effect design and operation. There has been considerable empirical laboratory work on overall heat transfer coefficients, but a real fundamental theory of these coefficients, based on a knowledge of the individual film coefficients, is still entirely lacking.

In the following bibliography no attempt has been made to list every article published in the United States that bears on the subject of evaporators or evaporation, but all the more important ones have been listed. The patent citations are based on a complete file of all patents listed by the patent office in class 159, sub-classes 2, 5, 6, 13, 14, 15, 17, 18, 19, 20, 22, 23, 24, 25, 26, 27, 28, 29, 31, 33, 43, 44, 45 46, 47 and 50. In making such a patent bibliography it is difficult to know what patents to include and what to exclude. No bibliography can take the place of an actual patent search. It is impossible to qualify briefly any patent in such a way as to indicate either what it protects or what it discloses. An attempt has been made to indicate in one sentence the general field covered by each of those patents that the writer considers of any real importance in this field. Those patents in the classes listed above that relate to open direct-fired pans, or types of equipment that would be called dryers rather than evaporators, or the special equipment used for concentrating acids, have been omitted. A very few patents from other classes related to this field have been included where they have seemed important.

Chronology of Evaporation, 1908-1933

[As shown by important American technical articles]

1908-9	Sadtler (59) published the first general discussions of evaporation to appear in the United States.
1912	McCormack (48) published the first report on evaporator experiments to appear in the United States.
1913	Kerr (35) published his first bulletin on his extensive laboratory investigations. This was the most elaborate study made anywhere up to this time.
1915	Kerr (36) published his second bulletin on tests of evaporators (and other sugar mill equipment) in actual operation.
1918	Moore (54) published an important summary of the principles of evaporator calculations. Sadtler and deBeers (60) announced the establishment of the coöperative evaporator laboratory at the University of Michigan. DeBaufre (27) rediscovered steam jet thermocompression.
1920	The first research papers from the University of Michigan appeared (13, 19, 20, 21).
1921	The most prolific year in the United States for the literature of evaporation. The A.S.M.E. published a tentative test code for evaporators (1). Baker (22, 23) showed that Dühring's rule was applicable to solutions.
1924	Evaporator test codes, prepared by coöperation of the A.S.M.E. and the A.I.Ch.E., adopted by both societies.

1926　Books on evaporation published for the first time in the United States (by Webre and Robinson and by Badger).

1927　First laboratory studies on the forced circulation evaporator published (8, 9).

1928　Revision of the evaporators at Searles Lake described by Teeple (63).

1930　Use of diphenyl heat for evaporators discussed (17, 53).

Bibliography of Articles on Evaporation

1. Am. Soc. Mech. Eng. Test code for evaporators. *Mech. Eng.*, **43**, I, 184 (1921) ; *Am. Inst. Chem. Eng.*, Bull. No. 29, 34-5 (1924).

2. Anon. The Sanborn multiple effect evaporator. *La. Planter*, **47**, 240 (1911).

3. Anon. Distilled water for boiler feed at River Rouge Plant. *Power*, **54**, 998-1033 (1921).

4. Austin, H. The case for the multiple effect evaporator in the paper mill. *Chem. Met. Eng.*, **29**, 974-5 (1923).

5. Badger, W. L. Studies in evaporator design, IV. The relation between hydrostatic head, temperature drop, and heat transmission in horizontal tube evaporators. *Trans. Am. Inst. Chem. Eng.*, **13** (II), 139-53 (1920) ; *Chem. Met. Eng.*, **25**, 459-63 (1921).

6. Badger, W. L. Modern types of evaporators. *Chem. Met. Eng.*, **29**, 475-8 (1923).

7. Badger, W. L. Vapor recompression systems for evaporators. *Trans. Am. Inst. Chem. Eng.*, **14**, 221-258 (1923) ; *Chem. Met. Eng.*, **28**, 26-31, 73-8 (1923).

8. Badger, W. L. A new method for the evaporation of electrolytic caustic. *Trans. Am. Inst. Chem. Eng.*, **18**, 231-48 (1927).

9. Badger, W. L. The evaporation of waste sulphite liquor. *Ind. Eng. Chem.*, **19**, 677-80 (1927).

10. Badger, W. L. Progress in evaporation. *Chem. Met. Eng.*, **35**, 576-7 (1928).

11. Badger, W. L. Evaporators for boiler feed make-up. *Trans. Am. Soc. Mech. Eng.*, **50**, 207 (1928).

12. Badger, W. L. Evaporator design shows modern trend. *Chem. Met. Eng.*, **38**, 223-5 (1931).

13. Badger, W. L., and Baker, E. M. Studies in evaporator design, III. The boiling points of salt solutions. *Trans. Am. Inst. Chem. Eng.*, **13** (I), 151-68 (1920) ; *Chem. Met. Eng.*, **23**, 569-74 (1920).

14. Badger, W. L., and Caldwell, H. B. Studies in evaporator design, VI. Evaporators for salts with inverted solubility curves. *Trans. Am. Inst. Chem. Eng.*, **16** (II), 131-43 (1925).

15. Badger, W. L., and Cutting, F. C. Studies in evaporator design, VII. A glass and stoneware evaporator. *Trans. Am. Inst. Chem. Eng.*, **16** (II), 145-57 (1925).

16. Badger, W. L., and France, J. S. Influence of the properties of aluminum sulphate on evaporator design. *Ind. Eng. Chem.*, **15**, 364 (1923).

17. Badger, W. L., Monrad, C. C., and Diamond, H. W. Evaporation of caustic soda to high concentrations by means of diphenyl vapor. *Trans. Am. Inst. Chem. Eng.*, **24**, 56-83 (1930) ; *Ind. Eng. Chem.*, **22**, 700-7 (1930).

18. Badger, W. L., and Othmer, D. F. Studies in evaporator design, VIII. Optimum cycle for liquids that form scale. *Trans. Am. Inst. Chem. Eng.*, **16** (II), 159-168 (1925).

19. Badger, W. L., and Shepard, P. W. The evaporator experiment station at the University of Michigan. *Trans. Am. Inst. Chem. Eng.*, **13** (I), 77-100 (1920) ; *Chem. Met. Eng.*, **23**, 159-64 (1920).

20. Badger, W. L., and Shepard, P. W. Studies in evaporator design, I. The effect of temperature drop and temperature level on heat transmission in vertical tube evaporators. *Trans. Am. Inst. Chem. Eng.*, **13** (I), 101-138 (1920) ; *Chem. Met. Eng.*, **23**, 239-41, 281-4 (1920).

21. Badger, W. L., and Shepard, P. W. Studies in evaporator design, II. The effect of hydrostatic head on heat transmission in vertical tube evaporators. *Trans. Am. Inst. Chem. Eng.,* 13 (I), 139-50 (1920); *Chem. Met. Eng.,* 23, 390-3 (1920).
22. Baker, E. M., and Waite, V. H. Boiling points of salt solutions under varying pressures. *Trans. Am. Inst. Chem. Eng.,* 13 (II), 223-32 (1922); *Chem. Met. Eng.,* 25, 1137-40 (1921).
23. Baker, E. M., and Waite, V. H. Vapor pressure of the system calcium chloride-water. *Trans. Am. Inst. Chem. Eng.,* 13 (II), 233-42 (1922); *Chem. Met. Eng.,* 25, 1124-8 (1921).
24. Carlsson, G. The vapor compression system of evaporation. *Chem. Met. Eng.,* 24, 645-7 (1921).
25. Carr, A. R., Townsend, R. E., and Badger, W. L. Vapor pressures of glycerol-water and glycerol-water-sodium chloride systems. *Ind. Eng. Chem.,* 17, 643-7 (1925).
26. Cook, R. V. Improvement in evaporator design. *Chem. Age* (N. Y.), 29, 409-10, 479-80 (1921).
27. deBaufre, W. L. A new system of regenerative evaporation. *Trans. Am. Soc. Mech. Eng.,* 40, 746 (1918).
28. Downing, W. F., Jr. Salt pans. *Chem. Age* (N. Y.), 30, 17-8 (1922).
29. Dunglinson, B. Evaporation by vapor compression. *Chem. Met. Eng.,* 25, 246-7 (1921).
30. Dunglinson, B. Multiple effect evaporation. *Chem. Met. Eng.,* 25, 110-5 (1921).
31. Forbes, J. Operating characteristics of flash evaporators. *Power Plant Eng.,* 27, 311-3 (1923).
32. Fuwa, T. Cost of installation and operation of the five general classes of evaporators. *Chem. Met. Eng.,* 31, 185-8 (1924).
33. Hoglund, B. Calculation shows minimum heating surface for evaporators. *Chem. Met. Eng.,* 35, 157 (1922).
34. Huttlinger, C. F. Vacuum pan evaporation in the sugar industry. *Chem. Met. Eng.,* 29, 498 (1923).
35. Kerr, E. W. An experimental study of heat transmission and entrainment in a vacuum evaporator. *Bull. La. Agr. Exp. Sta.* No. 138 (1913); *Trans. Am. Soc. Mech. Eng.,* 35, 731-71 (1913); *Met. Chem. Eng.,* 11, 333-8 (1913).
36. Kerr, E. W. Performance tests of sugar house heating and evaporating apparatus. *Bull. La. Agr. Exp. Sta.* No. 149 (1915); *Trans. Am. Soc. Mech. Eng.,* 38, 539-51 (1916); *Met. Chem. Eng.,* 13, 485-92, 551-7 (1915); 14, 603-8 (1916).

It is not clear to what extent the following references (37 to 41, inclusive) are reviews of parts of Bulletins 138 and 149.

37. Kerr, E. W. Test of a vacuum pan. *Met. Chem. Eng.,* 12, 81 (1914).
38. Kerr, E. W. Heating and evaporating with superheated steam. *Sugar,* June, 1914, p. 41.
39. Kerr, E. W. Radiation from multiple effect evaporators. *Sugar,* July, 1914, p. 41.
40. Kerr, E. W. Vacuum apparatus for sugar factories. *La. Planter,* 54, 217-21 (1915).
41. Kerr, E. W. Factors affecting economy in vacuum pans. *Int. Sug. J.,* 18, 24-9 (1916).
42. Kermer, M. J. Evaporators for black liquor. *Paper Mill,* 53, No. 24, 20-2 (1930).
43. La Bour, H. E. Phosphoric acid evaporation. *Chem. Met. Eng.,* 24, 466-8 (1921).
44. Lee, J. A. Evaporation of electrolytic caustic soda. *Chem. Met. Eng.,* 37, 404-8 (1930).
45. Linden, C. M., and Montillon, G. H. Heat transmission in an experimental inclined-tube evaporator. *Trans. Am. Inst. Chem. Eng.,* 24, 120-41 (1930); *Ind. Eng. Chem.,* 22, 708-13 (1930).

46. McCabe, W. L. Economic side of evaporator scale formation. *Chem. Met. Eng.*, **33**, 86-7 (1926).
47. McCabe, W. L., and Robinson, C. S. Evaporator scale formation. *Ind. Eng. Chem.*, **16**, 478-9 (1924).
48. McCormack, H., Dormitzer, H. C., and Roleson, E. P. Heat transmission in vacuum evaporator tubes. *Chem. Eng.*, **16**, 1-9 (1912).
49. Mantius, O. The evaporator and the power problem in electro-chemical plants. *Met. Chem. Eng.*, **12**, 722-4 (1914).
50. Mantius, O. Specifications for single and multiple effect evaporators. *Met. Chem. Eng.*, **15**, 449-50 (1916).
51. Miller, R. W. Concentrating waste sulphite liquor. *Can. Chem. Met.*, **14**, 19-21 (1930).
52. Monrad, C. C., and Badger, W. L. Boiling points of electrolytic caustic solutions. *Ind. Eng. Chem.*, **21**, 40-2 (1929).
53. Monrad, C. C., and Badger, W. L. The condensation of vapors. *Trans. Am. Inst. Chem. Eng.*, **24**, 84-119 (1930) ; *Ind. Eng. Chem.*, **22**, 1103-12 (1930).
54. Moore, H. K. Some general aspects of evaporation and drying. *Trans. Am. Inst. Chem. Eng.*, **10**, 367-401 (1917) ; *Met. Chem. Eng.*, **18**, 128-33 (1918).
55. Moore, H. K. The fundamental principles of multiple effect evaporative separation. *Trans. Am. Inst. Chem. Eng.*, **15** (II), 233-307 (1923) ; *Chem. Met. Eng.*, **29**, 1102-5, 1144-6, 1190-2 (1923) ; **30**, 274-8 (1924).
56. Othmer, D. F. The condensation of steam. *Ind. Eng. Chem.*, **21**, 576-83 (1929).
57. Pridgeon, L. A. Calculation of vapor recompression evaporators. *Trans. Am. Inst. Chem. Eng.*, **15** (I), 231-40 (1923) ; *Chem. Met. Eng.*, **28**, 1109-11 (1923).
58. Pridgeon, L. A., and Badger, W. L. Studies in evaporator design, V. Effect of surface conditions. *Ind. Eng. Chem.*, **16**, 474-8 (1924).
59. Sadtler, P. B. Notes on the theory and practice of evaporation. *J. Frank. Inst.*, **166**, 291-6 (1908) ; **167**, 56 (1909) ; *J. Ind. Eng. Chem.*, **1**, 644-53 (1909).
60. Sadtler, P. B., and deBeers, F. M. Some problems in evaporation and drying. *Trans. Am. Inst. Chem. Eng.*, **10**, 403-10 (1917) ; *Met. Chem. Eng.*, **18**, 543-4 (1918).
61. Sanger, W. E. Solving the evaporation problems of the soap industry. *Chem. Met. Eng.*, **29**, 478-81 (1923).
62. Spence, G. K. Some evaporator problems met in the paper-pulp industry. *Chem. Met. Eng.*, **29**, 972-3 (1923).
63. Teeple, J. E. Potash and borax from Searles Lake brine. *J. Soc. Chem. Ind.*, **47**, 345-7 T (1928).
64. Van Marle, D. J. Heat transmission in an inclined rapid circulation type vacuum evaporator. *Ind. Eng. Chem.*, **16**, 458-9 (1924).
65. Viola, B. Evaporators and vacuum pans. *Met. Chem. Eng.*, **9**, 206-9, 349-52 (1911) ; **10**, 31-6, 102-3, 267-9 (1912).
66. Webre, A. L. Theory and practice in the design of multiple evaporators for sugar factories. *J. Ind. Eng. Chem.*, **10**, 121-8 (1917).
67. Webre, A. L. Evaporation study of the various operating cycles in triple-effect units. *Chem. Met. Eng.*, **27**, 1073-8 (1922).

Important U. S. Patents on Evaporators and Evaporation

1907

Patent No.	Name	Remarks
849,579		Thermocompresser. Vapors compressed by live-steam jet.
868,275	Kaiser	Standard vertical, no downtake, auxiliary tubes inside regular tubes.

1908

Patent No.	Name	Remarks
880,080	Kaiser	Circulation plates in standard horizontal tube evaporator.
880,812	McArthur	Multiple effect with movable vapor and liquor lines, to make either vapor or liquid flow in any order desired.
881,351	Smith, A. P.	Details of steam distribution in standard vertical.
881,523	Winter	Several vertical heating elements in single shell.
881,990	Zaremba	Standard vertical, side downtake, hood from downtake extending over some of tubes.
882,043	Zaremba	Round-body horizontal.
882,322	Kestner	Details of climbing film evaporator.
894,407	Suzuki	Vertical tube evaporator with forced circulation by propeller.
896,414	Rogers & Rogers	Condenser built as part of milk pan.
896,460	Prache & Bouillon	Vertical tube thermocompressor with compartments for progressive liquor travel.
898,147	Von Seemen	Combined downtake baffle and entrainment separator for standard vertical.
899,738	Kirkwood	Long vertical tubes, bundle sets into a feed chamber, tubes discharge into vapor head.
905,568	Ordway	Collect salt in two external settlers operated alternately, drying by hot air in the settlers.

1909

Patent No.	Name	Remarks
920,997	G. Ray	Vapor piping as usually built on Manistee evaporators.
936,760	Childs	Multiple effect so arranged that during operation feed can be progressively shifted from effect to effect. This is apparatus patent— See 1,005,600.
939,143	Lillie	Details of feed distribution.
940,473	Parker	Kestner with dropped head.

1910

Patent No.	Name	Remarks
13,117 (Re-issue)	Kestner	Details of feed device to pocket and distribute vapor from flash.
948,376	Lillie	Lillie reversible, alternate ends adjacent, all valves operating at once.
951,322	Mantius	Special flowsheet for salt evaporation.
951,559	Duncan	Details of vacuum salt receiver.
965,388	Kestner	External long-tube heating element attached to a standard evaporator—natural circulation.
971,258	Dunn	The Jedun evaporator.
971,383	Kestner	Details of feed chamber.
971,394	Morris	Details of Kestner feed chamber.
971,395	Morris	Details of Kestner feed chamber.
972,572	Prache	Inclined tube evaporator.
972,880	Lillie	Feed heater in steam space of first effect.

1911

Patent No.	Name	Remarks
984,226	Lillie	Automatic reversing valves in vapor lines.
984,645	Bock	Control of evaporation by balance between weight of condensate and weight of crystals.
984,754	Eydman	Two-compartment vertical with forced circulation.

Patent No.	Name	Remarks
988,002	Lillie	Combination of salt evaporator and grainer.
988,477	Lillie	Closure of tube.
989,982	Kestner	Baffle for vapor space.
989,996	Parker	Baffle for vapor space of Kestner.
991,342	Mellor	Feed control for Kestners.
995,776	Dunn	Porcupine tube Jedun.
997,502	Kestner	Apparatus patent corresponding to 997,503.
997,503	Kestner	Concentrator for thick or viscous liquids. This is process patent. See 997,502.
1,000,285	Morison	Coil evaporator—coils removed through door.
1,002,866	G. Ray	Entrainment separator.
1,003,912	Kestner	Falling film.
1,004,087	Scheinemann	Steam baffles for standard vertical, extending also up into liquor compartment.
1,004,686	Dow	Open pans in series with vacuum-flash chambers above each, salt leg dropping into open pan.
1,004,858	Dow	Salt grainers in series, salt and liquor into counterflow.
1,005,553	Kestner	Falling film high concentrator. This is apparatus patent. See 1,005,554.
1,005,554	Kestner	Process patent corresponding to 1,005,553.
1,005,571	Parker	Combination of climbing and falling film Kestners.
1,005,600	Childs	Process patent. Apparatus patent is 936,760.
1,006,195	Frasch	Shower hot brine over layers of coarse salt.
1,006,196	Frasch	Use spray evaporation to produce fine salt, then hold hot brine with this salt in suspension.
1,006,197	Frasch	Salt evaporator with brine and steam spaces interchangeable to dissolve scale.
1,006,823	Block	External heater and spray chamber for salt evaporation. Back pressure on heater to prevent evaporation.
1,009,782	Ordway	Rectangular shell superimposed Yaryan.

1912

Patent No.	Name	Remarks
1,015,629	Newhall	Vapor separator consisting of annular rings of perforated metal. See 1,015,704.
1,015,704	Newhall	See 1,015,629. Same but with screen.
1,016,160	Kestner	Concentrated liquor finished in first effect.
1,028,738	Kestner	Several groups of tubes, in series as to liquor but in parallel as to steam and vapor.
1,028,777	Power	Griscom-Russell coil evaporator, rotatable coil assembly.
1,028,792	Sanborn	The Sanborn porcupine tube evaporator.
1,033,558	Dunn	Vertical tube porcupine evaporator. Vents in tubes instead of secondary tube sheet. See also 1,033,559.
1,033,559	Dunn	See 1,033,558.
1,033,580	Hall & Searby	Steam distributing belt for standard vertical. Slots to admit steam to tubes.
1,036,127	Lillie	Pumps salt out of cone to separate open settler.

1913

Patent No.	Name	Remarks
1,049,014	Weir	Weir flat coil evaporator.
1,049,425	Webre	Baffles in steam space of standard vertical.
1,054,926	Mantius	Mantius porcupine tube high concentrator.

Patent No.	Name	Remarks
1,060,607	Kestner	Feeding device for falling film Kestners.
1,067,010	Dunn	Details of long tube natural circulation evaporator.
1,068,789	MacGregor	Final effect operates as finishing pan and may be cut off from rest of evaporator.
1,069,566	Morris	Details of Kestner feed.
1,071,341	Prache	Inclined tube evaporator with super-imposed liquor compartments.

1914

1,086,457	Lillie	A Lillie, reversible as to liquor or vapor or both, with salt settlers.
1,087,409	Tremann	False inner shell. Liquid pumped up through annular space, overflows down inner shell, in which are standard vertical tubes.
1,090,628	Kestner	Rising and falling Kestner under pressure.
1,098,825	Moore	Apparently backward feed on standard vertical.
1,106,532	Zaremba & Mantius	Tile lined horizontal tube evaporator.
1,117,005	deBeers	Reinforced cast lead construction.

1915

1,125,998	Frasch	Settler tank between purifier and salt grainer.
1,126,491	Kuhnke	Slightly inclined tubes, liquid inside tubes, liquid cascades downward.
1,143,744	Bauer	Piping for a set of several bodies so that variable number of effects may be put in series or parallel.
1,149,939	Newhall	Series withdrawal of drips from multiple effect.
1,150,605	Kermer	Horizontal tube evaporator, drum surrounding all tubes, liquid inside tubes and outside drum.
1,150,713	Soderlund	Vertical stack of tubes, liquor down over these in film. Vapor recompressed not over 5 deg. C. and fed to inside of tubes.
1,152,977	Rossi	Inclined tube, natural circulation, with curved ends on tubes so that bottom tube sheet is horizontal.

1916

1,168,758	Stade	Inclined tube express pan with annular downtake.
1,179,636	Krug	External circulating tube for sugar pans.
1,182,220	Seeger	Variation of Heckmann separator.
1,190,317	Naudet	External circulators for any type of evaporator.
1,191,108	Kestner	One or more salting Kestners discharging into a separating head.
1,200,996	Söderlund & Boberg	Thermocompression in stages — series as to liquid, parallel as to vapor.

1917

1,213,596	DeBaufre	DeBaufre's steam jet thermocompressor.
1,215,140	Geller	Flash evaporator with pump taking liquor from bottom of pumping to sprays in vapor space.
1,216,187	Trump	N-effect evaporator for salting in which salts pass toward I and feed is toward N to dissolve soluble material from salts at high temperatures.

Patent No.	Name	Remarks
1,225,118	Evans	Makes distilled water from sea water by boiling sea water and superheating vapor in a second heating unit.
1,246,824	Smith	Details of basket type vertical.
1,246,939	Sadtler	Basket type with circulation by external pump.
1,249,557	Truscott	Express pan, large central downtake, inclined heating tubes, ring of large vertical downtake tubes around outside.

1918

1,252,962	Söderlund & Boberg	Feed divided into two streams, one pre-heated by thick, one by drips, relative volumes automatically proportioned.
1,263,467	Reavell & Mann	Kestner for salting with vapor head and settler separate from tube bundle.
1,288,480	Benjamin	Griscom-Russell type, permanent super-heating coils in vapor dome.

1919

1,297,737	Schaeffer	Coarse salt made in grainer, fine salt made in pan from grainer mother liquor and returned to brine mixing tank.
1,298,925	Garrigues	Vertical—outermost ring of tubes used as downtake, baffles in steam space.
1,299,955	Jones	Griscom-Russell evaporator—hood over tubes forces vapor sideways through liquid before escaping.
1,302,625	Benjamin	Griscom-Russell evaporator—details of connection between manifolds and shell.
1,318,793	Newhall	Special flow for liquor in multiple effect.
1,324,417	Thunholm	Flat tray evaporator with rotating stirring arms from central shaft.
1,325,461	Barbet	Special long tube natural circulation.

1920

1,329,786	Mabee	Adjustable vapor outlet for Mabee type evaporator.
1,331,373	Prache	Liquid pumped down into heater, up through circulating leg into large settler, back to heater from behind baffle.
1,334,014	Braun	Flat coil evaporator—claims rest on coils fixed to headers made as part of door.
1,346,624	Wood	Withdrawal of brine from a multiple effect, heating, passing through a graveler, and returning.
1,348,409	Grimwood	Salt evaporator with boot and elevator as usual—feed of fresh liquor to all boots to wash salt.
1,352,648	Beyer & Hall	Countercurrent condenser and rectifying column mounted directly on top of evaporator.
1,355,935	Benjamin	Vapor passed into space containing electric heating unit to remove entrainment.
1,363,323	Kehoe	Entrainment separator for basket type verticals.

1921

1,373,041	Witte	Studs holding packing plates on horizontal evaporators extended to act as stays for cover plate.

Patent No.	Name	Remarks
1,387,475	DeBaufre	Use of orifice on steam line to evaporator as regulating device.
1,390,676	DeBaufre	Steam jet thermocompressor. Applied to the combination of single and multiple effect evaporators.
1,390,677	DeBaufre	Same as 130,676 but several nozzles used.
1,393,221	Hughes	Horizontal—steam fed to tubes by manifolds instead of steam chests.
1,393,475	Wirth-Frey	Annular heating elements with sharp-edged tops.
1,396,316	Bogdanffy	Griscom-Russell type. Hanger to support element when removed from shell.

1922

1,402,238	Mabee	Jacketed kettle open at top, high speed stirrer arms to keep all liquid as film on wall.
1,405,244	Wirth-Frey	Series—parallel steam flow in multi-step thermocompression.
1,415,818	Engel	Entrainment collector. Centrifugal force in going around baffle.
1,417,943	Rogers	Details of superimposed flat coils.
1,420,641 to 1,420,650 incl.	Mabee	Apparatus and process patents on various features of Mabee evaporators.
1,424,992	Creighton	Standard vertical calandria divided into sections on steam side, each section with several large downtake tubes.
1,425,005	Gensecke	A thermocompressor with a connection from the condensate outlet to blower inlet to remove air.
1,425,020	Josse & Gensecke	Thermocompressor with condenser and vacuum pump to operate under vacuum, but remove non-condensibles.
1,428,557	Ray and Ray	Depressions in tube sheet to prevent salt starting around tubes.
1,433,141	Mabee	Open kettle-shaped body.
1,436,739	Webre	Long tube natural circulation. Claims really cover liquor collecting depression around upper tube sheet and baffle over vapor outlet.
1,437,698	Wirth-Frey	Tapered annular heating elements with scrapers on top edges.
1,438,502	Peebles	Concentrating sensitive liquids by forced circulation through a heater and then spraying into flash chamber. 4 ft./sec. claimed.
1,440,026	Milsson	Remove acid constituents from vapor before thermocompression.

1923

1,440,548	Mellott	Pusher block on shaft (Mabee type).
1,440,723	Dyson & Stuart	Process patent on evaporator of Griscom-Russell type—details of condensate removal.
1,449,313	Bollmann	Multiple compartments like Vincik-Turek.
1,451,168	Mabee	Vertical tapering shell, discharge at bottom.
1,451,829	Mellott	Mabee evaporator with balls instead of scrapers.
1,459,182	Mabee	Mabee evaporator with U-shaped stirrer to avoid filling center of cylinder.
1,461,640	Wirth-Frey	Compressor loading device for turbo blower thermocompressors.

Patent No.	Name	Remarks
1,466,357	Engel	Buffalo Foundry's "Express" pan. Inclined tube sheets, inclined tubes, stepped downtake wall.
1,473,373	Kermer	In a multiple followed by a single high-concentrator, interconnecting the steam supply to multiple and high concentrator, and using vapor space of I as catchall for concentrator.
1,476,331	Engel	Inclined tube express pan. Propeller with blades shaped to fit bottom, to circulate and also assist in discharge.

1924

1,481,924	Nelson	Basket type, steam inlets in form of jets to compress vapors.
1,482,143	Peebles	External heater, flash chamber, forced circulation.
1,486,387	Lebermuth	Similar to Vincik-Turek idea.
1,487,071	Mabee	Vertical cylinder.
1,491,544	Morison	Flat coil evaporator, returns from entrainment separator cast in body wall.
1,495,151	Bancel	By-pass from condenser to intercooler and ejector for quick evacuation.
1,498,440	Fothergill	Details of pancake coil evaporator.
1,501,646	Brown	Griscom-Russell coil with flattened tubing.
1,506,001	Hughes	Lillie type but with two tube sheets and a cover over the tubes to make vapor flow *down* with the liquid.
1,508,130	Sanger	Wurster & Sanger's glycerine evaporator. Side downtake, tube centers on arcs, arcuate baffles in steam space.
1,509,634	Brown	Special cycle for double-effect power plant evaporator.
1,514,819	Armstrong	Vertical central downtake, flat top tube sheet, stepped bottom tube sheet, congest tubes near center.

1925

1,524,184	Lawrence	Lawrence's superimposed evaporator, very similar to 1,145,728.
1,525,136	Kopke	Entrainment separator like Kestner's spiral blades.
1,536,873	Barthelmy	Tubular liquor preheater in vapor space.
1,536,894	Lillie	A Lillie with side baffles to retain liquor but leave passages for vapor escape.
1,537,563	Suczek	Jet thermocompressor involving cooling of jet.
1,538,254	Mellott	Scrapers carry inclined brushes.
1,548,063	Ray	Superimposed vertical tube cone bottom multiple effect.
1,552,534	Bancel	When the condenser is followed by an intercooler, non-condensed gases from last effect go direct to intercooler. See 1,552,562.
1,552,562	Kirgan	Same as 1,552,534 except that intercooler is independent of main condenser.
1,558,957	White	Calandria pan, inclined tube sheets, filler for downtake to reduce volume of pan.
1,562,525	Thunholm	Details of Thunholm's flat shelf evaporator.
1,562,713	Miles	Buflovac inclined evaporator with separate return pipe.

Patent No.	Name	Remarks
1,566,539	Kermer	Standard vertical. Bottom tube sheet contains trough for introduction of condensate from previous effects.

1926

1,581,545	Prache	Add sand to circulating liquor to scour off scale.
1,582,066	Moore	Moore's spray evaporator—62 claims cover: (a) feeding from an intermediate effect (X^{th}) backward to I, then to $X + 1$, then forward to end. (b) construction of Moore's spray evaporator.
1,582,067	Moore	Feed to an intermediate effect X, forward to last effect N, back to $(X - 1)$ (with or without liquor interchangers) and then backward to I.
1,586,814	Leonard	Special form of baffle for steam space of central downtake vertical.
1,591,583	Vila	Sugar pan with external heaters heated by vapor of juice itself without compression.
1,591,725	Mumford	Use of non-volatile emulsion colloid to prevent foam.
1,597,809	Lavett	Chemical and Vacuum Machinery Company's combined I.H.V. and drum dryer.
1,598,935	Robinson	Process for pure NaCl. Remove liquor from evaporator, settle suspended impurities, and return.
1,600,106	Foghergill	Forced circulation evaporator with closed discharge chamber to prevent boiling in the tubes, and sprays into evaporating space.
1,600,784	Aiken	Reversible double effect, so piped that each effect is always followed by a foam catcher.
1,609,853	Badger	External superheater for salts that form scale.
1,610,307	Nash	Separator for $CaSO_4$ inside cone of evaporator.
1,611,059	Nicolai	Special construction of basket type vertical.

1927

1,612,961	Badger	Closure for Yaryan liquor end.
1,615,287	McLaughlin	Sensitive liquids concentrated with thick-walled tubes so that area of liquor film is large and hence small temperature drop.
1,617,081	Price	Horizontal tube boiler feed evaporator, fixed headers, bowed tubes.
1,617,082	Price	Same evaporator as 1,617,081 but arranged for film operation.
1,617,119	Jones	Similar to 1,617,081.
1,621,862	Aiken	Basket type vertical—steam nozzle inside basket telescopically mounted.
1,622,918	Merlis	Special shapes of baffles for steam space of standard verticals.
1,631,162	Sebald	Vertical tube film type with thimbles in top of tubes.
1,638,697	Merlis	Special arrangement of tubes and baffles in steam space of standard vertical to control venting.
1,650,122	Grängdörffer	Vertical annular concentric heating elements.

1928

Patent No.	Name	Remarks
1,657,633	Martin	Spray process for salt manufacture. See 1,811,091.
1,664,133	Schedler	Plate attached to basket opposite liquor inlet on basket type evaporators.
1,677,987	Pokorny	Standard basket type with a long Kestner-type element in the downtake. Steam from ordinary H. S. can escape only by pumping liquid up the Kestner unit.
1,721,760	Zeitler	Horizontal tube evaporator with removable tube bundle.
1,717,927	Hughes & Hughes	Central downtake vertical. Liquor in body all below bottom tube sheet, external pump discharges it over top tube sheet.
1,733,476	Vogelbusch	Inclined tube evaporator.
1,735,979	Sadtler	Swenson's forced circulation evaporator. Apparatus patent. See 1,735,980.
1,735,980	Sadtler	Process patent corresponding to 1,735,979.
1,744,096	Baker & Prescott	Hard candy evaporator. Spiral syrup passages and tangential gas flames.
1,746,795	Rogers	Condenser built into top of pan.
1,756,673	Baumann	Coil pan with condenser inside vapor space.
1,760,907	Jones	Horizontal with fixed tube sheets, bowed tubes, and film feed.
1,770,320	Morterud	Porcupine tubes with tapered inner tube.
1,782,143	How	Circulator for vertical downtake pans, with lower end of downtake flared to become upper half of casing of open runner centrifugal pump.

1931

1,791,286	Wurster	Details of return connection from foam catcher.
1,793,174	Hofmeister	Horizontal tube evaporator, liquid showered over tubes, deep tube banks decreasing in cross-section toward bottom.
1,795,601	Hamill et al	Vertical calandria with steam baffles, and tubes spaced wide near steam inlet but progressively closer on opposite side.
1,799,478	Peebles	Alberger evaporating cycle with flash chambers superimposed.
1,810,181	McDonald et al	Circulating brine from evaporator to heater, superheating, and back to evaporator.
1,811,091	Martin	Martin's spray process for salt. See 1,657,633.
1,820,065	Guy	Horizontal tube evaporator, tubes of elliptical cross-section, long axis is vertical in lower layers and horizontal in upper.
1,831,121	Kermer	Salting forced circulation with external heater.
1,835,250	Webre	Method of operating sugar pan.
1,835,620	Webre	Screw pump circulator in downtake of sugar pan, and blades in upper part of charge above calandria. See 1,835,621.
1,835,621	Webre	Same apparatus as 1,835,250. Claims stirrer driven by constant speed motor, and an ammeter in motor circuit for indicating viscosity. See 1,835,620.
1,837,964	How	I.H.V. evaporator (Struthers-Wells).

1932

Patent No.	Name	Remarks
1,840,834	Davis	Non-circular tube using water-hammer to remove scale.
1,847,589	Brobeck	Heats sulphite liquor under velocity of 1.5 meters and prevents boiling.
1,860,118	Ray	Curved baffle below propeller in salt pan deflect circulation up through tubes, but heavy crystals fall through annular gap outside baffle.
1,860,741	Jeremiassen	The Jeremiassen salting evaporator.
1,864,349	Govers	Use of diphenyl alone as heating medium.
1,869,093	Crewson	Salt settlers for forced circulation evaporators.
1,869,651	Badger	Solution thermocompressor.
1,872,554	Badger	Deflector for forced circulation evaporators.

CHAPTER XXI

CONTINUOUS MECHANICAL SEPARATIONS IN THE CHEMICAL ENGINEERING INDUSTRIES

By JOHN VAN NOSTRAND DORR

President, The Dorr Co., Inc., New York

H E WHO WOULD TRACE the genesis of continuous mechanical separations and review their infiltration into the chemical industry and growth there, would do well to start with their birthplace—the cyanide process—shortly after the turn of the twentieth century. And, too, this is entirely appropriate, for the cyanidation of gold and silver ores was then and still is essentially a chemical process and in a certain sense the precursor of the interconnected, unit-operation concept which today our Institute recognizes as the basic contribution of chemical engineering to industry.

Coming, as it did, at a time when there was world-wide alarm at the falling production of gold, and when the hue and cry for the re-monetization of silver was being generally taken up in all quarters of the globe, the invention of the cyanide process in 1887 by two Scotchmen, MacArthur and Forrest, was of vast importance, both technically and socially. Their process, based on the dissolution of gold in a solution of cyanide of potassium, followed by subsequent precipitation of the precious metal by the use of zinc shavings, opened up for profitable exploitation, great areas of low grade ores that could not be developed profitably by the then-existing methods of gravity concentration and of amalgamation with mercury.

Rapidly the new chemical process grew and developed. First New Zealand, then Australia and South Africa and finally Mexico, the United States and Canada embraced the new technique, while year by year the world's gold production rose by leaps and bounds. In 1896, when Bryan was defeated on his free silver platform, the production had risen in 10 years from $106,000,000 to $211,242,000. A galaxy of chemists, metallurgists and engineers was drawn to the ranks of those developing and expanding the new process and, under the pressure of their contagious enthusiasm, advances in the practices of mechanical handling and, especially, mechanical separation followed one another in amazingly rapid succession. Here were first developed such tools of modern chemical engineering as the tube mill, the percolation vat, the mechanical classifier, the thickener, continuous counter-current decantation and the continuous vacuum filter. And yet it all took place in a relatively short time and was the work, not of one man or group, but of many scattered to the four corners of the globe, but freely exchanging their information for the betterment of the new process in which all were interested alike.

In recounting the growth and applications of continuous mechanical separations in the chemical industry, I am duly conscious that the field is overwhelmingly large and beyond the power of any one man to cover authoritatively. Screening, centrifuging, dust collection, crystallization, and several others, all come under this category, as well as those unit operations with which I personally am more familiar, namely, classification, sedimentation and vacuum filtration. I will, therefore, discuss these latter three, because fate placed me, then a metallurgical chemist, in the western gold fields when they were born as products of cyaniding development and because since then I have made the mechanizing continuously of chemical and hydrometallurgical processes my principal work. In other words this chapter is to be concerned with the handling and separation of finely divided solids suspended in liquids.

Classification

The forerunner of the mechanical classifier of today first saw the light of day almost 30 years ago at the little 50-ton per day cyanide mill of the Lundberg, Dorr & Wilson mine at Terry, South Dakota. It was born, after six months' mental gestation, as a child of direst necessity. A serious plant breakdown brought us to a realization that existing apparatus was incapable of properly separating the coarse and fine constituents of the ore prior to separate cyanide treatment. Some old correspondence of mine, written about that time, has come to light, recounting in the terms familiar to me then, how mechanical classification came into being.

A mill—in which three men with more faith than anything else had put practically all their funds and had borrowed to the limit from friends, banks, and the labor union—was steadily losing money, largely because of difficult classification and the production of sand that would not leach, and a slime product badly contaminated with sand. Preliminary experiments had indicated the practicability of mechanical classification. One Sunday afternoon we were working around the 22-ft. settling cone, to stop the foam from overflowing. One of the boys, walking on the rim, threw it out of a delicate equilibrium. The foundations were weakened by spills.

Down it dropped, on the point of the cone, spilling probably one-third of the slime pulp it carried, and nearly washing the plant down the hill.

It was a critical moment for us. You can imagine how discouraging a crumpled-up cone would look to men who knew that uninterrupted operation was absolutely essential to stand off the creditors. There was nothing to do however, but to "go to it." Recognizing that a week or ten days must pass before things could be straightened out, we decided to burn our bridges on the classification problem. We took out two cones, a Frenier pump, and a wet elevator, and designed a commercial size mechanical classifier based on a few weeks' small-scale experimental work. We went at it boldly, and by the time our cone was picked up we were ready to operate. Dimensions and slopes had been guessed at. When the machine started it would do good work for perhaps half an hour, and then clog up and quit. I myself spent about 60 hours on the job, lying down for naps, while alterations were being made. Its delicacy at that time was such that while able to handle continuously one ore, when called on to handle another ore, mined a short distance from the first, the machine would shut down. When the adjustments were made, however, it ran continuously, converting a monthly deficit into a profit.

The design of this first mechanical classifier remains basically unchanged to this day in spite of many mechanical improvements, and the development of a dozen or more types to meet widely varying applications. The purpose of this first mechanical classifier was to produce a continuous settling chamber with means for removing the settled material free from slime, while maintaining an undisturbed surface zone. Further requirements were freedom from wear and great flexibility of control with varying feeds.

An inclined bottom settling box with reciprocating rakes rigid below the water level for progressing the settled materials above the water level, proved the answer, giving an agitated zone at the bottom, a quiet zone above, and a free discharge, untrammelled by the fine adjustment needed to discharge under a hydraulic head.

The metallurgical history of the classifier must be passed over briefly, although metallurgy still served as the proving ground for classification in other industries. Following the invention of the classifier at the Lundberg, Dorr and Wilson mill and so long as the separate treatment of sands and slimes persisted in cyanide practice, its use spread in the gold camps of the world for efficient, easily controlled separations. A separation was generally made at 150 to 200 mesh, the fine slime overflow being thickened, agitated and filtered or decanted and the coarse sand discharge being leached in vats. Somewhat later, when the all-slime method came into use in cyaniding and later still when flotation began to be generally adopted in the base metal industry, the classifier was operated in closed circuit with the highly efficient ball and tube mills that then replaced or followed the old stamp batteries. A single product, a uniformly-sized classifier overflow, was made for further treatment, all coarse oversize was returned to the mill until ground to the requisite fineness with great reduction in grinding cost. Within the last 10 or 15 years, stage grinding has become accepted practice. The crushed ore passes through two or more ball or tube mills, each mill being designed to perform a definite part of the total reduction in the most efficient manner and being operated accordingly. All of these mills operate in closed circuit with classifiers and frequently additional classifiers are to be found performing special functions between the grinding stages. Products passing 65 to 100 mesh are common practice today in base metal work, 200-mesh separations are widely prevalent in precious metal milling while in the chemical industry 300-mesh separations are not unusual and the microscopic equivalent of a 700-mesh separation has been performed commercially.

Mechanical development, of course, had to keep pace with the spread of mechanical classification both within and outside of the metallurgical industry. As new industries were entered and new problems solved, new designs had to be introduced and new and improved materials of construction sought and applied. The descendants of the original "switch box" classifier of 30 years ago, handling about 50 tons of sand per day are now legion and range up to widths of 20 ft. and lengths of 35 to 40 ft. A moderately sized 1933 model, only 12 ft. wide and 25 long, weighs close to 25 tons and rakes 12,000 tons of sand per day and circulates 10 times the new feed through the mill with which it is closed-circuited.

The trend toward very fine separations in the 200- to 325-mesh range led many years ago to the development of the bowl classifier. Here the fine separation is made in a shallow, quiescent bowl, surmounting the classifier proper, while the coarse underflow from the bowl is reclassified below in the reciprocating rake compartment. Bowls up to 28 ft. in diameter have been built with overflow capacities of 3,000 tons per day. Counter-current decantation in thickeners, discussed later, led to the development of the multi-deck washing classifier for washing or leaching granular solids. Two to six classifier mechanisms, driven in unison and rigidly secured together, were installed in a single long classifier tank with individual, series-connected inclined decks for each rake. Solids introduced in the first compartment were raked successively through the other compartments and came in contact successively with weaker and weaker washing or leaching solutions, introduced initially in the last compartment and gravitating toward the first. This counter-flow principle assured a well-treated final discharge of solids from one end and from the other end a solution of maximum strength.

All of these types of classifiers have found an ever widening field of usefulness in the chemical industry. The rake and bowl classifier are used in many lithopone, whiting and pigment plants, operating in closed circuit with ball and tube mills and overflowing to thickening and filtration a uniformly sized product that in certain cases may be all finer than 325 mesh. Classifiers, too, are to be found at many phosphoric acid plants operating in open or closed circuit with the acid resisting tube mills that are now so widely used for grinding phosphate rock in weak phosphoric acid. In the alkali and chemical pulp industries the bowl classifier plays a useful rôle in removing grit, sand and unburned core from the milk of lime used in causticizing, while in the mineral field the classifier is used for concentrating phosphate rock, bauxite and barytes as well as for the preparation of finely divided ochre, sienna, clay, sand, etc. A uniformly sized slurry with virtually no stray oversize coarser than 100 mesh was found to be essential in the cement industry if correct chemical combination in the kilns was to be secured with a minimum of free CaO after burning. Two wet process cement plants have replaced open circuit grinding with closed circuit grinding and classification and report less grinding cost as well as a sounder cement displaying higher early strength.

The multi-deck washing classifier has proved useful in many chemical operaitons. The salt crystallized out in the evaporation of electrolytic caustic soda solutions is readily separated from the recycled liquor and after washing with brine and water, meets specifications for cattle and packing salt. Oxidized copper ores and pyritic sinter are readily leached with acid, yielding good extractions and high solution strengths. New Jersey green sands used in zeolite water softeners, and artificial abrasives, used for polishing wheels, are graded and at the same time washed free from soluble impurities. Even totally-enclosed, gas tight and insulated washing classifiers have been designed for operating at high temperatures and under vapor pressure.

Looking back over 30 years, the blacksmith-built machine of which the world's foremost engineer, just back from South Africa, said—"If you had sent me a blueprint of this to Africa I would have said it was impossible to do what I see it doing"—laid the foundation for developments that have contributed much towards our overproduced world of today in the metallurgical and chemical fields.

It seems a bit archaic today compared with its modern progeny, built not only of steel and wood, but also of such special materials as lead, aluminum-zinc, bronze, rubber, stainless steel and the many new alloys in use today.

Continuous Thickening

Two years after the invention of the classifier, I was engaged in remodeling the 100-ton dry crushing mill of the Mogul Mining Co. at Pluma, S. D., into a 300-ton wet-crushing mill, following the practice worked out earlier at the Lundberg, Dorr and Wilson mill. The settling of ore slimes and decantation of the gold bearing solution was at that time largely an intermittent operation carried out in flat-bottomed tanks, although following another engineer's experience, I had used a large cone and made the solution recovery continuous at Terry. I met much trouble from solids accumulating on the sides of the cone, which slid down and choked the discharge, and I felt the size units needed for this larger mill presented many other difficulties. At Terry, I had also proved the diaphragm pump as a reliable 24-hour tool for slime pumping and, with an alternate up my sleeve, proposed a plant scale demonstration, which to my more cautious mind today seemed quite foolhardy.

Realizing the advantages of continuous decantation the question arose in my mind—Was it possible to operate a stirring mechanism in the bottom of a flat-bottomed tank to prevent the bottom layer settling out as a solid and yet slow enough not to disturb the upper settling zone? The musty old file of correspondence, referred to before, contains a letter, written at the time to a friend, speaking of the development of the thickener as follows:

> Experience had shown the advantages of continuous thickening, but also the disadvantages of big cones. We had some 35 ft. tanks already installed and, wishing to use them, considered whether it would be possible by means of plows on the bottom to prevent the settled slime from packing solid and yet not interfere with settling out a clear overflow. We designed slow moving plows attached to a centrally suspended shaft for this purpose, and William M. McLaughlin, our general manager, had the courage of his convictions or confidence in me and authorized the trial on a plant size scale. . . . It was a thrilling moment when we started the mill and actually proved it would work.

The principle of the first thickener was a slowly revolving raking mechanism placed in a suitable round tank, by means of which the operation of settling could be made continuous, through the displacement of the clarified supernatant portion into a peripheral collecting trough at the surface and the mechanical removal of the deposited material to a discharge point at the center. Feed entered at the center surface through a cylindrical loading well, thickened solids were removed at maximum density by a diaphragm pump and the entire mechanism was capable of being raised vertically a foot or so to prevent its becoming embedded during a shut down. All parts moving upon one another and subject to wear were located above the solution level and an overload alarm was provided to record unusual rake loads and appraise the operator of the condition by an electric bell so that the load could be reduced before a breakage occurred. All of these principles have persisted to the present day, although, of course, the practice used to apply them and the size and type of machine have changed vastly.

The use of the thickener spread rapidly through the cyanide mills both here and abroad and soon became standard practice for the thickening of slimes as it later did in base metal work for thickening flotation and fine gravity concentrates and for dewatering tailings. Its success made its use for continuous counter-current decantation, tried before in large cones, quite feasible as a means of separating gold bearing solution from the residues. This principle, abbreviated, C. C. D., was first applied at the Vulture Mining Co. at Wickenburg, Ariz.

A series of four C.C.D. thickeners was used, the first one being built on the floor level and each successive one being on a foundation half a foot or so higher than that of the preceding one. Thus wash water, added in the last and most elevated thickener, might flow by gravity from one thickener to another to the head end of the system. The slime settled in each thickener was removed continuously at greatest density by a diaphragm pump and elevated to the next higher thickener where it mixed freely with the cascading counter flow of washing solution and was thickened once more.

Briefly, then, the slimes, as they were advanced mechanically through the system came in contact with weaker and weaker wash solutions and finally fresh water, being in this way successively impoverished in dissolved values before being discarded to waste. In the same way, the wash water, flowing from one thickener to another, came in contact with solids containing greater and greater amounts of dissolved values, and was successively enriched in solubles. Three products of uniform characteristics were thus made—first, a strong gold bearing solution, sent to be precipitated; second, a moderately strong solution, sent to the grinding system for return to the first thickener; and third, a low grade tailing, sent to waste. Thus C. C. D. plus the continuous thickener, classifier, filter and rotary mill made the cyanide process continuous for the first time and gave it very much the same flowsheet as is followed today.

In subsequent years the thickener underwent a great and significant development. The use of the original type of single compartment thickener with central shaft and bridge type superstructure was extended up to diameters of 100 ft. or more. For tanks beyond this range of size a traction type of mechanism was developed. In it the inboard end of the revolving raking arm was mounted on a turn table, surmounting a rigid column in the tank center, while the outboard end was a motor-driven truck traveling on a rail laid on the tank top. The largest built to date is 325 ft. in dia., provides almost 2 acres of settling area, dewaters 18,000 tons of tailings per day and clarifies 10,000,000 gal. of water, all at a power expenditure of only 5 H. P. One C. C. D. series of four 150 ft. diameter traction units, all constructed of acid resisting materials, has recently been leaching 500 tons of oxidized copper slimes per day with sulphuric acid.

Somewhat later the Anaconda Copper Co., at Butte, Montana, was confronted with a difficult problem in slime settling. The tonnage to be handled was large and the floor space available was insufficient to accommodate the number of single compartment thickeners needed. The problem was carefully studied and resulted in our development of the tray type thickener which provided the capacity of several single compartment machines in the space occupied by but one. The modern tray tank is subdivided into a multiplicity of superimposed settling compartments, by means of slightly conical steel trays or diaphragms suspended from the tank sides. A series of raking mechanisms, one for each compartment, is attached to a single, slowly-revolved, vertical shaft. A number of different methods is employed for feeding, overflowing and discharging, but the cumulative effect is greater capacity, less space and greater ease of insulation when handling hot solutions.

Modifications of the single compartment, traction type were made later, and led to the building of a rotary, oscillating mechanism that swept the bottom of the large, square tanks that are preferred today for settling such light, temperamental materials as sewage, trade wastes and chemically treated water. More recently, too, a new method of feeding through an inverted siphon and submerged diffuser has been worked out. The tray type of thickener, also, has gone through a metamorphosis and a new type has come forth with the compartments operated, not in parallel as before, but in series, thus giving in effect a complete C. C. D. plant in a single unit.

All of these types of continuous thickeners have become a part of the tools of chemical engineering and industrial processing. Thickeners as individual units are used for settling lithopone, whiting, ochre, sienna, clay and many other pigments or paint derivatives prior to final dewatering on filters and in dryers. They are found, too, in the reclamation of fiber and filler from white water at paper mills, and for dewatering coal, cement slurry, phosphate sands, fine artificial abrasives, salt, beet and cane sugar residues and other similar substances. They are widely used, too, for the treatment of sewage, trade wastes and water supplies and in myriad other liquid-solid separations where advantage may be taken of the natural laws of gravitation, supplemented by mechanical provision for continuous discharge of solids.

C. C. D. has probably reached its highest point of development in the chemical engineering industries, where, in conjunction with continuous agitation, it is in itself a process of wide application. The bulk of the phosphoric acid made today by the wet process is produced in this way. The pulverized phosphate rock is digested with sulphuric acid in a series of continuous agitators, followed by five to seven thickeners for decanting off the strong acid and washing the gypsum precipitate. The same is true in the manufacture of aluminum sulphate where the bauxite is similarly digested with sulphuric acid and the alum liquor and insoluble residues subsequently separated. The manufacture of caustic soda by the lime-soda ash process, the leaching of barium sulphide from reduced barytes cinder, the making of blanc fixe and other barium chemicals and even cane and beet sugar, are all susceptible to this method of continuous, wet processing. C. C. D.'s field of utility is constantly broadening, for it seems ideally suited to those processes where, first, a reaction must be carried out leaving a residue or precipitate suspended in a liquid; second, where the liquid and solid must be separated mechanically; and, third, where the solid must be washed commercially free from the liquid with a minimum amount of wash water. It works to advantage regardless of whether the liquid or the solid or both happen to be the products of value. In the manufacture of phosphoric acid, aluminum sulphate, caustic soda, and barium sulphide, the liquid, of course, is the valuable constituent and must be recovered as clear, hot and strong as possible, while in making lithopone, blanc fixe, and titanium pigment, the emphasis is on the precipitate which must be washed as free as possible of soluble salts and delivered with minimum water content.

Filtration

Gravity filters, simple false-bottomed boxes lined with fabric, paper or partially filled with sand or charcoal are as old as civilization itself and served the crude processing requirements of the Egyptians, Romans and Europeans of the Middle Ages. Though filter presses in the vintage industry are freely referred to in the Bible, Needham in England, about 1853, is said first to have conceived of pressure filtration in the modern sense and to have built a successful filter press for removing seeds from vegetable oils. The more recent significant advances made by Shriver, Merrill, Kelly, Sweetland, Vallez and Burt, and others are matters of common knowledge to chemical engineers and need no comment here.

Engineers of the Solvay group appear to have been working on continuous vacuum filtration as early as 1790. The outcome of these studies, the Solvay filter, was widely used for many years in the alkali industry for filtering bicarbonate crystals and precipitated calcium carbonate. It was of extra heavy cast-iron construction and had no blow back for cake discharging. Not being of the compartment type, no separation of filtrates was attempted.

As cyanidation got under way it became increasingly evident that a dependable method of filtering and washing slimes was needed. Filter pressing was used successfully, to be sure, on high grade ores, but was too expensive for average ores.

In the summer of 1903 I made a trip of inspection through the Western gold fields to check up on certain new equipment before designing the Lundberg, Dorr & Wilson mill. While at Salt Lake City I was introduced to George Moore, who at the time was running an experimental plant at Mercur, Utah, and was designing the first commercial size Moore process plant which subsequently was tried and abandoned at the Golden Gate mill.

Moore's filter consisted of a cluster of flat, canvas-covered frames or leaves. The leaves were connected to sources of vacuum and compressed air by a hose and could be raised, lowered and moved from tank to tank by means of a crane. The filter was first lowered into a tank containing slime for cake formation and then, cake and all, immersed successively in other tanks containing weak solution and water for cake washing. Finally, it was placed over the tailings bin and the washed cake discharged by a blow-back of compressed air.

Just about the time we were to start up our mill in the Black Hills, in January, 1904, word reached me that the Moore process had failed at the Golden Gate mill. This was bad news, indeed, for I had adopted the Moore process for our mill and upon its proper functioning depended our great problem of making our tailing stick on the 30 deg. slope of the hill on which the mill was built. My fears were, luckily, quite ungrounded, for after rectifying certain very evident mechanical errors in design, our Moore filter was finally made to run and continued to do so for the life of the plant. This was the first vacuum leaf filter plant to operate successfully, to my knowledge.

About the time I was working on the first continuous thickener at Pluma, S. D., word reached me of the significant work being done by Edwin L. Oliver at the North Star Mines in California, which led to the development of the first continuous, rotary vacuum filter with provision for cake washing. Oliver's principles were of far reaching importance and it is safe to say that the improvements made by others in later years were little more than modifications of Oliver's fundamental concepts of vacuum filtration.

The distinctive feature of the Oliver filter was the devising of a wire winding for holding the filtration medium securely on the drum. No other rotary filters developed before the time of Oliver used such a system and until this wire winding was put into practical use successfully operation was impossible, due to the difficulty of making the cloth adhere to the surface. The Oliver filter as finally developed embodied other desirable features such as the subdivision of the periphery of the drum into a number of segmental compartments, the special rotary port valve for the application of vacuum and blow-back air, and separate outlets and receivers for the collection of filtrates and wash solutions of different strengths. As a result of the new wire winding and other improvements, it then became possible for the first time to wash continuously on a vacuum filter.

The American vacuum filter, introduced in 1917, and invented by A. Genter, differed chiefly from the Oliver in that the filtration medium was applied upon both sides of a number of rotating disks instead of on the exterior of a drum. The Feinc, developed in 1923, by Arthur Wright, differed chiefly from the Oliver in the manner of discharging the cake, which was by means of a series of endless strings or wire mesh. The Dorrco filter, introduced in 1926 at the Chino mine, Hurley, N. M., differed in that the filtering medium was applied on the interior of the drum which acted as its own pulp container.

The continuous, rotary vacuum filter filled a real need in the metallurgical field and spread rapidly, first in cyanide plants and shortly after in the treatment of flotation concentrates. Placed at the end of a series of thickeners in a C. C. D. plant it saved valuable solution, gave the cake a final water wash and dewatered the tailing so it could be more easily disposed of. Later, fuller use of its washing ability was made by arranging two or more in series for what has come to be known as "series filtration." The slime was given a spray wash on each filter in turn and the cake from each filter was repulped with solution in a small agitator before being fed to the next filter. In the flotation and gravity concentration of the base metals the vacuum filter was widely adopted for dewatering the concentrates prior to pyrometallurgical treatment and in certain cases, too, it was used on the tailings.

Machine development in the vacuum filtration field has kept abreast of the special requirements of the new industries entered. The largest built to date are 14 ft. dia. x 16 ft. face width and are capable of handling 700 tons of cyanide slime per day. A type used in paper mill work has 90 or more per cent of its drum submerged in the pulp to give great capacity and has extra large filtrate ports leading to barometric legs for carrying off the vast amount of water removed from this dilute stock.

Trending in the opposite direction is a type developed for filtering the cachaza or cane fiber at sugar mills, this type having not more than one-quarter of its drum submerged, but being copiously supplied with washing sprays over its exposed surface. Another type, used both for filtering and drying salt and other granular substances, is totally enclosed and supplied with heated air which dries the crystals as it is drawn through the interstices of the cake. Flappers, rollers and pressure-loaded, endless belts, etc., have been developed for squeezing the cake and thus reducing its final moisture content. A great variety of materials of construction may be used for corrosive work and special metallic and fabric filtration media have been perfected for severe acid and corrosive conditions.

In the chemical industry the continuous vacuum filter has found a field wherever dewatering must proceed to a point beyond the physical limitations of simple gravitational settlement in a continuous thickener. Dewatering is frequently done in three stages —thickening, filtering and drying—and for this reason the fields of the vacuum filter and the thickener are largely identical. Broadly speaking, though, each unit is most efficient in its own particular range of dewatering and consequently the most efficient and cheapest way to dewater a dilute suspension is to use all three, the thickener first, the dryer last and the vacuum filter in the middle range.

Salt and other crystalline materials filter extremely rapidly and supplemented by the use of heated air may be dewatered to 2 to 2½ per cent moisture at the rate of 2 to 6 tons per sq. ft. per day. The dewatering of calcium carbonate in alkali mills and the causticizing departments of chemical pulp mills, has become a real field for the filter since all but a fraction of a per cent of caustic must be washed out and frequently the mud is reburned in rotary kilns. Lithopone, blanc fixe, titanium and the mineral pigments are widely dewatered and sometimes washed on vacuum filters as also are gypsum wastes from phosphoric acid plants, magnesium carbonate and hydrate, clay slip, cement slurry and beet and cane sugar muds.

One of the greatest fields of filtration today is the pulp and paper industry where vacuum filters now perform a dozen or so separate and distinct operations. Among these are deckering, pulp thickening, bleaching, pulp washing, recovering the fiber and filler from white water, lime mud dewatering and washing. Among the most difficult problems is the filtration of sewage sludge where even with chemical preconditioning the 98 per cent moisture feed can only be reduced to a 77-84 per cent moisture cake and where the capacity seldom exceeds 30 lb. of dry solids per sq. ft. per day.

The continuous unit operations of classification, thickening and vacuum filtration in the modern sense are all industrial developments of this century and their useful life to date coincides closely with the 25 years of chemical engineering progress in America which this volume commemorates. This triad of unit operations sprang from the then-infant chemical-metallurgical process of cyanidation and was developed, expanded and fathered by many men in all parts of the world whose professional connections covered the fields of chemical, metallurgical, civil, mechanical and electrical engineering. Thus, those chemists and chemical engineers who at the turn of the century were struggling each with his own particular problem, were aided and helped along the often rough and devious way by members of those professional Founder Societies with whom today our Institute has so much in common.

Reviewing the quarter century of progress and my contact with it, a few things stand out clearly. In the field of which I write positive mechanical action for continuous operation is needed. In chemical engineering, as in most other fields, continuous operation with proper regulation offers better products at less cost than intermittent operation. The greatest field for advancement lies in opportunity for transfer of knowledge and experience from one field to another, tempered always with that "good sense" which must be mixed with any operation—physical, chemical or social—as a catalyst to produce success.

CHAPTER XXII

PURIFICATION OF WATER FOR SANITARY AND INDUSTRIAL USES

By SHEPPARD T. POWELL

Consulting Chemical Engineer, Baltimore, Md.

I T IS ONLY WITHIN RECENT YEARS that water has been considered as an engineering material and the treatment of water has been recognized as a specific chemical engineering problem. A review of the early history of water conditioning indicates that many of the specific problems involved in present day practice required little or no consideration a few years ago. The scope of water treatment, prior to the past 25 years, was limited largely to filtration and softening by chemicals. Current practice includes a number of mechanical, electrical and chemical processes, the efficacy of which is of vital importance to domestic and industrial water consumers. Our intensive industrial era has focused attention on the demands for water of satisfactory quality to meet the exacting requirements of improved chemical processes and industrial experience.

Although the treatment of water for purely domestic and for industrial consumption is similar, there are special requirements in each field requiring specific treatment.

Filtration. The earliest filtration plants installed in America for the purification of municipal water supplies, were of the slow-sand type. The efficacy of this process depends upon biological action and requires low rates of filtration. A number of slow-sand filters were built in this country prior to 1904, but since that time practically all municipal water purification systems have been rapid-sand filters, frequently termed mechanical or American filters. The operating principle of this latter type differs radically from slow-sand filtration. The rapid-sand filtration process depends upon precoagulation of the water by chemicals, and the removal of suspended solids by subsidence prior to filtration through the sand beds. The rates of filtration employed are relatively high and cleaning of the sand is effected by backwashing with filtered water. This is accomplished with or without agitation of the sand and while the washing is in progress.

Few changes in the design and operation of this process have been made in recent years. The broad experience gained by the operation of a vast number of these systems, however, has resulted in much more efficient control than was formerly possible.

There is a trend at the present time toward the use of coarser sands and higher rates of filtration. Hand operated valves have been replaced in the larger plants by hydraulically or by electrically operated valves. In recent years, many designers of municipal filtration plants have used perforated pipes and other simplified underdrains in place of strainer systems. These changes in design have been made to reduce the cost of construction and to avoid some inherent difficulties of strainers.

Pressure Filters. Pressure filters, as their name indicates, are for the purpose of filtering water under pressure through a bed of sand or other media which is contained in a pressure vessel. Units of this type are used largely for the clarification of water for industrial uses. Twenty-five years ago a few installations of this type were also employed for the purification of municipal water supplies but this type of filtration equipment is now generally considered inefficient for such service. Pressure filter shells are usually cylindrical, but a radically new design was placed on the market a few years ago. This is the Cochrane conical filter for which a number of advantages are claimed.

Effect of Mixing. Efficient coagulation requires that the water and chemical shall be thoroughly mixed and that the mixing period shall be sufficiently prolonged to insure complete flocculation of the suspended solids present in the water supply. Recent experimental studies have demonstrated that thorough mixing of coagulants results in an appreciable saving of the chemical over that which would otherwise be required without mixing. The time necessary for satisfactory mixing varies with different waters. As a general condition, mixing for less than 10 minutes will give poor results and mixing for more than one hour will be unnecessary and impractical. Various designs of mixing equipment have been employed, but the best results are obtained by use of power-driven appliances.

Softening by Chemicals. Water softening by lime, was discovered by Clarke in England in 1842. Porter, also in England, improved the process about 20 years later, using soda ash in addition to lime. The development of water softening began in this country about 1890 but relatively few plants were installed prior to 1900. At first, all softening was done in cold water, but after the Adolph

Sorge, Jr., patent was issued in 1900, hot chemical process softening advanced fairly rapidly and many installations were made for the treatment of industrial waters. Numerous patents, relative to the design and operation of softening equipment and auxiliary appliances have been taken out since that time. This form of water softening has wide application and many large units have been installed within recent years. Hot chemical softening plants, installed since 1914, have a combined capacity in excess of 10,000,000 gal. per hr. or more than 250,000,000 gal. per day. The largest hot process softener installation in the world is the plant of the Texas Gulf Sulphur Co. at Gulf, Texas. This plant has a capacity of 420,000 gal. per hr.

There is a decided advantage in softening hot water since the residual hardness can be reduced to a much lower point than by cold water softening and less chemicals are required. This is indicated graphically in Fig. 1.

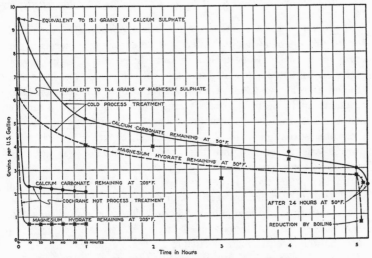

Fig. 1. Advantages in Softening Hot Water Are Shown by the Increased Velocity of Chemical Reactions Due to the Influence of Heat.

Courtesy of the Cochrane Corporation

The softening of water by chemicals for municipal purposes is limited to cold treatment while the hot process softening is adaptable specifically for the treatment of industrial waters. In addition to softening reagents, coagulants are frequently employed to produce more rapid subsidence of suspended solids and to effect a lower residual hardness in the treated water. The latter condition depends entirely upon local conditions and the type of coagulant used.

Lately, phosphates have been used extensively in conjunction with other chemicals for softening water for industrial uses. These salts are employed primarily to reduce the residual hardness of the treated water and to inhibit the formation of adherent boiler scales.

Municipal and industrial supplies requiring completely clarified water are filtered to remove all suspended matter thrown out of solution by the softening chemicals.

It is desirable to filter water from hot process softeners through non-siliceous [1] material. Experience has demonstrated that the passage of hot alkaline water through sand or other siliceous materials may result in the formation of silicate boiler scales when the water so treated is used for boiler feed purposes.

Manufacturers of water softening equipment have greatly improved control devices for accurately regulating the quantities of chemicals required to produce efficient softening, and many novel and accurate appliances for this purpose have been designed and patented.

Softening by Base Exchange Materials (Zeolites). The credit for the process of softening water by base exchange minerals is generally given to Dr. Robert Gans, a German chemist. Gans' investigations were made about 20 years ago although these materials were studied as early as 1848. Gans discovered how the base exchange reactions might be used for softening water and he also originated methods for producing synthetic zeolites. Through his efforts zeolite water softening was put on a practical, commercial basis. The process was introduced into this country about 20 years ago and since that time has been used extensively in the industries where soft water is desired. It is estimated that at present there are upward of 40,000 industrial zeolite water softening plants in operation in this country and the number of household softeners exceeds 150,-000. The zeolite business trebled from 1922 to 1929 according to information recently made available by the Permutit Co.

A number of zeolite installations have also been made for softening municipal water supplies. It is the practice, in softening public water supplies by zeolites, to soften completely only a portion of the supply and to mix the softened water with hard water to produce the desired degree of softening. The justification for this type of treatment will depend largely upon local conditions and the relative cost of the zeolite softened water as compared with softening by chemicals.

---

[1] U. S. No. 1,638,803 issued August 9, 1927.

The principal development in the manufacture or processing of zeolite minerals has been improvement in the durability of the products and a reduction in the salt consumption required for regeneration. The earlier types of zeolites required for regeneration 1.25 to 1.50 lb. of salt for each 1,000 grains of hardness removed by the softening material. This has now been reduced to from 0.35 to 0.50 lb.

Combination lime-zeolite plants for the treatment of boiler feedwater are a recent development in this art. The process consists of first treating the water with lime in order to remove the major portions of the bicarbonate hardness, and simultaneously lowering the total solids of the treated water by a corresponding amount. Then the lime-softened water is treated with acid, alum or ferrous sulphate to prevent after-precipitation and finally passed through a bed of zeolite mineral to remove the residual hardness. Zeolites have also been used for softening water prior to distillation by evaporators in order to eliminate scale from the evaporator coils.

Softening water by the zeolite process has been introduced on some railroads and under certain conditions is desirable and has a definite sphere of usefulness. One railroad system now uses zeolite treated water at about 100 water stations. This railroad has reported annual savings of from 80 to 300 per cent on the investment. An interesting application of zeolite water softening has been the treatment of cooling water for diesel and gas engines for the prevention of scale formation in the cooling jackets.

The most recent development in the design of zeolite equipment is an apparatus which is operated entirely automatically by an electric control mechanism. The manufacturer claims these units effect a saving in salt and rinse water, require less operating labor and result in other economies.

Boiler Feed-Water Treatment. In practically all stationary boiler plants some form of water treatment is employed. Operators of small boilers rely almost entirely upon boiler compounds to correct problems arising from bad water but in larger installations water purification systems are generally used. Many of these are elaborate and produce a high degree of purification. The value of such plants has been demonstrated by extensive steam station operation. The conditioning of boiler feed water by zeolites, chemical softeners and evaporators for the removal of encrusting solids, and the exhaustion of dissolved gases from water by degasing apparatus has marked a distinct advance in the art of water purification.

Steam generating conditions in power plants and on steam railroads have undergone such radical changes in recent years that the necessity for satisfactory water for these purposes has established boiler feed-water treatment as an important engineering problem. There has been a decided trend toward higher steam pressures and temperatures and increased ratings of boilers. (See Fig 2.)   Ten

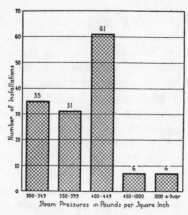

Fig. 2. Trend Toward High Steam Pressures as Indicated by Recent Boiler Installations

(Based on data compiled by the author and supplemented by records presented before the Phila. Section, A. S. M. E., by P. W. Swain, March 26, 1929.)

years ago steam pressures of 250 to 300 lb. were considered high. Since 1926 there have been built, or are now in the course of construction, many boilers which are operating at 400 lb. pressure or higher.   Many of these installations have been designed to operate at pressures in excess of 1,000 lb. and one at 1,800 lb.   These conditions are a natural sequence of engineering development, resulting from the desire for greater economy in the generation of steam.

Cracking of Boilers.   During the past 25 years a number of boilers have cracked while in service.   A study of the conditions responsible for these failures has indicated that the primary cause of the difficulty has been the presence of relatively high concentrations of caustic soda in the boiler water salines in the absence of appreciable amounts of sulphates.   This theory was first advanced by the late Prof. S. W. Parr who conducted extensive research at the University of Illinois to determine the mechanism of this type of failure. His early work was later substantiated and confirmed by the data of his associates, notably by F. G. Straub who has contributed much to the literature on the causes and prevention of boiler failures. Briefly, the conditions which result in failures of this type may be characterized as a combination of stress and chemical attack of the metal. In order to inhibit these conditions and to insure proper adjustment of the water the American Society of Mechanical Engineers [2] has recommended that the following ratio of sodium sulphate to total hydroxide and carbonate alkalinity be maintained:

Working Pressure of Boiler (Pounds, gage)	Sodium Sulphate Ratio		Total Sodium Hydroxide and Carbonate Alkalinity calculated to equivalent sodium carbonate
0 to 150	1	to	1
150 to 250	2	to	1
250 and over**	3	to	1

Under conditions where the sulphate content of the feed water is too low to meet these standards various forms of sulphates are added to the feedwater to make up for the sulphate deficiency. Sulphuric acid, sodium sulphate, sodium bi-sulphite and other chemicals are employed for this purpose.

Elaborate investigations concerning the mechanism of cracking of boiler steel have been carried out both in this country and abroad and numerous reports [3] and papers have been published on this subject.

Chlorine and Its Compounds. In 1904 and 1905 Sir Alexander Houston, director of water purification for the city of London, England, experimented with sodium hypochlorite for the sterilization of the raw water. The bacteriological results obtained by this treatment were entirely satisfactory. A similar process was used as a temporary expedient at Maidstone, England, during the 1897 typhoid epidemic. Credit for the first systematic use of chlorine for the treatment of a large water supply, however, is generally given to Sir Alexander Houston, and his associate, Dr. McGowan.

The earliest experiments for the chlorination of water, in America, were conducted at the Louisville Experimental Station in 1896, then under the direction of George W. Fuller. J. W. Ellms and

---

[2] Recommended revision of item six paragraph CA-5 of The American Society of Mechanical Engineers Boiler Operating Code relative to conditioning of boiler waters for the inhibition of caustic embrittlement as approved by the Committee on December 5, 1931.

** For cases where this ratio should be higher, see Bulletin No. 216 of the Engineering Experiment Station, University of Illinois entitled "Embrittlement in Boilers," 1930, pages 76-77-78.

[3] "Boiler Feed Water Purification," by Sheppard T. Powell, McGraw Hill Book Co., 1927.

Robert Spurr Weston assisted Mr. Fuller in this important work. Colonel George A. Johnson in 1908 probably carried out the first commercially successful chlorination treatment by the application of hypochlorite of lime to the water supply at the Bubbly Creek Filter Plant in Chicago. In the same year, Colonel Johnson and Professor Leal initiated chlorination of the water supply for Jersey City, N. J. So successful was this experiment that by 1911 over 800,000,000 gal. of water per day were being treated by hypochlorite in America.

In 1910 Major C. R. Darnell of the United States Army proved that liquid chlorine could be applied to water on a practical basis to replace bleaching powder which had been used previously. The first commercial use of liquid chlorine for the sterilization of a public water supply was made at New Niagara Falls, N. Y., in 1912. The

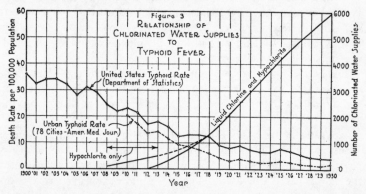

apparatus employed was developed by Dr. Georg Ornstein, for the Electro Bleaching Gas Co. This development was followed in 1913 by the Wallace & Tiernan chlorinator. With the development of equipment to apply the more easily handled liquid chlorine, the chlorination of public water supplies advanced rapidly and by 1918 over 3,000,000,000 gal. of water per day were so treated. It is estimated that, at the present time, over 6,000,000,000 gal. of water per day are being chlorinated. This is 85 to 90 per cent of the country's domestic water consumption.

Improved methods of filtration, more adequate facilities for disposal of sewage and other sanitary measures, developed in recent years, have influenced the reduction of morbidity and mortality rates of water-borne diseases, but the chlorination of public water supplies has been the greatest single factor responsible for the reduction. This condition is graphically illustrated in Fig. 3. Reference to this chart shows clearly that the rapid rise in chlorination of public water supplies was followed immediately by a marked reduction of typhoid fever rates.

Chlorination was instituted, primarily, for the disinfection of water supplies, but has been proved to be a valuable aid also to other forms of water treatment. It has been demonstrated that chlorine aids coagulation under some conditions and is especially adaptable to the treatment of colored waters and waters containing a high organic content. The application of chlorine to unfiltered water, or when used as an aid to coagulation, reduces the cost of filtration processes. Some of the specific advantages resulting from this treatment are:

1. A reduction of bacterial loadings on filters, permitting better and more consistent over-all quality of water than is possible by chlorination of filtered water only.
2. An increased factor of safety by the double application of the chlorine.
3. Improved coagulation, resulting in better clarity of effluents with a lower residual iron and alumina content of the water so treated.
4. Reduction of coagulant required to produce a satisfactory water.
5. Better color removal.
6. Prolongs filter runs with resulting economy of wash water and the maintenance of cleaner filters.
7. Control of plankton (microscopic life) in coagulating basins and filters.

Superchlorination and subsequent dechlorination by permanganates and sulphur dioxide has been successfully used in a number of cases for the prevention of tastes and odors.

In industrial fields, chlorination is now employed successfully in 100 or more paper mills for the prevention of slime growths. Chlorination of water is practiced, also, in many bottling plants for the final sterilization of rinsing water. Chlorination of circulating water used in surface condensers is now practiced at a number of steam generating stations. In this process the chlorine solution is applied to the condenser cooling water either continuously or intermittently. The purpose of this treatment is to control slime growths on the condenser tubes and thus ensure clean tubes and high vacuum. At present there are more than 20 installations of this kind in this country and many more in Europe. It is anticipated that the use of this process will advance rapidly, since the saving resulting from the maintenance of clean condensers can frequently justify the whole cost of treatment.

Water purification experience and research has shown that under some conditions chloramines, formed by the reaction of ammonia and chlorine, are superior to straight chlorine. The principal difference between the action of chlorine and chloramine is believed to be an electrochemical reaction, although there may be some chemical differences. It is claimed by some investigators [4] that—"The oxidation potential is a value which gives the oxidizing power of a compound a numerical expression. The oxidation potential, while the characteristic property of a compound, is also dependent upon the compound, the pH value of the solution, and other influences. Other things being equal, the oxidation potential of chlorine and chloramines is very important."

The recent popularity of the ammonia-chlorine treatment may be traced to the gratifying results obtained for the correction of certain specific conditions which chlorine treatment alone could not completely control. Some of the specific conditions where this process has proved advantageous are:

1. The prevention of bacterial after-growths occurring at times in chemically treated waters.
2. Control of microscopic growths, principally algae and similar aquatic organisms.
3. Permitting the maintenance of high residual amounts of chlorine in treated water without producing chlorinous tastes and odors.
4. Ability to maintain, without difficulty, high residuals of chlorine doses in water to insure protection of public water supplies arising from secondary pollution after initial chlorine treatment.

Ammonia-chlorine treatment of municipal water supplies has passed the experimental stage and although it has not always been as satisfactory as expected, it has proved to have a specific sphere of usefulness. In many cases the apparent failure of the process to produce the desired results may be traced to the inexperience or ignorance of the operators attempting the treatment. The important factors to be considered in ammonia-chlorination are:

1. Prompt and complete mixing of both ammonia and chlorine with the water to insure rapid formation of chloramine and to prevent local reaction of chlorine with phenol.
2. Reasonably short periods between the point of application of ammonia and chlorine to prevent dissipation of the ammonia and to prevent the necessity for high doses of ammonia or the danger of reaction of unprotected chlorine with phenol.
3. When post-chlorination, in addition to pre-treatment with ammonia and chlorine is practiced, it is necessary also to have ammonia present in order to avoid taste formation.

Chemical Coagulants. Progress in the art of water purification in the past quarter of a century has resulted from critical studies of the physico-chemical properties of the soluble and suspended

---

[4] "Ammonia Chlorine Process and Its Application in the Treatment of Water," by John C. Baker and Franz C. Schmelkes, Wallace & Tiernan, Bulletin 305.

solids contained in natural waters. The colloidal chemist has contributed much to our knowledge of the mechanism of coagulation and by this contribution, the art of water purification has advanced greatly.

In the past aluminum sulphate has been the most widely used coagulant for the clarification of water and still leads all others in tonnage of material employed for this purpose. During recent years, however, there has been a trend toward the use of combinations of chemicals for coagulating purposes. Much valuable work has been done on the coagulation of water by chemicals and the literature has been enriched by the contributions of John R. Baylis, Abel Wolman, A. M. Buswell, G. J. Fink, C. P. Hoover and other members of the chemical engineering profession.

Ferrous sulphate and lime possess some advantage over alum for clarification of certain waters, especially surface supplies which contain excessive amounts of suspended matter. These coagulants may also be used to advantage for the removal of manganese. Coagulation of certain types of water by ferric chloride and chlorinated copperas has been shown to be superior to alum under some conditions and has been adopted in a number of places where effective coagulation by alum has proved difficult. Combination of these chemicals and alum and sodium aluminate has greatly widened the field of chemical treatment of public and industrial water purification processes.

Although ferric chloride was employed as a coagulant many years ago, until recently its use for this purpose was limited. The relative cheapness and availability of aluminum sulphate made the use of this iron coagulant unattractive. The classical studies of L. B. Miller of the U. S. Public Health Service in 1925 again directed attention to the value of ferric salts for water coagulation and their adaptability and specific value for the coagulation of certain types of water. These coagulants are useful especially for the clarification of water containing low alkalinities. This development has led to securing a cheaper source of a ferric iron coagulant than ferric chloride and has resulted in the direct oxidation of ferrous sulphate with liquid chlorine. These coagulants also have merit since coagulating at low pH values, there is less tendency to the formation of colloidal or complex soluble iron compounds. The coagulum formed by these iron salts is bulky and possesses high adsorptive properties—desirable qualities for effective coagulation of certain waters.

The tonnage of ferric coagulants used in water purification is still much less than that of alum. There are indications, however, that their use will increase. It is probable that these materials will have a specific usefulness and will not displace aluminum sulphate for general water purification uses.

Recarbonation. Recarbonation of lime softened water at municipal water treatment plants for the prevention of after deposits is growing in favor and a number of installations of this type are now in use. Frequently, water softened by lime is not stable, owing to supersaturation of the normal carbonates of magnesium and lime, and as a result of these unbalanced equilibria, carbonate deposits occur on sand used to filter the treated water, in water mains and elsewhere in distribution systems. This condition is always encountered where excess lime, over that required for theoretical reaction, is used.

By recarbonation of lime softened water with carbon dioxide gas, the excess lime or caustic alkalinity in the water is neutralized, and the normal carbonates are converted into bicarbonates. The bicarbonates have a high solubility and, therefore, are not deposited unless the water is heated. The process is relatively simple and consists merely of bubbling the gas through the water in as inexpensive and convenient a manner as possible. Various sources of gas production are utilized and this method of generation depends upon local conditions. According to C. P. Hoover [5] who has been largely responsible for this development in America, states:

Perhaps the simplest type of plant yet built consists of a tall tank provided with a gas burner, another similar tank for cooling the gases, a compressor or blower and a diffuser. Carbonation equipment of this kind has been used when the quantity of water to be treated was less than 10,000 gal. per hour. For plants of large capacity, say, 40,000 gal. per hour or more, a coke burning stove, a scrubber and dryer, a moisture trap, a compressor and a diffuser are provided. Instead of a stove, a brick furnace provided with a coke hopper has sometimes been used. It is customary to provide one square foot of grate area for each 10 lb. of coke burned per hour. In larger plants a marine boiler is very often used instead of a stove. This boiler can be made to produce a considerable quantity of hot water which can be used advantageously for slacking the lime used in the softening process. At larger water softening plants, a gas producer type of plant may be used to advantage. This consists of six principal parts:—a gas producer, a gas burner, a return tubular boiler, a steam driven air compressor, a combination scrubber and dryer, and a diffuser. In operation, coke is burned in a gas producer, which is a closed furnace with controlled air supply furnished by a blower. The products of combustion pass from the gas producer to a gas burner where they are mixed with air and burned to complete combustion under a boiler. The steam produced in the boiler is used to drive the air compressor and blower in order to make a closed cycle for the process. The air compressor takes its suction from the boiler stack of the producer gas burning boiler, through a scrubber and dryer and

---

[5] Chemist, Filtration Plant, Columbus, Ohio. (Private communication.)

forces the washed gases through diffusers into the water to be carbonated. Making producer gas from coke and burning it under a boiler is perhaps the most economical method of producing carbon dioxide gas, because the steam generated is readily available and it is possible to produce a gas containing as much as 18 to 19 per cent carbon dioxide, thus requiring an air compressor of much less capacity than if coke were burned in an open furnace.

Treatment With Activated Carbon. An interesting recent development in the art of water purification is the use of activated carbon. Various forms of carbon have been used in small pressure filters for many years, but the direct application of carbon to municipal water supplies is an innovation. This type of water treatment is specifically important to the chemical engineering profession, since it has opened up a new and growing market for activated carbon. Data supplied by the Industrial Chemical Sales Co. indicate that the number of water treatment plants using activated carbon of the Aqua Nuchar type has increased from fewer than 10 in July, 1930, to approximately 375 at the end of 1932.

As a result of war time research on activated carbon for use in gas making, much information was gained concerning the physical and chemical properties of these products and this knowledge and experience have been utilized in the present practice of supplying this type of carbon for the removal of tastes and odors from domestic water supplies. Although taste and odor removal has been the primary reason for the addition of carbon to water, there are a number of other incidental benefits derived from these products. Investigation of this process has demonstrated that activated carbon improves coagulation, assists chlorination by adsorption of organic matter, reduces the residual aluminum content of water coagulated with aluminum salts and insures less difficulty from putrefaction of sludge deposits in the coagulating basin.

Chemical and Engineering Contributions. In a number of places in this brief review the author has mentioned the individual contributions of members of the American Institute of Chemical Engineers and others in the chemical profession. Much, or perhaps even more, credit is due to the achievements of such men as Professors William P. Mason and Edward Bartow. The former trained many of the engineers who have since played important rôles in water purification. His book on the "Examination of Water," which has gone through a half dozen editions, has long been a classic text and reference source. Dr. Bartow, as head of the Illinois State Water Survey and subsequently at the University of Iowa, trained an impressive group of chemists and engineers for work in water purification. Among these are W. D. Hatfield, R. C. Bardwell, Frank Bachmann, F. W. Mohlman, L. I. Birdsall, J. J. Hinman and many others. Reference should also be made here to the early contributions of W. Miller Booth, a founder of the Institute, and to W. M. Barr, whose work with the Union Pacific System has attracted national attention. There are literally scores of others who have helped during the past 25 years to lift the art of water treatment to its present high plane of efficiency as a branch of chemical engineering.

CHAPTER XXIII

STREAM POLLUTION AND WASTE DISPOSAL

By ROBERT SPURR WESTON

Weston & Sampson, Consulting Engineers, Boston, Mass.

IN THE PAST 25 years a great change in attitude regarding the relation between stream pollution and waste disposal has taken place among sanitary engineers and others. More and more attention is being paid to the necessities of the streams and the utilization, for economic reasons, of their great capacities for self-purification and consequently, disposal of sewage by dilution.[1] Formerly, the amount of dilution, with little regard for the quality of the diluting water and the degree of self-purification, was considered the important factor.

Because in England where rivers are small and the population dense it had been held for years that rivers were not long enough to purify themselves from the effects of sewage pollution, this belief became established; although as stated in the Second Report of the Royal Commission on Sewage Disposal, 1903, the River Severn near Shrewsbury was shown to purify itself to a substantial extent, as indicated by chemical tests.

While the amount of dilution was considered without reference to the quality of the diluting water, engineers were accustomed to give the opinion that dilutions of from 3 to 7 or even more cu. ft. per second per thousand population were required to prevent offensive anaërobic decomposition in the stream. For example, on October 12, 1911, G. M. Wisner, chief engineer of the Chicago Sanitary District, reported results obtained with a dilution of 3.3 cu. ft. per sec. per thousand population and found it too low for local conditions.

---

[1] *Editor's Note:* In a paper entitled "The Use, Not the Abuse of Streams," which Mr. Weston presented before the Stream Pollution Symposium of the Institute at Atlantic City in December, 1931, he developed the modern criteria for judging the sanitary condition of streams and presented comprehensive data correlating the biochemical oxygen demand with a stream's definite capacity for self-purification. It is suggested that the reader consult that paper in the *Transactions*, A. I. Ch. E. Vol. XXVII, pp. 1-8 (1931) for these phases of the subject of stream pollution.

TABLE I.—Comparison of Characteristics of Sewages and Various Industrial Wastes

(Parts per Million)

| Constituent | Sewage | | | Wool Scouring Waste | | Chrome Dye Liquor | Logwood Blue Liquor | Textile |
	American Manuf. Cities	Domestic	English Manuf. Cities	(A) Combined	(B) First Bowl			Stronger Wastes for Treatment
Turbidity								300.
Color								.500
Total organic nitrogen	24.1	18.0						8.80
Ammonia nitrogen	11.9	7.8	14.8	6.64		11.3	123.4	7.64
Albuminoid nitrogen	26.5	27.2	36.5	71.4		17.1	22.0	5.40
Nitrite nitrogen	0.26							
Nitrate nitrogen	1.19							
Oxygen consumed	133.	71.	266.	230.		3.82	335.	562.
Biochemical oxygen demand	230.	143.		702.				378.
Chlorides	109.	47.	162.		850.			20.
Alkalinity	129.			550.	6100.		21.	392.
Residue on Evaporation								
Total	1058.	603.	1896.	1960.	50882.	5026.	5359.	1860.
Volatile	635.	393.		1530.		1271.	4497.	1380.
Fixed	423.	210.		430.		3755.		480.
Suspended Residue								
Total	384.	342.	668.	700.	24127.			300.
Volatile	288.	260.		520.				270.
Fixed	96.	82.		180.				30.
Dissolved Residue								
Total	608.	261.	1288.	1260.	26755.			1560.
Volatile	270.	133.		1010.				1110.
Fixed	338.	128.		250.				450.
Fats	37.			520.	18620.			
pH Value								

[1] Proc. A. I. Ch. Eng., Besselievre & Anable. Vol. 27—Liquid Wastes from Indus. Plants.

F. B. Stearns, chief engineer of the Massachusetts Board of Health, in his report on pollution of streams in 1890 arrived at the conclusion that volumes of 2.5 and 7 cu. ft. per sec. are required per thousand population. This opinion was based largely upon free ammonia determinations, a yardstick whose accuracy is debatable and which has largely been superseded.[2]

Later on, Allen Hazen in his special report for the State of Ohio in 1898 stated that "in the case of sluggish streams or streams which are already somewhat polluted, the quantity required for proper dilution may be increased (from 4 cu. ft. per sec.) to 6, 8 or even 10 cu. ft. per sec. per thousand of population." The modern position is that stated by Fuller,[3] namely, that each stream must be considered upon its merits.

While from a theoretical standpoint, the dissolved oxygen in the water may be nearly or quite exhausted before any nuisance arises,

[2] See Trans. A. I. Ch. E. Vol. 27, p. 4.
[3] Sewage Disposal, 1912.

TABLE I.—Comparison of Characteristics of Sewages and Various Industrial Wastes

Wastes			Paper Wastes										
Kier Liquor	Finishing Plant		Sulphite Liquor [1]	Machine Waste [1]	Rotary Boiler Liquor	Beater Waste	Washer Waste	Beet[3] Sugar Wastes	Tannery Waste [1]	Dairy Waste [1]	Slaughter House Waste[1]	Cannery Wastes	Pea[2] Canning
	Raw	Effluent											
250.	215.	5.			3500.	600.	1200.					234.	
3500.	181.	60.				160.	200.						
62.4			40.					33.	96.	48.	640.		
11.8	1.63	0.46		19.2		0.3	0.82		19.2	28.	112.		
42.2	2.78	1.20	12.8	19.2		1.4	8.68		25.6	19.2	96.		
			0.					0.22	0.	Trace	0.		
			0.	0.				0.08	0.	0.	0.		
1350.	254.	27.	4690.	330.	2500.	172.	275.	1100.	5000.	20.	356.	1650.	
	257.	25.	1300.	20.	2000.				14000.	260.	600.	1593.	
			18.5	7.4					185.	18.5	3800.		
3040.	404.	288.			6800.	153.	530.						
8140.	1441.	734.	35260.	2000.	59275.	1350.	1550.	2260.	40140.	720.	13440.	4558.	
5480.	717.	166.			38975.	820.	1020.	1868.					
2660.	724.	568.			20300.	530.	530.						
550.	258.	3.	80.	180.	24905.	480.	870.	516.	10820.	280.	3580.	324.	
540.	187.	1.			19205.	170.	560.	396.					
10.	71.	2.			5700.	310.	310.						
7590.	1183.	721.	35180.	1820.	34370.	870.	680.		29320.	440.	9860.	4234.	
4940.	530.	115.			19770.	650.	460.						
2650.	653.	606.			14600.	220.	220.						
					50.								
			3.0	7.6				6.1	6.6	6.6	6.3		

[2] Stream Pollution in Wisconsin. Sp. Report p. 26—Treatment Pea Canning Wastes.
[3] Sewage Works Jour., Vol. 1, No. 1, Levine & Nelson—Expts. on purifying beet sugar wastes.

it is not good practice in most cases to burden the stream to such a degree that this condition will exist. How much should be left is a matter of opinion. Major fish life requires at least 2.5 p.p.m. of dissolved oxygen which is about 30 per cent of that required for saturation at ordinary summer temperature (25 deg. C.) In few cases is it wise to reduce the per cent of saturation to as low as 20 per cent, while in general, 50 per cent, or about 4.2 p.p.m. at ordinary summer temperatures is a desirable minimum.

Character of Industrial Wastes. No generalization regarding the character of industrial waste is of much value. Wastes differ widely. How widely various wastes differ from one another and from domestic sewage in composition is shown in the Table I.

Methods of Treatment. No review of the work of the past 25 years would be complete without mention of the work of the Lawrence Experiment Station of the Massachusetts State Board of Health. This work began in the early 90's and has been continued until this writing, although not so extensively in recent years. The important early work of the station in the field of waste treatment was reviewed by Mr. Harry W. Clark in the Report of the Board for 1909. In this review, methods of treatment of wastes from tanneries, paper mills, carpet mills, paint mills, woolen mills, wool scouring works, dye works, shoddy mills, creameries, yeast factories, glue works, etc., were discussed in great detail. Many satisfactory methods were worked out which are in use today. In general, the successful methods included subsidence, straining through coke, and intermittent filtration through sand. Chemical precipitation was tried quite extensively and its economic limitations noted.

Many wastes, especially when mixed with some domestic sewage like that derived from the toilets of a mill and from the sewers of the village in which a mill is located, may be disposed of by using biological and other methods which are used successfully to treat ordinary municipal sewage. Among these are screening, plain subsidence, trickling filters, intermittent sand filters, activated sludge treatment with secondary subsidence, and chlorination.

If the same results be obtained as with ordinary sewage, one may expect the following degrees of purification:

Method	*Per cent of Purification*
Screening	10 to 15
Screening and plain subsidence	30 to 40
Screening and plain subsidence and chlorination	40 to 50
Screening and plain subsidence and trickling filters	85
Plain subsidence and intermittent sand filters	90 to 95
Screening, grit chambers, plain subsidence, and activated sludge treatment with secondary subsidence	90 to 95
Same as above but with chlorination	95 to 98

There are many industrial wastes which cannot be treated by biolysis like domestic sewage. The chief difficulties are:

(1) Certain wastes, or certain portions of wastes, from some manufacturing processes contain antiseptic substances which prevent bacterial action or nitrification.
(2) The wastes may contain excessive amounts of settleable solids, especially carbonaceous matter, as indicated in Table I.
(3) The economic problem of handling enormous volumes of wastes.
(4) The varying character of liquor coming from different plants doing similar work. This limits the value of data obtained from one plant in solving the problems of another.
(5) The changes in the character of the waste due to market and industrial conditions.

For these reasons special methods must be used, and, in general, the waste from each plant, not each type of plant, must be treated as a special problem. In the following paragraphs are described a few of the methods which are used for certain classes of wastes:

Wool Scouring Waste. Wool scouring waste results from the washing of wool with soap and alkali. Under the best practice it is a highly concentrated liquor containing, in addition to the soil and other matter washed from the wool, lanoline and other wool greases, soap and alkali.

Two methods of purification are in common use, namely, centrifugalization and the acid-cracking process. The first process in its simplest form consists of passing the waste through subsiding basins and thence through centrifugal machines where most of the mineral suspended matter and about half of the ether-soluble matter are recovered. In its more elaborate form, the scouring plant is operated as a closed system, that is, primary and secondary centrifugal machines are used for the continuous treatment of the scouring liquor as it flows through the bowls and only a small amount of concentrated waste is discharged into lagoons or on beds, thereby relieving the stream of practically all pollution and greatly increasing the yield of marketable grease.

In some cases where the simpler process is used, the effluent from the centrifugal machines is stored in lagoons during periods of low stream flow and released during periods of high water when it may be discharged without damage to downstream owners.

In the acid-cracking process the waste is treated in tanks with sulphuric acid which precipitates the sludge containing fully 90 per cent of the grease and suspended matter. This sludge is then thickened, heated and the grease extracted in steam heated presses by the usual methods. The effluent from the tanks and the water from the presses are much lower in grease content than the effluent from the centrifugal machines. It is high in sulphates and contains free sulphuric acid, making it unsuitable for discharge under some conditions.

Waste From the Paper Industry. This waste is of three principal types:—(1) That resulting from the processing of wood to make wood pulp, or, resulting from the boiling of raw stock in alkali. (2) That discharged from beaters and washers. (3) That discharged from paper-making machines.

The first class of waste is almost impossible to treat except when quite highly diluted with other wastes or when evaporated and incinerated. Many northern rivers are burdened with sulphite pulp liquor which is the worst waste of this class. It is highly antiseptic and decomposes with difficulty. After a considerable period of storage it loses its antiseptic character, begins to ferment and may then be disposed of by dilution or by addition to other wastes. The recovery of byproducts of value from the evaporated liquor is the most promising method under discussion at present. Unfortunately, overproduction would destroy such values.

For the disposal of beater and washer wastes, subsidence, with or without coagulants, is the most valuable method and one which is adequate for stream protection in most cases. Paper manufacturers are realizing more and more the possibility of recovery of valuable material from some of their wastes, particularly those from papermaking machines. The use of mechanically-cleaned subsiding basins has stimulated this work. Manufacturers of higher grade papers can often sell recovered fiber to manufacturers of lower grade paper products. The possibilities in this direction have been well described by C. M. Baker.[1]

Sometimes chemical treatment accelerates subsidence but in most cases the cost of chemicals prohibits their addition. For the further treatment of wastes, beds of cinders, not too fine, are most useful. In designing beds for winter use, the low temperature of the wastes should be taken into consideration.

Textile Dyeing and Finishing Plant Wastes. These wastes are of wide variety. They include alkaline mercerizing waste, spent dye and mordants, including acid chrome liquor and tin salts, kier liquors, diastatic ferments, spent bleach, soapy waste water, wastes containing starch, saccharine bodies, gums, clay and other waste materials from the finishing processes, waste color from print works, and various acid and alkaline wash waters.

It is fortunate that many textile wastes are relatively clean and may be discharged into most streams with impunity, leaving but from one-quarter to one-half of the volume of waste to be treated. Only where fabrics and fibers are loaded with various insoluble substances, or where logwood or other vegetable dyes are used, are textile wastes high in suspended matter. Even kier liquor, high in solids, holds them in colloidal suspension.

Kier liquor, like sulphite liquor from pulp mills, is the most difficult textile waste to treat. When uniformly diluted with other waste and domestic sewage, it does not interfere greatly with biological processes of treatment or with subsidence. By itself it has been hitherto best treated by lagooning and dilution, but quite recently

---

[1] *Trans., Am. Inst. Chem. Engrs.* **27**, 147 (1931).

William S. Wise[2] has described a promising method in which the free caustic in the kier liquor is converted to carbonate by treatment with flue gases in an absorption tower, after which the solids in the liquor are precipitated with calcium chloride. The process, while not yet fully worked out, promises the removal of over 90 per cent of the organic matter and the discharge of an effluent which will not interfere with other processes when mixed with other wastes to be treated, in other words, one which may be discharged into most streams with impunity.

Waste containing starches, clay and other suspended matter may be purified by subsidence and filtration. Unless the kier liquor, waste bleach and other textile substances are specially treated or removed from the other wastes, double treatment by filtration (trickling filters and intermittent filters) is often indicated, although intermittent sand filters at low rates may be depended upon to give good results.

The activated sludge process is suited to few textile wastes. This is because of the low specific gravity of the suspended matter, resulting in poor separation of the sludge and liquor and frequent loss of sludge from the aerating tank.

While many wastes may be purified by chemical precipitation, while low priced chemicals, notably ferric sulphate and ferric chloride, are coming on the market, and while chemical precipitation processes are greatly facilitated by mechanically-cleaned subsiding basins, it must be borne in mind that the treatment of a heterogeneous waste demands strict supervision and considerable storage and mixing to equalize the varying characters of the raw wastes. For this work the automatic pH recorder in train with electrical relays and valves is useful, where its cost is warranted.

Ferrous Metal Wastes. These commonly result from the treatment of iron and steel with sulphuric acid. Chemical engineers are generally familiar with methods for treating ferrous wastes by dilution, or neutralization, or by recovering byproducts therefrom. The neutralization process may be greatly facilitated by the use of mechanical devices, as described by Besselievre and Anable[3] but the process has many disadvantages due to the cost of lime used to neutralize the acid and to the increase in the calcium sulphate content of the water in which the treated waste is discharged. In many cases, however,

---

[2] Work of the Connecticut State Water Commission. *Trans. Am. Inst. Chem. Engrs.,* **27,** 99 (1931).

[3] Liquid Wastes from Industrial Plants and Their Treatment, *Trans. Am. Inst. Chem. Engrs.,* **27,** 138 (1931).

neutralization is demanded in order to prevent a stream from becoming acid.

These statements regarding waste pickling liquor apply equally well to acid mine waters whose discharge raises such a sanitary problem in the coal mining regions.

Non-Ferrous Metal Wastes. Considerable work has been done, particularly in Connecticut, in devising methods for the removal of copper and zinc from the sludge produced by neutralizing pickling liquors treated with lime and soda ash; also, in recovering copper by precipitation on scrap metals followed by neutralization, precipitation and recovery of zinc. As yet, however, these processes are not in wide use.

Laundry Wastes. Methods for treating laundry wastes by precipitation with calcium chloride and ferric or aluminum salts have been developed in recent years and may be employed for batch treatment followed by subsidence and discharge of other wastes into the stream, or further purification by treatment on beds as occasions require. The cost of chemicals for precipitation is often unreasonably high and conditions often favor plain subsidence and treatment on intermittent sand filters at low rates.

Packing House Wastes. The highly odorous and putrescible waste from packing houses contains grease, fertilizing elements and other products which are usually recoverable by processes conducted as part of the plant operations. Screening and treatment in continuous, mechanically-cleaned sedimentation tanks, with the screenings and sludge de-watered by vacuum filters or otherwise, and the effluent treated by the activated sludge process, or by double filtration, or by dilution with city sewage for further treatment are accepted methods for handling this troublesome waste. The addition of chlorine is often useful to reduce nuisance and to facilitate precipitation and oxidation. Its use, however, introduces an economic factor because of the high chlorine demand of the waste.

Glue and Gelatine Wastes. These are concentrated and contain waste animal parts, lime used in the de-hairing process, dirt, etc. While of disagreeable appearance, they may be greatly improved by screening and clarification in a continuous subsiding basin which is cleaned mechanically. The sludge and screenings may be handled like those derived from packing-house wastes.

Gas Works Wastes. The chief wastes from gas works are tar and ammonia liquors. From the tarry waste the tar is collected and sold as such. The ammonia liquors were formerly subjected to distillation.

It has been usual to recover ammonia from the crude ammonia liquor, distilling first the free ammonia and then the fixed ammonia, lime being added for the second process. This resulted in the production of either liquid ammonia or ammonium sulphate and the discharge of the so-called still waste, or "devil liquor," containing lime and some organic matter.

Recently, the recovery of ammonia has been unprofitable and in cities like Milwaukee, Rochester and Providence the crude ammonia liquor is mixed with domestic sewage and disposed with it at the municipal treatment works. Experience has shown that when added uniformly in the concentration of not over 1 part of waste to 750 parts of sewage and when the amounts of phenol-like bodies are kept at the minimum by skimming the wastes before discharge, the ammonia liquor has no material ill effect upon the disposal of sewage by biological methods including the activated sludge process.

One great achievement in the field of chemical engineering has been the process for recovering by absorption the phenols from the wastes from byproduct coke ovens, thus preventing their discharge into streams used for water supply. The alternative was the use of the waste for coke quenching, an expensive expedient at best because the quenching had to be done in the coke wagons with consequent great loss of equipment through corrosion.

Canning Wastes. Improvements made in treating the wastes from canning processes, in fact the wastes from food producing factories in general, have been in the line of removing the waste matter by screening and subsidence and the de-watering of the screenings and sludge by the use of continuous filters and dryers. The treatment of the settled waste from the various canning industries presents no unusual problems; neither have any material improvements been made in the processes in this regard which have not had their first use for treating domestic sewage.

Starch and Sugar Wastes. Prof. Edward Bartow [4] has reviewed the methods for the disposal of these readily fermentable carbohydrate wastes. Here again, improvements in the processes of treatment of the starch factory waste have consisted in the use of chemical engineering methods for reducing the amount of waste discharged, namely, in using for steeping and other processes the effluents from certain other processes, instead of fresh water. These methods have been successful in reducing by 90 per cent the amount of polluting matter

---

[4] *Trans. Am. Inst. Chem. Engrs.*, **27**, 110-122 (1931).

discharged from starch factories. For the treatment of the concentrated waste from starch factories after subsidence, the activated sludge process, either by itself or in combination with trickling filters, has proved most useful.

In beet sugar factories the three principal wastes, wash water, diffusion water and the Steffens waste, are the ones which must be considered. The former presents no technical difficulties, the volume of wash water being easily reduced by re-circulation with screening and subsidence in the circuit. The diffusion water may be purified by biological methods but at rather low rates, because of the tendency toward the formation of lactic acid which interferes with biolysis.

The Steffens waste presents the greatest difficulty and in recent years the possibility of recovery of byproducts, especially potassium salts, betaine hydrochloride and glutamic acid, have occupied the attention of many chemical engineers. If glutamic acid can be recovered at a low price, it can compete with a similar product from wheat gluten and thus conserve values by placing a valuable chemical product upon the market.

The problem of the treatment of waste from cane sugar factories is similar to that of treating the beet sugar waste with the exception that, because cropping takes place in the dry season, disposal by dilution is commonly more difficult and the prevailing higher temperatures promote fermentation. As in the case of the beet sugar waste, re-circulation and treatment with the assistance of aeration offers the most promising way out of a difficult problem.

Tannery Wastes. While tannery wastes can be treated by chemical precipitation, the method described in the Report of the Pennsylvania Sanitary Water Board seems more economical, as does the method of subsidence followed by filtration through intermittent sand beds as worked out by the Massachusetts Board of Health 25 years ago.

In Pennsylvania it was advised that the mixed wastes from the tannery should be first subjected to plain subsidence and then to primary filtration through deep trickling filters of coke. After a second subsidence, with the aid of coagulants if necessary, the effluent from the primary filters is passed through secondary filters and is then ready for discharge into most streams. This process differs but little from that required for treating the waste from textile finishing plants. Its novelty consists in the using of chemical coagulation after primary subsidence and filration, it being uneconomical to apply chemicals to the raw waste.

Milk and Dairy Wastes. In milk plants and dairies, economy of water is the first essential for successful treatment. The second essential is to prevent waste of milk products, notably lactose, which greatly interferes with treatment of the waste on bacterial beds. Many chemical engineers are probably familiar with the experiments using trickling filters made up of bundles of laths which are able to effect a reduction of 90 per cent in the biochemical oxygen demand.

In general, treatment in a septic tank followed by filtration in primary and secondary filters suffices. In many cases treatment with chlorine greatly reduces the odor nuisance due to fermentation and often permits the discharge of the waste on land without causing complaint.

In treating all wastes containing fermentable carbohydrates, rapid handling in basins is essential, and sludge digestion in Imhoff tanks is rarely practicable.

Mechanical Devices. The most marked change in methods of treating industrial wastes has been the increased employment of mechanical devices, notably automatic screens, self-cleaning grit chambers, mechanically-cleaned subsiding basins, vacuum filters for sludge and the activated sludge process, the latter employing compressed air in large volumes. While great advances have been possible through the use of these devices and excellent results are obtained, it is doubtful if, where natural sand in place can be used, the new devices produce better or more economical results. They have, however, been a great boon to industries located where natural filters are out of the question or where filter materials are difficult to obtain and costly.

Chemical Precipitation. Quite recently the production of cheap ferric salts by the action of chlorine on scrap iron, or as a byproduct of certain other industries, has revived attention to the chemical precipitation process. A notable example of this is the work of Guggenheim Brothers in New York, at present being applied on a semi-plant scale to domestic sewage only.

In brief, the process consists of chemical precipitation with the de-watering of the sludge by means of vacuum filters and the subsequent incineration of the de-watered sludge, the ash from the incinerator being treated with sulphuric acid and used over again. The effluent from the subsiding basin is then passed through a special zeolite which exchanges sodium for the basic nitrogen in the sewage. The zeolite is regenerated with brine in the usual way and ammonia is recovered from the salt wash water by distillation.

While this process is extremely interesting from a chemical standpoint, one must await its trial on a large scale for determinations of cost factors before making predictions regarding its economy. Such a trial is about to be made by the Sanitary District of Chicago.

Profitable Byproducts. During the past 25 years chemical engineers have made much progress in recovering byproducts from wastes with consequent lifting of some of the burden which streams have had to carry. Knowledge is not lacking for further recoveries but market conditions frequently prevent the disposal of recovered products at any price.

An example of this was the recovery from the Milwaukee sewage of dried sewage sludge, a product known as "Milorganite." When first placed on the market it found a ready sale, notably as a fertilizer for golf greens. Present market conditions prevent its sale and consequently the method of disposal is costly. Milwaukee conditions have, therefore, turned the attention of engineers towards the disposal of sewage sludge by de-watering followed by incineration without reference to its utilization.

Similar conditions have obtained in the gas industry. Formerly, there was a market for aqua ammonia and ammonium sulphate. Recently European manufacturers have sold synthetic ammonium sulphate at a price below the cost of its recovery from gas works waste.

On the other hand, there are many industries, like paper making and silk dyeing, where valuable waste products were formerly discharged with the waste and are now recovered at a profit. There are other opportunities for work of this kind but under present conditions the attention of engineers is being turned more toward reducing cost of treatment with little attention toward the possibilities of recovering valuable byproducts. One reason for this is that if recoverable byproducts were placed upon the market the resulting lowered price would in many cases make the products unsaleable.

Chemical engineers can well view with pride their record of accomplishment during the past 25 years. With them the sanitary engineer has cooperated and their combined efforts have resulted in lowered costs of production and a reduction in stream pollution.

CHAPTER XXIV

A STATISTICAL SURVEY OF THE CHEMICAL ENGINEERING INDUSTRIES, 1908-1933

By E. R. Weidlein and Lawrence W. Bass

Respectively, Director, Mellon Institute of Industrial Research, Pittsburgh, Pa., and Director of Research, The Borden Co., New York

THE QUARTER-CENTURY that has elapsed since the organization of the American Institute of Chemical Engineers has witnessed profound changes in our industries. Throughout our manufacturing activities there has been a remarkable growth. But the expansion in that group of industries characterized by dependence on chemical engineering processes has been especially noteworthy.

A sharp differentiation of chemical engineering manufactures from other manufactures is, of course, not possible. The list of industries selected for inclusion in the present chapter represents in our best judgment those manufacturing operations permeated to a major degree with the spirit of the chemical engineer.

Economic Importance of the Process Industries. A summary of the basic data for the entire group of process industries, as well as the corresponding figures for all manufacturing industries, is given in Table I. From these totals it is seen that the chemical engineering manufactures have steadily increased in importance from 16.2 per cent of the value of all manufactured products in 1909 to 19.5 per cent in 1931. The magnitude of this change is more clearly seen in the following comparisons: in the period 1909 to 1929 the value of the products of the process industries has increased nearly 280 per cent, while the total for all industries shows a rise of about 240 per cent; between 1929 and 1931 the process industries suffered a decrease of 36 per cent in value of products, as compared with a decrease of 38 per cent in the totals for all industries. The noteworthy increase of nearly 2 per cent in the ratio of chemical engineering products to all manufactures in the two-year period 1929 to 1931 illustrates the relative stability of the group under the stress of adverse economic conditions.

From Table I it is also seen that the chemical engineering manufactures, although carried on in only 8 per cent of the total number

329

TABLE I.—Economic Importance of the Process Industries

	(1) Number of establishments	(2) Number of wage earners	(3) Number of salaried employees	(4) Wages	(5) Salaries	(6) Cost of materials, containers, fuel, energy	(7) Value of products	(8) Value added by manufacture
				Thousands of dollars				
1909								
All manufactures.	175,142	6,472,616	790,267	3,427,038	938,575	12,064,573	20,449,588	8,385,015
Process industries.	21,813	747,588	108,380	381,515	135,446	1,969,722	3,306,762	1,337,040
Percentage.	12.5	11.6	13.7	11.1	14.4	16.3	16.2	15.9
1919								
All manufactures.	214,383	9,000,059	1,438,219	10,461,787	2,880,868	37,232,702	62,041,795	24,809,093
Process industries.	18,729	1,065,613	233,081	1,239,484	457,892	6,804,592	10,596,943	3,791,754
Percentage.	8.7	11.8	16.2	11.8	15.9	18.3	17.1	15.3
1921								
All manufactures.	196,267	6,946,570	1,146,380	8,202,324	2,563,103	25,321,055	43,653,283	18,332,227
Process industries.	15,132	841,438	166,766	1,017,865	375,337	5,236,665	7,968,793	2,732,124
Percentage.	7.7	12.1	14.5	12.4	14.6	20.7	18.3	14.9
1929								
All manufactures.	210,959	8,838,743	1,358,775	11,620,973	3,595,064	38,549,580	70,434,863	31,885,284
Process industries.	16,249	1,096,011	191,438	1,422,438	489,331	7,397,626	12,489,716	5,092,094
Percentage.	7.7	12.4	14.1	12.2	13.6	19.2	17.7	16.0
1931								
All manufactures.	174,136	6,511,647	....	7,225,587	....	21,420,124	41,333,109	19,912,985
Process industries.	14,029	832,982	....	961,922	....	4,525,346	8,042,436	3,517,090
Percentage.	8.1	12.8	....	13.3	....	21.1	19.5	17.7

of establishments in recent census periods, give employment to approximately 12 per cent of the wage earners in all manufacturing operations, and to a still higher proportion of salaried employees. Between 1909 and 1921 there was a decided trend toward larger establishments as compared with manufactures in general, this fact being illustrated by the change in actual number of establishments as well as in the percentage figures.

Economic Characteristics of the Process Industries. In Table II are given the basic data for the various process industries as compiled from U. S. Censuses of Manufactures. Certain generalizations characteristic of the group can be drawn, before proceeding to the discussion of individual industries.

From an inspection of the data it is apparent that the comment made regarding the expansion of the chemical industries as a group is generally true for the individual industries. There has been, of course, an exceedingly rapid growth in some branches of manufacture, while in others the change has been moderate.

Operation of chemical engineering processes is in general conducted on a somewhat larger scale than the average for all industries, as shown by a greater output per establishment. Because of the great diversity of products included in this group of manufactures, it is not possible to fix too definite an explanation of this condition, but it is perhaps safe to assume that the production of a change in the chemical composition of matter is a more complicated manufacturing procedure than a fabrication not involving chemical reactions. In any case, economic justification is afforded by the larger production per wage earner as compared with the average for all manufacturing industries.

The process industries show a ratio of wages to value of products slightly below the average for all manufacturing industries. When the comparison is made between wages and value added by manufacture, however, chemical engineering industries show a ratio markedly lower than the average. The group, on the other hand, shows a higher expenditure for salaries as compared with value of products than other industries, a reflection, perhaps, of the greater amount of technical supervision required in this type of manufacture.

TABLE II.—Basic Data on the Process Industries

Explanatory Notes. The classification of industries here is the same as that used in the U. S. Census of Manufactures. The following combinations of related industries have been made to render the data more compact:

Chemicals: include compressed and liquefied gases, and rayon.

Coke: includes manufactured fuels.

Coloring and finishing materials: printing and writing inks; blackings, stains, and dressings; boneblack, carbon black, and lamp black; bluing; cleaning and polishing compounds.

Oils and greases: grease and tallow; lubricating greases; cottonseed oil, cake, and meal; linseed oil, cake, and meal; essential oils; oils not elsewhere classified; candles.

Sugar: beet and cane sugar; cane sugar refining; corn syrup, corn sugar, corn oil, and starch.

Wood chemicals: turpentine and rosin; wood distillation and charcoal manufacture; tanning materials, natural dyestuffs, mordants and assistants, and sizes.

Miscellaneous products of process industries: ethyl alcohol and distilled liquors; salt; glue and gelatin.

Adequate data could not be obtained throughout the period for ethyl alcohol alone, and hence it was necessary to include distilled liquors; the effect of the 18th Amendment on the data for this classification must be borne in mind.

		(1) Number of establishments	(2) Number of wage earners	(3) Number of salaried employees	(4) Wages	(5) Salaries	(6) Cost of materials, containers, fuel, electric energy	(7) Value of products	(8) Value added by manufacture
					Thousands of dollars				
Chemicals	1909	401	25,981	3,923	15,591	6,137	69,531	127,625	58,094
	19	836	76,918	18,200	105,062	39,039	301,519	614,279	312,760
	21	728	49,*38	12,184	62,161	30,870	200,273	412,231	211,959
	29	934	104,695	18,652	144,755	47,357	411,441	939,784	528,344
	31	934	90,046	....	108,420	....	292,880	707,403	414,523
Clay products	1909	5,037	132,696	9,353	66,892	11,252	45,647	168,895	123,248
	19	2,786	105,353	10,607	108,578	21,980	88,857	285,005	195,528
	21	2,178	97,591	9,315	109,443	22,343	94,004	279,766	185,764
	29	2,102	129,311	11,410	151,350	30,627	109,651	408,528	298,877
	31	1,558	78,725	....	72,596	....	55,073	196,440	141,367
Coke	1909	326	29,361	1,874	15,504	2,094	64,180	96,008	31,828
	19	289	29,490	3,579	42,521	7,740	225,653	318,490	92,836
	21	190	16,441	3,176	24,318	8,480	171,071	224,491	53,419
	29	176	20,978	3,040	33,973	7,716	287,511	425,846	138,335
	31	135	14,684	....	22,491	....	165,828	231,077	65,249
Coloring and finishing materials	1909	728	4,584	2,738	2,385	3,438	13,154	28,217	15,064
	19	962	8,135	4,797	8,271	10,566	49,338	93,582	44,245
	21	660	6,585	3,603	7,606	8,455	37,790	77,544	39,755
	29	872	9,214	4,084	12,442	12,119	58,507	144,342	85,835
	31	776	7,300	....	9,515	....	43,258	110,560	67,302
Drugs, medicines, and cosmetics	1909	3,667	23,817	15,618	10,361	17,275	53,830	147,949	94,119
	19	3,591	39,764	23,562	31,420	45,282	181,661	403,307	221,645
	21	2,294	31,316	16,054	31,984	32,495	138,962	340,223	201,260
	29	2,792	40,908	19,436	45,837	53,684	202,520	646,795	444,275
	31	2,337	34,428	....	36,827	....	151,765	525,952	374,187
Explosives, fireworks, and matches	1909	154	11,308	1,448	6,273	2,074	28,307	53,762	25,455
	19	196	14,197	7,697	16,560	15,375	54,872	115,601	60,729
	21	168	10,246	3,811	12,006	9,273	45,801	94,176	48,374
	29	166	11,185	1,327	14,537	3,481	46,755	99,475	52,719
	31	126	9,215	....	9,994	....	31,384	67,520	36,135
Fertilizers	1909	550	18,310	3,317	7,477	4,406	69,522	103,960	34,438
	19	600	26,296	6,007	25,363	11,572	185,041	281,144	96,103
	21	588	16,898	4,376	16,026	9,820	144,978	180,375	35,397
	29	638	20,926	4,051	17,884	9,398	159,801	232,511	72,710
	31	590	14,803	....	12,314	....	106,900	155,151	48,251
Gas, manufactured	1909	1,296	37,215	13,515	20,931	12,385	52,428	166,814	114,387
	19	1,022	42,908	20,393	52,759	25,172	157,551	329,279	171,728
	21	954	34,956	18,681	53,306	25,959	202,253	411,196	208,942
	29	754	43,065	22,559	61,060	40,774	188,416	512,653	324,236
	31	638	35,726	....	50,750	....	152,580	467,751	315,172

Table II (Continued)

		(1) Number of establishments	(2) Number of wage earners	(3) Number of salaried employees	(4) Wages	(5) Salaries	(6) Cost of materials, containers, fuel, electric energy	(7) Value of products	(8) Value added by manufacture
							Thousands of dollars		
Glass	1909	363	68,911	3,575	39,300	4,994	32,119	92,095	59,976
	19	371	77,520	6,076	87,527	13,365	90,780	261,884	171,104
	21	329	54,748	4,993	68,224	12,440	86,036	213,471	127,435
	29	263	67,527	5,869	87,795	15,587	103,294	303,819	200,525
	31	230	48,830	....	57,543	....	73,080	214,811	141,731
Leather	1909	919	62,202	4,114	32,103	6,744	248,279	327,874	79,595
	19	680	72,476	6,418	88,205	20,179	646,522	928,592	282,070
	21	608	48,955	4,714	57,741	13,398	277,725	383,365	105,640
	29	471	49,932	4,291	63,414	15,649	337,598	481,340	143,742
	31	412	42,096	....	49,594	....	172,400	271,070	98,671
Lime and cement	1909	988	40,672	3,687	21,300	4,733	36,075	81,157	45,083
	19	599	36,929	5,815	44,064	11,492	93,807	209,235	115,429
	21	417	36,576	5,576	44,218	12,504	116,574	234,642	118,068
	29	411	41,922	6,216	58,325	16,034	109,150	303,325	194,175
	31	369	30,996	....	35,884	....	64,855	170,934	106,079
Linoleum, oilcloth, and artificial leather	1909	43	5,644	345	3,042	649	17,583	26,467	8,884
	19	49	8,555	1,361	9,882	3,015	59,642	94,392	34,751
	21	48	8,084	1,818	10,346	5,636	46,166	77,829	31,663
	29	47	11,891	2,177	18,161	4,739	78,961	145,207	66,247
	31	48	7,964	....	10,398	....	34,191	71,720	37,530
Oils and greases	1909	1,472	25,424	6,626	10,786	8,171	191,249	243,759	52,508
	19	1,596	42,378	9,833	38,591	19,581	768,879	934,677	165,799
	21	1,195	27,108	6,573	25,640	14,502	350,292	415,937	65,643
	29	1,173	28,872	6,595	30,101	16,383	474,247	607,994	133,748
	31	1,030	22,032	....	21,043	....	261,656	348,200	86,544
Paints and varnishes	1909	791	14,240	7,200	8,271	10,378	79,016	124,889	45,874
	19	830	21,507	12,225	24,118	26,523	217,112	340,347	123,234
	21	804	18,015	9,836	23,293	23,010	171,398	274,310	102,912
	29	1,063	29,211	12,888	42,245	38,034	334,132	568,976	234,844
	31	1,010	22,300	....	29,122	....	192,593	348,855	156,262
Paper and pulp	1909	777	75,978	5,245	40,805	9,510	165,442	267,657	102,215
	19	729	113,759	11,005	135,691	29,953	467,483	788,059	320,577
	21	738	105,294	10,050	127,029	29,089	445,992	667,436	221,443
	29	883	128,049	13,629	173,077	43,468	723,361	1,206,114	482,754
	31	846	107,901	....	126,396	....	494,108	851,530	357,422
Petroleum refining	1909	147	13,929	2,669	9,830	3,929	199,273	236,998	37,724
	19	320	58,889	14,525	89,750	26,619	1,247,908	1,632,533	384,624
	21	366	63,189	11,039	102,294	27,903	1,382,170	1,727,440	345,270
	29	390	80,596	13,797	131,177	33,578	2,031,341	2,639,665	608,324
	31	358	67,936	....	106,815	....	1,200,918	1,511,598	310,679
Roofing, wall, and floor compositions	1909	315	7,256	1,792	3,730	2,430	18,465	32,008	13,543
	19	339	13,994	4,173	16,178	7,871	64,409	112,770	48,361
	21	280	11,806	2,656	16,210	5,895	61,130	108,547	47,417
	29	338	13,489	2,873	19,132	7,145	89,705	174,169	84,465
	31	273	9,678	....	11,694	....	49,491	108,728	59,237
Rubber products	1909	267	49,264	5,948	25,137	6,821	122,745	197,395	74,650
	19	477	158,549	45,932	193,763	82,350	594,344	1,138,216	543,872
	21	496	103,273	20,755	123,613	46,130	377,879	704,903	327,024
	29	525	149,148	22,834	207,306	55,353	578,678	1,117,460	538,783
	31	445	97,269	....	110,810	....	249,028	596,004	346,977
Soap	1909	420	12,999	5,065	6,227	5,506	72,179	111,358	39,178
	19	348	20,436	8,300	21,228	14,172	238,519	316,740	78,221
	21	283	16,558	6,361	18,865	13,701	150,356	240,195	89,839
	29	282	14,363	4,688	18,995	11,504	180,353	310,192	129,839
	31	223	13,762	....	17,330	....	119,522	254,164	134,642

Table II (Continued)

		(1) Number of establishments	(2) Number of wage earners	(3) Number of salaried employees	(4) Wages	(5) Salaries	(6) Cost of materials, containers, fuel, electric energy	(7) Value of products	(8) Value added by manufacture
							Thousands of dollars		
Sugar	1909	409	25,503	4,080	14,958	5,573	311,747	376,171	64,425
	19	363	43,879	6,762	54,590	13,747	923,646	1,124,140	200,514
	21	278	37,914	6,286	52,258	13,492	616,272	708,714	92,442
	29	208	30,457	5,082	39,387	11,954	625,868	800,252	174,384
	31	196	26,587	....	31,771	....	461,729	592,652	130,923
Wood chemicals	1909	1,888	45,260	3,342	12,370	2,975	20,918	51,860	30,941
	19	1,491	37,564	3,054	27,174	5,933	68,843	139,930	71,088
	21	1,293	32,545	2,839	14,434	4,566	33,033	61,290	28,257
	29	1,400	47,260	2,858	23,443	6,227	50,421	105,712	55,291
	31	1,134	32,832	....	12,325	....	27,585	53,491	25,906
Wood preserving	1909	53	2,403	471	1,066	517	9,328	14,099	4,771
	19	73	3,978	636	4,342	1,293	23,242	33,239	9,997
	21	78	4,153	532	4,502	1,273	34,432	47,422	12,990
	29	199	13,077	1,413	14,940	3,622	147,703	190,945	43,242
	31	210	9,700	....	8,212	....	85,129	106,494	21,365
Miscellaneous products of process industries	1909	802	14,631	2,435	7,176	3,455	48,705	229,745	181,040
	19	182	12,139	2,124	13,847	5,073	54,964	101,502	46,539
	21	159	10,049	1,538	12,348	4,103	52,078	83,290	31,211
	29	162	9,935	1,669	13,102	4,898	68,212	124,612	56,400
	31	151	8,172	....	10,078	....	39,393	80,331	40,936

Economic Development of Individual Industries. While it is of interest to survey the process industries as a unit, the effect of the various factors involved in the changing industrial picture is damped by the inclusion of such a large sector of manufacturing operations. In order to trace more accurately the influence of technological progress, economic histories of individual industries are more illuminating.

Even in the study of groups of establishments devoted to the manufacture of the same products, however, it must always be borne in mind that there may be startlingly large variations in operation in individual establishments. In the case of plants refining crude petroleum, for example, L. P. Alford and J. E. Hannum (*Mech. Eng.*, December, 1932) have shown that the rates of productivity had a ratio of 1 : 224 from lowest to highest.

TABLE III.—Variations in Productivity of Individual Petroleum Refining Plants

Limits of groups, barrels of crude petroleum refined per kilo-man-hour	Number of establishments in the group	Quantity of product processed, barrels of crude petroleum per kilo-man-hour
Under 1,000............	9	633
1,000 to 2,499......	59	2,008
2,500 to 4,999......	97	3,734
5,000 to 9,999......	72	5,810
10,000 to 24,999......	49	12,709
25,000 to 49,999......	13	29,972
50,000 to 99,999......	4	56,570
100,000 and over.......	3	141,829

Brief reviews of manufacturing economics in a number of process industries are presented in the following sections. The index numbers have been adapted from data on a larger group of industries discussed in a recent invaluable contribution to the literature of industrial economics, "Economic Tendencies in the United States" (National Bureau of Economic Research, Inc., 1932) by Frederick C. Mills. As a measure to economize space in the tables, the recurring full titles of the indexes have been abbreviated as follows from the terms employed by Mills:

physical volume of production = production volume
physical volume of production per wage earner = production per wage earner

cost of materials per unit of product = unit material costs
cost of fabrication plus profits per unit of product = unit value added
labor costs per unit of product = unit labor costs
overhead costs plus profits per unit of product = unit overhead and profit

selling price per unit of product = unit selling price

It should be emphasized that the index numbers in Tables IV to XVI are adjusted for physical volume of production.

In Table IV are given weighted average indexes for the entire groups of industries in the three periods studied by Mills. These averages, representing a cross section of all manufacturing industries, will serve as a basis of comparison for the data on individual process industries given in the following tables.

TABLE IV.—Average Values of Index Numbers for Manufacturing Industries

Year	35 Industries				52 Industries				62 Industries			
	1899	1904	1909	1914	1914	1919	1921	1923	1923	1925	1927	1929
Production volume..	100.0	118.5	164.3	165.6	100.0	125.3	99.7	145.3	100.0	101.5	103.6	119.0
Production per wage earner..........	100.0	107.4	117.7	119.9	100.0	95.5	95.3	112.8	100.0	105.3	109.7	117.8
Unit material costs.	100.0	106.0	136.0	143.9	100.0	200.6	163.3	174.1	100.0	98.1	90.3	83.8
Unit value added..	100.0	95.3	108.9	102.0	100.0	230.2	175.9	187.6	100.0	99.2	96.3	101.4
Unit labor costs...	100.0	100.0	103.4	111.6	100.0	225.1	205.1	188.6	100.0	95.4	92.5	86.6
Unit overhead and profit............	100.0	94.3	113.5	98.6	100.0	235.8	164.8	187.5	100.0	100.9	99.6	110.1
Unit selling price...	100.0	104.6	124.6	127.4	100.0	208.4	175.1	182.2	100.0	97.2	90.6	90.3
Output per establishment.........	....	....	....	....	....	....	....	....	100.0	107.3	114.9	124.4
Wage earners per establishment....	....	....	....	....	....	....	....	....	100.0	99.9	101.2	102.3

It will be noted that the index numbers are grouped into three periods, 1899-1914, 1914-1923, and 1923-29, the initial year of each period being the base year. In the following data relating to individual industries, index numbers for the entire period covered have been calculated on 1909 or 1914 as a base year.

Considering as a group the 14 process industries discussed below (including the three classifications under sugar as separate industries), we observe noteworthy increases in physical volume of production during the period 1909 or 1914 to 1929 in all except cottonseed products, lime, and cane sugar. Expansion is most marked in petroleum refining, followed by rubber products, manufactured gas, paints and varnishes, and coke, while fertilizers, cement, clay products, soap, beet sugar, and cane sugar refining have shown a more moderate growth. When listed according to increase in physical volume of product per wage earner, the industries arrange themselves in a somewhat different order: the coke industry leads, followed by rubber products and manufactured gas; beet sugar, soap, petroleum refining, fertilizers, and cement show a considerable increase; clay products, lime, cane sugar refining, paint and varnish, and cane sugar appear to be somewhat lower than the average for all industries; in the cottonseed products industry, however, the output per worker has increased only very slightly in the past fifteen years.

In nearly all these industries unit material costs reached a maximum of two to three times the pre-war value in either 1919 or 1921; the maximum material costs of rubber products, however, were only 27 per cent greater than in 1914, and by 1929 this index had dropped to 69 per cent of the 1914 figure. Throughout the group there has been a notable decline in material costs since 1919 and 1921. A similar course is observed in the unit labor costs, the maximum having been reached in 1919, except for cement (1923), manufactured gas (1925), lime (1921), and paint and varnish (1921). The maximum for manufactured gas and rubber products was much lower than in the rest of the industries, amounting to but 50 per cent increase over 1914. Two industries—coke and rubber products—have reduced unit labor costs below their pre-war values, while in beet sugar and manufactured gas the 1929 index is only slightly higher.

The majority of these industries reached a maximum unit selling price in 1919, only cement, coke, manufactured gas, and lime showing a maximum in 1921 or 1923. Manufactured gas and rubber products are noteworthy for their low maxima, 138 and 132, respectively. Since 1919-21 the unit selling prices have decreased considerably; the index for rubber products was 73 in 1929, with the cane sugar, cane sugar refining, beet sugar, manufactured gas, and petroleum refining industries moderately above pre-war levels, while the remaining manufactures are considerably higher.

The individual industries of this group reached maximum indexes of unit overhead and profit over a somewhat wider range of time than for the other indexes given: seven maxima in 1919, three in 1923, one in 1925, two in 1927, and one in 1929. Rubber products and manufactured gas have maintained low indexes throughout the period studied. The sugar industries experienced particularly sharp declines from their maxima. Eight of the 14 industries reached their maximum indexes of value added by manufacture per unit of product in 1919, two in 1923, one each in 1925 and 1927, and two in 1929. Manufactured gas and rubber products have very low indexes for the post-war period, the latter reaching a maximum of 138 in 1919 and declining to 77 in 1929.

Cement. The notable increase in volume of physical output per wage earner during the period 1923-29 was effected with a slight increase in the output per establishment, the index figures at 2 year intervals being successively 100, 109, 105, and 102. The number of wage earners per establishment showed a marked decrease, the indexes for the same period being 100, 101, 86, and 73.

TABLE V.—Manufacturing Indexes for the Cement Industry

Year	1914	1919	1921	1923	1925	1927	1929
Production volume	100	93	98	127	150	161	156
Production per wage earner	100	102	104	101	109	123	141
Unit material costs	100	164	201	153	146	144	114
Unit value added	100	207	208	259	250	217	209
Unit labor costs	100	196	194	216	197	182	168
Unit overhead and profit	100	213	217	284	280	237	232
Unit selling price	100	185	205	205	197	180	160

Clay Products. The data include non-clay refractories but do not include pottery. During the period 1923-29 there was a considerable increase in output per establishment, the index numbers being 100, 109, 115, 113, accompanied by a smaller increase in number of workers per establishment.

TABLE VI.—Manufacturing Indexes for the Clay Products Industry

Year	1914	1919	1921	1923	1925	1927	1929
Production volume	100	76	73	126	135	135	127
Production per wage earner	100	97	103	120	128	131	131
Unit material costs	100	210	222	194	176	175	155
Unit value added	100	202	189	199	190	178	186
Unit labor costs	100	191	189	183	176	169	160
Unit overhead and profit	100	217	189	222	208	191	222
Unit selling price	100	204	200	198	183	177	176

Coke. The data do not include gas-house coke. The physical volume of production per wage earner has increased by roughly 240 per cent in 20 years; this shift, of course, reflects the influence of the transition from bee-hive to byproduct ovens. Between 1923 and 1929 the average output per establishment increased about 120 per cent, the indexes for the census years being 100, 100, 142, 222; in this same period the index numbers of wage earners per establishment increased 34 per cent.

TABLE VII.—Manufacturing Indexes for the Coke Industry

Year	1909	1914	1919	1921	1923	1925	1927	1929
Production volume	100	96	136	94	197	178	182	240
Production per wage earner	100	133	136	171	203	224	252	336
Unit material costs	100	112	258	281	280	244	246	186
Unit value added	100	99	214	176	261	179	165	177
Unit labor costs	100	96	201	164	158	134	121	93
Unit overhead and profit	100	102	226	188	359	222	207	257
Unit selling price	100	108	243	246	274	222	219	183

Cottonseed Oil, Cake and Meal. The physical volume of production in this industry has shown a broken line of decline since 1914, and the increase in physical volume of production per wage earner has increased only slightly. The output per establishment has increased considerably however during the period 1923-29, as has also the number of wage earners per establishment.

TABLE VIII.—Manufacturing Indexes for the Cottonseed Oil, Cake and Meal Industry

Year	1914	1919	1921	1923	1925	1927	1929
Production volume	100	83	60	52	81	91	75
Production per wage earner	100	68	81	90	109	108	105
Unit material costs	100	330	179	209	167	134	185
Unit value added	100	333	119	177	204	198	199
Unit labor costs	100	292	242	178	166	185	173
Unit overhead and profit	100	348	74	177	218	204	209
Unit selling price	100	330	170	204	172	143	187

Fertilizers. During the period 1923-29 the output per establishment has increased 17 per cent, the successive index numbers being 100, 111, 108, 117. This increase has been effected with only a slight increase in the number of wage earners per establishment.

TABLE IX.—**Manufacturing Indexes for the Fertilizer Industry**

Year	1909	1914	1919	1921	1923	1925	1927	1929
Production volume	100	149	137	102	130	148	152	170
Production per wage earner.	100	119	95	110	128	137	149	148
Unit material costs	100	104	195	203	142	134	131	136
Unit value added	100	88	204	101	123	136	100	125
Unit labor costs	100	95	249	211	169	161	156	141
Unit overhead and profit...	100	86	192	70	111	129	84	120
Unit selling price	100	99	198	170	136	135	120	132

Gas. The data refer only to manufactured illuminating and heating gas. The increases in physical volume of production and in physical volume of product per wage earner are especially noteworthy. During the period 1923-1929 the output per establishment has increased over 50 per cent with an increase of 30 per cent in the index of number of wage earners per establishment.

TABLE X.—**Manufacturing Indexes for the Manufactured Gas Industry**

Year	1909	1914	1919	1921	1923	1925	1927	1929
Production volume	100	140	189	180	213	218	252	251
Production per wage earner.	100	119	163	190	187	172	192	217
Unit material costs	100	105	159	216	172	157	161	142
Unit value added	100	90	81	102	106	111	106	112
Unit labor costs	100	92	134	143	134	149	131	114
Unit overhead and profit...	100	89	67	93	100	103	101	112
Unit selling price	100	94	104	137	127	125	123	121

Lime. This industry has remained almost stationary in the period 1923-29 in regard to size of establishment as measured by the average number of workers. During the same period, however, the output per establishment has increased 26 per cent.

TABLE XI.—**Manufacturing Indexes for the Lime Industry**

Year	1914	1919	1921	1923	1925	1927	1929
Production volume	100	82	63	100	109	99	100
Production per wage earner	100	88	73	97	108	108	123
Unit material costs	100	235	306	269	251	239	208
Unit value added	100	227	254	265	270	236	205
Unit labor costs	100	224	266	233	221	212	186
Unit overhead and profit	100	230	239	304	331	266	230
Unit selling price	100	230	276	267	262	237	206

Paints and Varnishes. While the physical volume of production in the industry has increased 140 per cent in 20 years there has been an increase of 18 per cent in the index of physical volume of production per wage earner. Since 1923 the index of output per establishment has increased nearly 14 per cent.

TABLE XII.—Manufacturing Indexes for the Paint and Varnish Industry

Year	1909	1914	1919	1921	1923	1925	1927	1929
Production volume	100	107	136	115	169	195	217	242
Production per wage earner	100	95	90	90	105	109	110	118
Unit material costs	100	105	202	190	186	191	180	174
Unit value added	100	116	197	196	200	198	212	210
Unit labor costs	100	115	214	246	214	220	224	210
Unit overhead and profit	100	117	194	185	197	193	210	210
Unit selling price	100	109	200	192	191	193	191	187

Petroleum Refining. In spite of the tremendous increase in physical volume of production, amounting to 400 per cent between 1909 and 1923, and to 785 per cent between 1909 and 1929, the physical volume of production per wage earner remained low until after 1923; since that year it has increased about 50 per cent.

TABLE XIII.—Manufacturing Indexes for the Petroleum Refining Industry

Year	1909	1914	1919	1921	1923	1925	1927	1929
Production volume	100	157	306	363	498	645	714	882
Production per wage earner	100	86	72	80	104	138	140	152
Unit material costs	100	104	205	191	144	147	123	116
Unit value added	100	120	333	252	196	200	145	183
Unit labor costs	100	126	298	286	212	165	162	15 1
Unit overhead and profit	100	118	345	239	190	212	138	194
Unit selling price	100	106	225	201	152	155	126	126

Rubber Products. The physical volume of production in this industry has shown a very great rise with steady intensity, the increase being over 400 per cent in the last 15 year period. The physical volume of production per wage earner has likewise shown a tremendous increase of 157 per cent in the same period. In the period 1923-29 the index of output per establishment has increased 43 per cent.

TABLE XIV.—Manufacturing Indexes for the Rubber Products Industry

Year	1914	1919	1921	1923	1925	1927	1929
Production volume	100	287	219	369	438	467	513
Production per wage earner	100	134	157	198	228	243	257
Unit material costs	100	127	106	83	101	87	69
Unit value added	100	138	109	90	89	88	77
Unit labor costs	100	153	128	112	99	96	91
Unit overhead and profit	100	130	99	80	85	84	70
Unit selling price	100	132	107	86	96	87	73

Soap. This industry has shown a continued growth in both physical volume of production and in physical volume of production per wage earner. In the period 1923-29 the index of output per establishment has increased 13 per cent while the index of wage earners per establishment has decreased 19 per cent.

TABLE XV.—Manufacturing Indexes for the Soap Industry

Year	1914	1919	1921	1923	1925	1927	1929
Production volume	100	127	115	133	133	139	153
Production per wage earner	100	88	98	110	121	146	153
Unit material costs	100	211	148	147	157	139	129
Unit value added	100	158	201	199	181	211	216
Unit labor costs	100	207	204	195	173	176	152
Unit overhead and profit	100	145	200	200	183	221	233
Unit selling price	100	195	164	163	164	161	156

Sugar. In accordance with the practice used in the Census of Manufactures, the cane sugar refining industry, as distinguished from the cane sugar industry, embraces establishments engaged in the refining of raw cane sugar, the greater part of which is imported. During the period 1923-29, the index of output per establishment shows an increase of 50 per cent for beet sugar, of 105 per cent for cane sugar, and of 10 per cent for cane sugar refining.

TABLE XVI.—Manufacturing Index for the Sugar Industries

Year	1914	1919	1921	1923	1925	1927	1929
Beet Sugar							
Production volume	100	98	140	100	145	121	147
Production per wage earner	100	67	82	106	129	129	156
Unit material costs	100	214	210	171	145	158	117
Unit value added	100	299	58	224	148	101	121
Unit labor costs	100	246	245	153	127	122	103
Unit overhead and profit	100	323		257	157	92	129
Unit selling price	100	243	159	189	146	139	118
Cane Sugar							
Production volume	100	96	92	63	49	26	74
Production per wage earner	100	57	122	81	86	98	115
Unit material costs	100	290	116	209	147	139	103
Unit value added	100	251	116	174	66	146	145
Unit labor costs	100	269	161	177	184	156	143
Unit overhead and profit	100	244	98	173	21	142	146
Unit selling price	100	279	116	200	126	141	114
Cane Sugar Refining							
Production volume	100	106	113	133	162	153	153
Production per wage earner	100	66	82	98	125	123	123
Unit material costs	100	236	143	195	129	136	109
Unit value added	100	256	140	132	139	118	178
Unit labor costs	100	274	220	193	150	148	149
Unit overhead and profit	100	249	104	105	134	105	191
Unit selling price	100	238	143	189	130	135	115

Industrial Changes Since 1929. A detailed study of the changes in physical production, industrial productivity, and manufacturing costs for the process industries during the period 1929-32 is not available, but the following data from a recent report by Frederick C. Mills (Bulletin 45, National Bureau of Economic Research, Inc., 1933) apply to the process industries as well as to manufacturing industries in general. It should be borne in mind, however, that the decline in some of the chemical engineering industries has been less severe than in the total for all branches of manufacture.

Comparing the elements of manufacturing costs for the two depression periods 1919-21 and 1929-31, Professor Mills finds the declines in unit material costs to be approximately the same, 23 and 24 per cent, respectively. Fabrication costs, including profits, however, have been decreased only 13 per cent during the later period, as compared with 18 per cent for 1919-21. Separating fabrication costs into labor and overhead plus profit, it is seen that the former has decreased 14 per cent in 1929-31 as compared with only 6 per cent for the earlier depression period; this difference Mills ascribes to an increase of 20 per cent since 1927 in the productivity of labor, as measured by output per man-hour. Overhead plus profits, on the other hand, decreased 27 per cent during 1919-21 and only 12 per cent in 1929-31. To quote the conclusion of Professor Mills' bulletin:

A drastic decline in the total volume of physical goods produced, a sharp increase in average industrial productivity per man-hour as less efficient plants and machines were stopped, a drop in the selling prices of manufactured goods which lags behind the general fall of wholesale prices, a reduction of labor costs per unit of manufactured product and a decline in the costs of the services of capital and management in manufacturing industries—these are notable features of the period of business depression which dates from the summer of 1929. They are not features peculiar to this depression, for, in differing degrees, these changes are characteristic of all periods of business contraction. The recent decline as reflected in the records of physical production, industrial productivity and costs, has distinctive characteristics in the magnitude of the changes which have occurred, and in certain of the interrelations among the movements of different economic elements. But these and other features of the current depression may be most readily understood when this depression is viewed in perspective, as the latest of many similar interruptions to the course of economic development.

Fuel and Power Consumption in the Process Industries. In Table XVII are given data on the consumption of fuels and purchased electric energy in the various groups of chemical engineering industries. The classification according to manufactures is the same as that used in Table II. It should be noted that the figures given in Table XVII for the total cost of fuel and purchased energy in the petroleum refining, manufactured gas, and coke industries include the cost of fuel produced and consumed in the manufacturing operations.

The extent of mechanization of the process industries may be judged by the primary horsepower installed; in 1909 35.6 per cent of the total for all manufacturing industries was used in plants employing chemical engineering processes, and by 1929 this figure had increased to 43.6 per cent. It will be recalled that the corresponding percentages of total value of product for the process group as compared with all manufacturing industries are respectively 16.2 and 17.7.

Another measure of the importance of the chemical engineering industries as consumers of fuel and power is the total cost of these items. In 1929 the process industries expended a sum equal to 44 per cent of the total for all industries. This represents over 10 per cent of the total of $7,397,000,000 expended in that year by this group for raw materials, containers, and fuel and purchased energy.

According to a study made by G. L. Montgomery (Chaplin Tyler, "Chemical Engineering Economics," McGraw-Hill, 1926; pp. 32-33) the average ratio of fuel used for process to fuel equivalent of total power is 2.3 in the chemical engineering industries.

Foreign Trade in Products of the Process Industries. In Table XVIII is given a survey of exports and imports of the various chemical engineering commodities for 1909 and 1929. The classification of industries is approximately the same as that employed in Tables II and XVII.

Estimates are given in Table XVIII of the increase in dollar value of foreign trade in each group of products during the period 1909-29, and also of the relative volume of foreign trade as compared with the value of products in each class manufactured in the United States in 1929. It must be emphasized that the percentages given cannot be interpreted too literally, because of the inherent differences in classification. In the case of foreign trade data for 1909 and 1929 changes have been made in the groupings of commodities which are difficult to compensate for. The discrepancy is perhaps even greater in the case of comparisons between data from the Census of Manufactures and data relating to exports and imports. In particular, it must be remembered that establishments are classified in the Census of Manufactures according to major product, and that the same commodity may occur in considerable quantity as a byproduct of another industry; the effect of this situation is especially evident in the classification "oils and greases" in Table XVIII.

From an inspection of the table it is apparent that there has been a noteworthy increase in both imports and exports in the last twenty years in the process industries. Even taking the data for 1929, however, it is seen that in general the total volume of either imports or exports is small when compared with the value of products of the same industry produced in this country. As a measure of comparison, Mills ("Economic Tendencies," page 468) estimates that in 1929 the value of exports of manufactured goods represented 8.1 per cent of the value of manufactured goods produced in the United States.

TABLE XVII.—Fuel and Power Consumption in the Process Industries

		(1) Primary horse-power	(2) Total cost of fuel and purchased energy $1,000	(3) Anthracite coal—1,000 tons (2,240 lb.)	(4) Bituminous coal—1,000 tons (2,000 lb.)	(5) Coke 1,000 tons (2,000 lb.)	(6) Fuel oil, kerosene, gasoline 1,000 gals.	(7) Natural and manufactured gas 1,000,000 cu. ft.	(8) Purchased electric energy 1,000 kw-hours	(9) Number of establishments
Chemicals	1909	208,604	8,047	650	2,162	64	4,632	1,300	....	(285)
	29	1,135,495	58,133	273	5,936	196	163,066	4,721	6,206,021	
Clay products	1909	451,186	25,349	334	9,658	46	59,251	26,369	....	(4,226)
	29	603,101	52,647	174	8,778	57	120,509	32,004	414,121	
Coke	1909	63,892	60,922	6	59,037	35	61	5,616	....	(148)
	29	408,104	287,331	194	83,158	1,749	6,209	117,898	182,815	
Coloring and finishing materials	1909	11,268	368	15	28	1	2,213	12,543	....	(334)
	29	46,510	2,906	9	73	......	3,287	321	30,674	
Drugs, medicines and cosmetics	1909	28,981	789	92	114	1	81	115	....	(1,101)
	29	81,413	3,080	74	209	1	5,527	159	37,606	
Explosives, fireworks, and matches	1909	35,342	917	40	967	1	6,070	285	....	(127)
	29	71,355	2,287	36	242	......	16,693	56	47,667	
Fertilizers	1909	64,711	1,453	21	462	6	828	112	....	(485)
	29	166,984	2,781	5	125	1	5,790	170	97,843	
Gas, manufactured	1909	128,350	39,196	899	4,668	759	496,284	605	....	(973)
	29	544,024	130,998	197	10,073	1,445	924,297	103,207	282,464	
Glass	1909	123,132	7,524	18	1,859	17	19,694	43,712	....	(353)
	29	341,979	30,179	97	2,310	2	57,412	53,435	502,314	
Leather	1909	148,140	3,293	99	1,028	1	1,937	599	....	(829)
	29	229,660	6,741	33	1,064	3	4,682	20	74,186	
Lime and cement	1909	399,470	16,593	366	5,490	75	65,051	16,147	....	(485)
	29	1,274,265	58,883	346	10,090	71	135,178	36,100	1,447,767	
Linoleum, oilcloth, and artificial leather	1909	16,125	526	39	150	2	7	....	....	(31)
	29	71,314	2,027	133	153	......	1,122	....	57,963	

TABLE XVII.—Fuel and Power Consumption in the Process Industries (Continued)

		(1) Primary horse-power	(2) Total cost of fuel and purchased energy $1,000	(3) Anthracite coal— 1,000 tons (2,240 lb.)	(4) Bituminous coal— 1,000 tons (2,000 lb.)	(5) Coke 1,000 tons (2,000 lb.)	(6) Fuel oil, kerosene, gasoline 1,000 gals.	(7) Natural and manufactured gas 1,000,000 cu. ft.	(8) Purchased electric energy 1,000 kw-hours	(9) Number of establishments
Oils and greases	1909	227,955	4,413	49	1,195	2	18,612	457	.....	(1,231)
	29	389,088	9,850	29	1,099	4	30,135	4,396	268,656	
Paints and varnishes	1909	56,162	1,306	67	300	25	824	269	.....	(672)
	29	180,315	6,860	83	539	48	16,429	678	149,610	
Paper and pulp	1909	1,304,265	18,320	559	5,460	1	24,551	6,485	.....	(777)
	29	2,968,431	75,266	1,136	9,811	1	130,300	12,057	2,826,017	
Petroleum refining	1909	90,268	8,376	1,348	1,265	100	145,898	7,520	.....	(130)
	29	789,849	92,068	191	2,597	.....	2,164,119	206,970	660,625	
Roofing, wall, and floor compositions	1909	35,323	1,048	55	250	4	7,261	133	.....	(278)
	29	176,145	6,544	26	503	14	41,485	1,922	195,637	
Rubber products	1909	101,965	1,797	69	582	.....	77	52	.....	(224)
	29	821,312	19,678	84	2,306	.....	20,166	1,329	882,450	
Soap	1909	28,360	1,266	56	461	1	2,913	57	.....	(317)
	29	65,856	3,529	125	580	6	3,752	188	52,998	
Sugar	1909	246,062	7,455	633	2,322	30	134,549	.....	.....	(404)
	29	396,495	15,940	481	2,977	44	103,711	8,273	18,783	
Wood chemicals	1909	36,196	3,583	70	390	1	24	2,461	.....	(1,320)
	29	50,079	2,876	11	438	.....	4,492	617	22,411	
Wood preserving	1909	10,647	264	2	58	.....	3,743	615	.....	(47)
	29	57,913	2,226	5	382	3	10,349	1,444	14,867	
Miscellaneous products	1909	88,979	3,708	203	1,732	7	6,112	1,888	.....	(630)
	29	62,670	4,936	17		.....	44,024	654	32,184	
Total, all process industries	1909	3,905,383	216,513	5,690	99,638	1,179	1,000,673	127,340	.....	(15,407)
	29	10,932,357	877,766	3,759	144,123	3,645	4,012,734	586,619	14,505,679	
Total, all manufacturing industries	1909	18,675,376	570,068	14,339	163,490	37,960	1,441,929	451,302	.....	(185,042)
	29	42,931,061	1,973,863	9,281	214,025	52,392	6,631,672	1,688,277	37,393,833	

TABLE XVIII.—Exports and Imports of Products of the Process Industries

	EXPORTS				IMPORTS			
	1909	1929			1909	1929		
	Millions of dollars	Millions of dollars	Percentage increase over 1909	Percentage of 1929 manufactures	Millions of dollars	Millions of dollars	Percentage increase over 1909	Percent age of 1929 manufactures
Chemicals........	12.0	53.2	340	6	64.7	66.6	3	7
Clay products.....	1.6	11.0	590	3	9.8	20.6	110	5
Coke.............	2.9	8.4	190	2	0.9	13.3	1380	3
Coloring and finishing materials ..	1.1	12.6	1050	9	0.1			
Drugs, medicines, and cosmetics....	8.2	30.2	270	5	4.6	12.1	160	2
Explosives, fireworks and matches.........	3.8	5.0	30	5	1.3	4.3	230	4
Fertilizers........	9.3	20.4	120	9	13.9	72.3	420	31
Gas, manufactured.								
Glass............	2.2	10.9	400	4	5.3	14.0	160	5
Leather..........	30.4	42.9	40	9	5.3	44.6	740	9
Lime and cement..	1.2	3.3	180	1	0.9	2.4	170	1
Linoleum, oilcloth, and artificial leather..........	0.4	7.0	1650	5	1.9	1.1	—40	1
Oils and greases...	76.8	163.9	110	27	19.4	128.7	560	21
Paints and varnishes........	4.8	20.7	330	4	1.7	25.3	1390	4
Paper and pulp....	8.2	36.6	350	3	9.5	251.9	2550	21
Petroleum products	105.5	523.4	400	20	0.6	63.6	10500	2
Roofing, wall, and floor compositions	0.8	5.1	540	3				
Rubber products ..	6.6	74.4	1030	7	1.5	2.7	80	
Soap.............	3.5	7.3	110	2	1.0	1.3	30	
Sugar............	8.6	20.4	140	3	97.0	226.4	130	28
Wood chemicals...	15.4	33.3	120	32	3.3	8.9	170	8
Wood preserving ..								
Miscellaneous products........	2.4	1.9	—20	2	9.0	3.9	—60	3

The position of various countries in world trade in chemicals is shown in Table XIX, based on data compiled by Die Chemische Industrie in 1932. The decline in American chemical exports between 1929 and 1931 represents a decrease of 36.1 per cent in dollar value.

TABLE XIX.—Chemical Exports of the World

	1928 Per cent	1929 Per cent	1930 Per cent	1931 Per cent
Germany...........................	27.2	27.8	27.7	29.1
United States......................	14.7	15.2	14.7	14.4
Great Britain......................	14.1	13.9	14.0	12.8
France............................	10.7	10.0	11.4	11.2
Chile.............................	10.7	10.5	7.4	6.7
Italy.............................	5.0	4.6	4.7	4.8
Holland...........................	3.8	3.6	4.0	4.6
Belgium...........................	3.4	3.5	3.5	4.7
Switzerland........................	3.5	3.5	3.8	4.5
Norway...........................	1.1	1.2	1.9	1.6
Sweden...........................	1.7	1.7	1.6	1.5
Czechoslovakia.....................	1.0	1.5	1.8	1.4
Japan.............................	1.5	1.4	1.6	1.5
Austria...........................	1.0	0.9	0.9	0.8
Spain.............................	0.6	0.7	1.0	0.4

Financial Aspects of the Chemical Engineering Industries. As a conclusion to this brief review of the economics of production in the process industries, it is of interest to survey the records of corporate earnings and investment in these branches of manufacturing.

An exhaustive compilation of the financial records of 2,046 manufacturing corporations during the period 1919-28 has recently been made by R. C. Epstein in collaboration with F. M. Clark ("A Source-Book for the Study of Industrial Profits," U. S. Department of Commerce, 1932). Included in this group of corporations are 210 chemical companies which are subclassified as 9 crude chemical and fertilizer companies, 42 paint companies, 52 petroleum refining companies, 56 proprietary preparation companies, 9 toilet preparation companies, 16 manufacturers of cleaning preparations, including soap, and 26 manufacturers of miscellaneous chemicals and chemical products. The 114 ceramic companies are subclassified as 48 manufacturers of ceramic products, 18 glass companies, 21 portland cement companies, and 27 manufacturers of miscellaneous clay and stone products. Manufacturers of rubber products, including 26 corporations, are given as a separate group.

Some of the most interesting data regarding these groups of corporations have been assembled in Table XX. From the total sales of the companies represented—nearly $5,000,000,000 dollars in the chemical group in 1927 and over $27,000,000,000 for all manufacturing industries—it is seen that we are dealing with such a large cross section of industry that the following generalizations are justified.

The chemical group shows a low bonded debt in comparison with the capitalization; in these corporations the bonded debt is considerably less than 10 per cent of the capitalization (sum of preferred stock, common stock, and surplus and undivided profits), while the totals for all industries show the bonded debt to be over 10 per cent throughout the period studied. As pointed out by C. R. DeLong (*Chem. Met. Eng.*, *32*, 853 (1925) the chemical engineering industries tend to show a capital ratio (ratio of capital invested to value of products) well above 1, whereas the averages for all manufacturing industries are in general less than 1; this conclusion is likewise borne out in the present data by comparison of sales with capitalization. It is also interesting to observe the comparatively low value set on patents and goodwill by the chemical companies—despite their obvious importance in this industry.

One very striking observation from Table XX is the large sums received by the chemical group as dividends from other companies, well over half the totals of the figures for all industries. In the 3 years for which values are given it is also apparent that the chemical companies have maintained a high standard in payment of their own dividends.

As a further analysis of the earning power of the 210 corporations in the chemical group, Table XXI presents the frequency distribution of the percentage of total net income to capitalization or of total profit to total capital during the period 1919-28. In the first row of this table, "under zero" means that the total net income (or total profit) of the corporation in question is negative.

TABLE XXI.—Frequency Distribution, Percentage of Total Net Income to Capitalization or of Total Profit to Total Capital for 210 Chemical Corporations

	Percentage of total net income to capitalization				Percentage of total profit to total capital		
	1919	1921	1923	1928	1925	1927	1928
Under Zero.............	2	41	13	7	3	13	7
Zero to 4%.............	9	38	21	26	18	28	26
5 to 9%.............	18	41	37	37	48	36	38
10 to 14%.............	23	27	38	41	43	45	47
15 to 19%.............	30	15	30	29	27	31	24
20 to 24%.............	26	14	22	29	18	15	27
25 to 29%.............	21	5	11	8	13	9	9
30 to 49%.............	38	15	22	21	25	22	20
50 to 74%.............	22	8	7	6	7	4	6
75 to 99%.............	8	3	4	1	4	4	2
100 to 199%.............	11	2	4	2	2	....	1
200 to 499%.............	2	1	1	3	2	3	3

The financial position of the chemical engineering industries in the period since 1929 is seen from Table XXII. The data used there have been published by the National City Bank in annual studies of the reports of a large number of companies classified in 45 to 50 industrial groups. The size of the corporations comprising each classification is indicated by the following values (in millions of dollars) of the net worth of the companies as of January 1, 1932: chemicals 775, drugs and sundries 279, fertilizers 115, paint and varnish 95, paper and products 210, petroleum 663, rubber tires, etc., 358, all industries 16,059.

TABLE XX.—Financial Aspects of the Chemical Engineering Industries

Explanatory Notes. All values are given in millions of dollars.

Capitalization is invested capital as measured by the total of the following balance sheet items: preferred stock, common stock, and surplus and undivided profits.

Sales are dollar volume of output or merchandise disposed of, after returns and allowances.

Total net income is net earnings (after payment of all business expenses and fixed charges including interest on funded debt), but before Federal income taxes. It includes income items which are not taxable.

Dividends received are amounts received out of the earnings of other corporations on stock holdings in such other corporations. Cash dividends paid are actual cash amounts or the equivalent paid by the corporations in question to their own stockholders.

	1919	1921	1923	1925	1927	1928
Capitalization						
Chemicals	2,447	3,794	4,578	5,003	6,205	6,737
Ceramics	320	412	505	586	661	697
Rubber products	489	607	546	607	660	583
All industries	13,491	17,331	19,800	21,109	23,713	24,925
Bonded Debt						
Chemicals	....	....	....	256	477	495
Ceramics				13	21	41
Rubber products				180	232	224
All industries				2,326	2,680	2,701
Capital Assets						
Chemicals	....	....	....	2,209	3,288	3,437
Ceramics				344	394	436
Rubber products				269	295	303
All industries				11,167	12,312	12,868
Sales						
Chemicals	3,132	2,944	3,276	3,952	4,885	4,469
Ceramics	344	330	525	560	543	550
Rubber products	770	580	763	1,030	948	935
All industries	21,466	16,378	22,538	26,736	27,057	28,219
Total Net Income						
Chemicals	440	109	307	608	467	780
Ceramics	53	26	99	95	81	89
Rubber products	93	—77	33	115	45	8
All industries	2,471	504	2,210	2,564	2,252	2,736
Dividends Received						
Chemicals	42	57	102	145	162	235
Ceramics	....	....	1	1	2	2
Rubber products				21	8	9
All industries	60	85	163	245	265	347
Federal Income Tax						
Chemicals	90	18	29	59	42	63
Ceramics	11	5	12	12	10	10
Rubber products	22	1	1	12	6	3
All industries	704	174	240	297	270	294
Cash Dividends						
Chemicals	....	....	....	329	414	550
Ceramics				43	49	44
Rubber products				25	52	20
All industries				1,276	1,624	1,783
Patents and Goodwill						
Chemicals	....	....	....	106	....	....
Ceramics				10	....	....
Rubber products				73	....	....
All industries				1,025	....	....
Inventories						
Chemicals	....	....	....	994	1,013	1,043
Ceramics				101	104	103
Rubber products				245	229	207
All industries				5,255	5,317	5,346

TABLE XXII.—Industrial Corporation Profits for the Period 1929—1932

Percentages of net profit return upon capital and surplus in the chemical engineering industries. A dash indicates a deficit for the group taken as a whole.

The number of companies included in each group for a given year is shown in parentheses following the percentage return for that year.

	1929	1930	1931	1932
Chemicals.........................	18.3 (23)	12.1 (22)	9.1 (17)	5.4 (17)
Drugs and sundries...............	21.8 (15)	22.1 (16)	17.0 (14)	9.9 (14)
Fertilizers........................	3.9 (5)	4.8 (6)	— (6)	— (6)
Paint and varnish................	13.3 (7)	4.5 (8)	4.6 (7)	1.1 (7)
Paper and products..............	9.0 (23)	3.9 (26)	1.5 (21)	— (21)
Petroleum	10.8 (41)	5.0 (21)	— (23)	1.8 (23)
Rubber tires, etc.................	6.6 (18)	— (17)	— (14)	— (14)
All industries....................	13.3 (900)	7.1 (900)	3.3 (840)	— (840)

From the data it is apparent that the companies engaged in the manufacture of chemicals and of drugs and sundries have maintained an outstanding record of earning power. In 1932 they ranked seventh and third, respectively, among the 45 groups when listed in order of percentage return on capital and surplus.

CHAPTER XXV

CHEMICAL ENGINEERING EDUCATION

Building for the Future of the Profession

By Alfred H. White

Professor of Chemical Engineering, University of Michigan, Ann Arbor, Mich.

THE FOUNDERS of the American Institute of Chemical Engineers were a group of leaders in chemical industry with only a small number of teachers among them. It might have been expected that the emphasis of their early discussions would be upon technical subjects and the advancement of the economic status of their profession. But listen to these quotations from the address of Dr. Charles F. McKenna, chairman of the Philadelphia meeting at which the Institute was organized on June 22, 1908:

> But the noblest aim before us, gentlemen, the one which most amply justifies us before all the world, is our ambition for the enlightenment and ample equipment of our successors; that is for the improvement of the training of the chemical engineer of the future. . . . While this society may probably have no junior grade, what it can and should do for juniors must be its first care. . . , I said in the opening that we begin as brothers. We inevitably will close our careers as fathers, passing on to our sons in the profession a heritage of knowledge and light that shall increase as the flame increases with the increase of fuel. No man who works for the success of this society works for himself. He can expect no reward other — than the pleasure which comes from fostering a worthy cause close to his heart. . . . You who call yourselves chemical engineers, who know the science and the art, who feel your potency and your latent forces, you are to blame if you do not demand to be heard, to show by your efforts what stock you come from, and to demand of educators that in the future the title of chemical engineer be clear, the training adequate and the public encouragement the strongest.

The proper education of chemists for industrial positions was a live topic in chemical circles at that period and the following quotation from an address of one of the captains of chemical industry, J. B. F. Herreshoff[1] will indicate the feeling of a progressive manufacturer.

> The greater the application of chemistry, the more important becomes the combining of mechanical engineering with chemical engineering. Our colleges should consider this matter more seriously than ever, and do their

---

[1] *Science*, 19, 561, April 8, 1904.

best to make the course in chemical engineering as complete and perfect in every way as possible. . . . Chemical engineering necessitates a greater variety of engineering than all the other branches of engineering combined. . . . My experience forces me to feel that a complete understanding of the various problems must come from a brain that can think in both chemistry and engineering.

This paper was discussed by a number of representatives of education and industry, and not all of them agreed that the schools should teach a course such as indicated by Mr. Herreshoff. Several teachers of chemistry dissented and expressed the view that they were doing the best they could for their students if they gave them a thorough course in chemistry and left them to acquire a knowledge of its applications by practical experience.

The organization of the American Institute of Chemical Engineers marked the formal recognition by a national society of the need for chemical engineers as distinct from the technical chemists who were then being prepared for industry by the various colleges of the country. The demand for men with such training had arisen spontaneously, for the Institute was not formed by men who had been educated in chemical engineering in other countries and felt the need and desire to form an association with men of similar training. Probably not a single charter member of the Institute had received formal education as a chemical engineer. They had all acquired their knowledge of chemical engineering through experience after leaving school and they saw the need of a training different from that which they had themselves received.

Why was it that there were no courses in chemical engineering at the time when these founders of the Institute received their professional training? What was the situation, and why had not education in these lines been developed further? In trying to answer these questions I am frankly going back into my memory of conditions as they were when, returning from a year's graduate study under Lunge and Gnehm at the Polytechnicum in Zürich, I commenced to teach chemical technology at the University of Michigan thirty-five years ago. It has been impossible to give due credit to all the forward-looking teachers of that era, and I hope that those who recall with gratitude names that are not included in this short list will kindly excuse the forgetfulness or ignorance of the writer.

We forget how very rapid progress has been within our own generation. Three generations take us back to Liebig and the other pioneers of chemistry. Two generations find the commencement of the expansion of the chemical industry which first attracted public attention through the great industrial development in Germany after 1870. Chemistry could not be applied to industry until methods of analysis were developed, and the first duty of the plant chemist was to analyze raw materials, intermediates and finished products. Until forty years ago the emphasis in teaching at least in this country, was placed upon analytical chemistry, and professional chemists usually confined their efforts to the laboratory because methods of analysis were not well worked out or standardized, and it required all the resources of a skilled chemist to obtain the required analytical data. Chemical plants were small and were concerned with quality of product rather than with large-scale operation or economies in manufacturing.

Analytical chemistry had to be developed before quality could be properly appraised, but analytical chemistry did not in itself tell how to control a process. The most powerful tool in the development of chemical industry was furnished by the physical chemists and the physicists. Le Chatelier, van't Hoff, Nernst, Roozeboom and Gibbs led their active lives in the quarter century before the organization of our Institute. Their researches, published in many journals and in different languages, were not collected in books which were available to students until about the time of the founding of the Institute. It was the correlation of the discoveries of these and many other investigators which made possible the scientific control of chemical reactions and the prediction of conditions under which reactions might be made to proceed in a desired direction.

During the last quarter of the nineteenth century the United States looked to Europe and especially to Germany for leadership in chemistry and its applications. The German universities were famous not only for their contributions to theoretical chemistry but also for the services which their professors as well as their graduates rendered to the chemical industry. The schools of engineering in Germany and Switzerland were founded later and grew up outside of the universities. These technische Hochschule were established to meet the demands of manufacturers for men trained for industrial positions. They adopted curricula in technical chemistry and developed courses in chemical technology. Lunge, Witt, Ost, Franz Fischer and Bunte were notable teachers and writers. The students in these courses studied mathematics, physics and some of the engineering courses taken by the other groups of engineers as well as chemistry, but nowhere were there coordinated courses in chemical engineering.

354 TWENTY-FIVE YEARS OF CHEMICAL ENGINEERING

At the close of the last century there were a number of schools in the United States giving courses in what was sometimes called industrial chemistry and sometimes chemical technology. These courses were all built around teachers of energy and ability—C. F. Chandler at Columbia, S. P. Sadtler in Philadelphia, Edward Hart at Lafayette, William McMurtrie and later S. W. Parr at the University of Illinois, A. B. Prescott and E. D. Campbell at the University of Michigan. These courses were weaker than those at the European schools, mainly because of too great a concentration on analytical and descriptive chemistry, and insufficient acceptance of the importance of mathematics, physics and engineering studies. Physical chemistry was just emerging from the descriptive stage. The introduction of the inductive method of teaching and the use of numerous problems which required students to really understand physical chemistry is due to A. A. Noyes, whose influence was then only beginning to be felt.

The status of education in applied chemistry at the commencement of the era we are discussing may be judged in part by the textbooks which were available in the English language. There was an excellent book by S. P. Sadtler, the first president of the Institute, entitled "Industrial Organic Chemistry" and also a more elementary book by F. H. Thorp, "Outlines of Industrial Chemistry." Dr. Charles E. Munroe had prepared a special report on chemicals for the U. S. Bureau of the Census in 1905 which deserved to rank as a monograph. In England there was Crookes' revision of the one volume of Wagner's "Chemical Technology" and also the large three-volume set of Thorpe's "Dictionary of Applied Chemistry." These books described processes used in manufacturing plants but did not attempt to discuss the underlying theory or indicate for the student the reasons for the procedures which had been evolved— largely because the theory had not been developed. There was only one book whose title carried the words chemical engineering. This was a two-volume work by George E. Davis of Manchester, published in 1904 and entitled "Handbook of Chemical Engineering." It is important as the first attempt to resolve chemical engineering into its unit operations, although the term itself had not yet been coined. There were chapters on evaporation and distillation, separating solubles from insolubles, absorbing and compressing gases, treating and preparing solids, and most of the other unit operations. The treatment was, however, mostly qualitative and descriptive.

There was also in existence in America a monthly journal, *The*

Chemical Engineer, founded in 1904 and edited by Richard K. Meade, who three years later issued the first call for the founding of this Institute. The editor in the initial issue stated:

> We have called our publication *The Chemical Engineer,* because the vast majority of the technical chemists of the present day are not only workers in the laboratory but have active supervision of the operation of our great chemical and metallurgical industries and hence are, strictly speaking, engineers, i.e., those to direct an enterprise.

The colleges had not lagged entirely behind the industrialists in sensing the demand for chemical engineering training. The first program in chemical engineering to be established in this or any other country was announced by the Massachusetts Institute of Technology in 1888. The announcement stated the aims of the new course as follows:

> The course is arranged to meet the needs of students who desire a general training in mechanical engineering and at the same time devote a portion of their time to the study of the application of chemistry to the arts, especially to those engineering problems which relate to the use and manufacture of chemical products.

This emphasis on mechanical engineering did not provide a satisfactory basis for a course in chemical engineering and the course languished until Dr. William H. Walker was called to control and revise it in 1904.

The second program in chemical engineering to be established was announced by the University of Michigan in 1898. This course had the advantage of being located in the engineering college and of being launched with the hearty cooperation of the chemistry department and it commenced its career under favorable auspices. Several years later a program was formulated at the University of Wisconsin, where C. F. Burgess, trained as an electrical engineer, brought an unusual viewpoint to the framing of the curriculum. Armour Institute of Technology, under Harry McCormack, initiated its course in chemical engineering in 1900 with the first class graduating in 1904. The first laboratory work in chemical engineering was offered here in 1908 and directed study to such unit operations as evaporation, crystallization, filtering and drying. Columbia University announced its program in chemical engineering in 1905. Several other universities had established programs labeled chemical engineering by the time this Institute was founded.

These first programs in chemical engineering were formulated without precedents and, because of economy if for no other reason, had to be pieced together from courses offered to the chemists and courses offered to engineers of other divisions, without many courses planned especially for the new group of chemical engineers. The new curriculum was usually placed within the department of chemistry but occasionally within one of the older departments in the college of engineering. Its prosperity depended largely upon the attitude of the fostering group. It has been mentioned that at Massachusetts Institute of Technology the program in chemical engineering failed to flourish during its first fifteen years. In 1903 Dr. William H. Walker, at that time a partner of Arthur D. Little in consulting practice, was asked to return to Massachusetts Institute of Technology and develop its course in chemical engineering. He found considerable opposition to his plans and prepared a thesis setting forth his ideas. Published later in *The Chemical Engineer*,[2] this won him the right to revise the course. After dwelling upon the development of civil engineering and mechanical engineering he stated:

> . . . When electricity became such a factor in human progress a new name had to be evolved to describe the workers in this field. They were not simply physicists who had specialized in electricity, but men who made use of their knowledge to accomplish results of general utility—men who adapted electrical forces to human necessities. They were engineers, and as their chief active agent was electricity they were called *electrical* engineers. . . . In a prfectly analogous way has been evolved the term *chemical* engineer. It describes an engineer who deals primarily with *chemical* forces. As before, this engineer is a man of practical achievements; a man who utilizes his knowledge of chemical reactions in the solution of industrial problems; a man who can devise, construct and operate industrial plants based upon chemical reactions. In contrast to the purely research or strictly laboratory chemist this man must be sufficiently familiar with mechanics and related subjects to enable him to carry his work to the point where it becomes a factor in the economy of the art.

In a recent letter to the writer Dr. Walker has given this interesting incident:

> This thesis did the work, and I organized the course along the lines with which you are familiar. I was most fortunate in early "discovering" a farmer's boy from Delaware, who had carried at the same time the full course in chemistry (5) and the course in mechanical engineering (2). This was Warren K. Lewis, who, as you know, has been of the greatest help to me and to whom is due a great portion of the success which the course later achieved.

The history of chemical engineering education in the United States has been discussed by this author in another place [3] and only the salient points will be touched on here. At the time of the organization of this Institute the total number of graduates from

---

[2] *The Chemical Engineer*, 2, 1 (1905).
[3] *Trans.*, A. I. Ch. E., 21, 55 (1928).

courses in chemical engineering in the United States was probably less than one hundred. Statistics compiled in 1910 by the Bureau of Education showed 869 students attending courses which were labeled chemical engineering. The outbreak of the World War, with the cessation of imports from Germany and the shortage of many products of chemical manufacture, caused much publicity to be given to chemical engineering, and the census of 1920 showed that there were 5,743 students in these courses, more than six times the number in 1910.

The instruction in chemical engineering did not develop at a rate commensurate with the number of students. The post-war programs were for the most part still composites of courses selected from those offered regularly to chemists and those offered regularly to engineers in other lines of specialization. Various schools had tried the experiment of increasing their programs to five years and Columbia had increased the length of its course to six years in order to permit the added engineering courses to be added to what was essentially the full chemical program. The University of Cincinnati had extended its cooperative program to students in chemical engineering. Robert Kennedy Duncan had popularized the idea of engineering research as an adjunct to schools of chemical engineering. M. C. Whitaker returned to Columbia University in 1911 to put into practice the policy which he had outlined before this Institute in 1910.[4] I quote from his paper of that date:

Is there any reason why chemical engineering should not and could not be taught by the tried methods of the normal schools, the medical schools, the agricultural schools and other engineering schools? Only with proper chemical engineering laboratories, equipped with real working models of standard appliances to illustrate the basic applications of the industries, and a proper curriculum arrangement to permit the student to study and use these appliances and the principles involved in their application will we be on a basis comparable with the methods and the facilities now existing in other educational fields.

But we can accomplish still more with proper laboratory facilities. We can so construct and administer these laboratories that the student will be surrounded by an "atmosphere" of manufacturing and business efficiency, where he will learn by *example*, by *daily contact*, by "*attrition*" the modern methods and practices of office and works management. Chemical engineers should have this knowledge. It is fundamental to the proper fulfillment of their job. Instances where failure has been converted into success and industries saved by a knowledge of proper administrative practices, and the application of business and works efficiency methods, are too numerous to mention. Refinements in chemical processes and ingenious mechanical devices are all ineffective and often useless if inefficient organization and management are permitted to absorb the earnings. Successful chemical manufacturing is based upon three general principles: First, chemical and physical facts; second, mechanical applications; third, organization and management.

4 "The Training of Chemical Engineers," *Trans.*, A. I. Ch. E., 3, 163.

Two noteworthy innovations were made at Massachusetts Institute of Technology. One was the School of Chemical Engineering Practice, which was outlined by Arthur D. Little and consummated through the energy of William H. Walker as a graduate program with stations at several manufacturing plants. The second was a comprehensive treatment of unit operations which culminated in the publication of Walker, Lewis and McAdams, "Principles of Chemical Engineering," appearing in 1923. In this book there was presented for the first time a comprehensive outline of the unit operations treated in a mathematical manner and with numerous illustrative problems. It was the first text in any language to deal adequately with this important subject.

A standing committee on chemical engineering education had been appointed at the first meeting of our Institute. This committee under the successive chairmanships of Charles F. McKenna and F. W. Frerichs sponsored symposia and questionnaires which will be found in the *Transactions* of the first few years. Subsequent committees have always been sympathetic and willing to be of service to the schools, but it remained for the committee under the chairmanship of Dr. Arthur D. Little to leave a lasting impression upon chemical engineering education. A careful survey of curricula followed by discussions during several years led to a report which, as finally adopted by the Institute in 1922, carried a declaration of independence in the statement,

> Chemical engineering, as distinguished from the aggregate number of subjects comprised in courses of that name, is not a composite of chemistry and mechanical and civil engineering, but itself a branch of engineering, the basis of which is those unit operations which in their proper sequence and coordination constitute a chemical process as conducted on the industrial scale.

This declaration was bitterly resented by some of the colleges offering programs in chemical engineering, as limiting the independence of the schools. The reply was that the national associations of the legal and medical professions went much further in their insistence on standards of education and that adequacy of professional preparation was of the greatest importance to any professional body. There is, of course, no compulsion which may be put by the Institute upon colleges, but those who wish to be accredited by the Institute must recognize this definition of chemical engineering, and its indirect effect has been extremely powerful.

The last decade has seen chemical engineering win its way to full recognition in industry and in education. The wave of students which followed war-time publicity found the schools unprepared, but it did force presidents and deans to give serious consideration to this youngster which outgrew its clothes every year, and as a consequence better equipment and facilities were usually provided. The curve of enrollment in the undergraduate courses is given in Figure 1. The post-war wave receded, giving the teaching staffs a chance to re-organize their work, and then a new wave started in 1925 carrying the number of undergraduates to 9,154 in the college year 1930-31. This total does not include those registered in curricula labeled metal-lurgical engineering, gas engineering, ceramic engineering, or other fields which are really specialized divisions of chemical engineering.

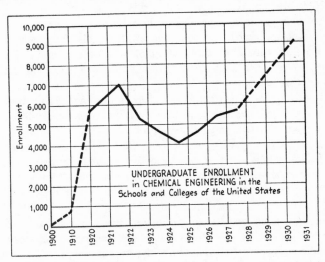

Methods of teaching chemical engineering also developed during this decade. Mathematics has been more generally used, problems have been stressed. The teaching of unit operations has become better organized. Chemical technology has changed from a descrip-tive study of existing manufacturing processes to a critical analysis of the development of processes with consideration of the underlying theory and of economic conditions.

Chemical engineering has reached its present development through a recognition that manufacturing operations involving chemistry can-not be economically controlled by one who does not have a thorough understanding of the forces involved and the methods of controlling them. Equilibrium in chemical processes is controlled by temperature, pressure and concentration of the reacting substances. The means of controlling temperature and pressure and insuring the desired concentrations are physical, not chemical. Chemical engineering is based on the triple foundation of mathematics, physics and chemistry. The chemical engineer in his work uses physics more than chemistry, but he cannot commence to be a chemical engineer without a thorough knowledge of chemical reactions.

It has been repeatedly emphasized by writers that four years is too short a time to train a chemical engineer. The industries have recognized this in recent years and have paid a premium for selected men with graduate training. This demand has, of course, been reflected in the supply of men with graduate training and at present one out of every three who receive their Bachelor's degree continues for at least one year of graduate work. It is this group with graduate training, with a firm grasp of fundamental theory and skill in its application to actual problems which will furnish the leaders in technical developments.

If we appraise the position which chemical engineering now occupies in our colleges and compare it with its status twenty-five years ago, we find remarkable progress—probably beyond the fondest expectations of the founders of the Institute. Then there were only a handful of schools which offered programs labeled chemical engineering. Now chemical engineering is taught by almost all schools which offer engineering courses. It is recognized as one of the five major divisions in the report on engineering education prepared by the Society for the Promotion of Engineering Education and is also so recognized by the Engineering Foundation. Its students are approaching in numbers those in the other four older major groups. The United States looks with respect to the chemical industries of Europe and recognizes many great chemical engineers among those who direct them. Chemical engineering education has, however, been an American development, and Europe recognizes our leadership in this field and is patterning after us.

So many individuals have contributed to the notable growth of the last decade that it is unfair to single out any for special mention. It has been an era of building upon foundations already laid. There are, now, textbooks and monographs of high quality in most of the fields and the volume of literature is increasing rapidly. *Chemical and Metallurgical Engineering, Industrial and Engineering Chemistry* and a number of professional journals in specialized fields are printing reviews and research papers with a wealth of disclosure in both the technical and economic fields which is raising the whole profession. Dr. McKenna in the same address from which quotation has earlier been made urged the Institute to assist in tearing aside the veil of secrecy. Much progress has been made, but, it must be said regretfully, much remains to be accomplished, especially with the large corporations which are in other respects leaders. The subject of catalogues of chemical equipment received study at the second semi-annual meeting of the Institute. A committee was appointed and through its efforts and the energy of the Chemical Catalog Company have come the successive annual editions of the Chemical Engineering Catalog, valuable to the profession and, thanks to the generosity of the publishers, available freely to students.

The curricula in chemical engineering have developed in the individual schools with very little attempt at cooperation or direction. The committee on chemical engineering education has made a study of curricula and tabulated the results but has not attempted to do more than indicate the general distribution of time which it believed desirable. This is probably wise, for no one can foresee what future demands will be and it is probably better to let each school experiment as seems best. One factor which is certain to be controlling in the long run is the attitude of the employer. One of the large department stores coined the phrase, "The customer is always right." That same phrase holds measurably true in education. A school may appeal to a select clientèle and fit its graduates for that clientèle with great success. If it fits its graduates for a non-existent market, that school will be forced to modify its policies. In the last analysis it is the employers who control chemical engineering education. They may also exert a powerful direct influence through the teaching staff. The successful teacher must keep some vital contact with industry either through consulting work or vacation employment, in order to understand and interpret wisely and broadly the changing needs of industry. Employers who assist in providing such contacts make a distinct contribution towards better teaching.

The demand for graduates from the courses in chemical engineering was greater than the supply until the depression of 1930.[5] In the present year, 1932, the graduates of chemical engineering courses are having difficulty in obtaining employment and there are numbers of older graduates who are out of employment. It is expected that with the resumption of normal business conditions there

[5] White, "Occupations and Earnings of Chemical Engineering Graduates," *Trans.*, A. I. Ch. E., 27, 221 (1931).

will again be a strong demand for chemical engineers. The larger corporations recognize the value of the chemical engineer fully, but small manufacturers have not yet learned the services he can render them. Whole groups of industries are as yet employing few chemical engineers and as a more truly scientific basis for their operations is developed they will appreciate the help which the chemical engineer can give and will open avenues of employment which are now non-existent.

The older divisions of engineering are coming to recognize that chemical engineering occupies a unique field, not only in that it controls the operation of great industries recognized as chemical, but also in that it has evolved a new technique. The chemical engineer has made it a point of honor not to be content with an overall appraisal of an operation but to take it to pieces and determine the value of the individual components. This method of operation is not original with him, but it has not become standard in other divisions of engineering. The chemical engineer has therefore become a pioneer in fields which do not involve definite chemical operations. For instance, the operation of heat transfer does not call for any distinctively chemical operation. Its control does, however, require a study of film resistances, and the properties of gaseous and liquid films are so different from the properties of the materials in a free state that the older branches of engineering have not attemped to consider their properties and have left this and similar fields to the chemical engineer. The chemical engineer finds his field of usefulness in the process industries in which chemical reactions play an important part, where automatic controls and machines may be used profitably and where accurate regulation of operation is essential. The higher wage scale in this country and the magnitude of our potential markets has promoted the development of chemical engineering and of chemical engineering education. So long as the American chemical industry continues to grow, so long will chemical engineering education flourish. The two are dependent on each other, for if chemical engineering education is defective, to whom will the torch of leadership in industry be passed? As Dr. McKenna said at the first meeting of this Institute:

We begin as brothers. We will inevitably close our careers as fathers passing on to our sons in the profession a heritage of knowledge and light that shall increase as the flame increases with the increase of fuel.

NAME INDEX

SUBJECT INDEX

369